LONDON BENEATH THE PAVEMENT

By the Same Author

NOVELS
Weep for Lycidas
Spring in Tartarus
All the Trees were Green
Vernal Equinox
Battered Caravanserai
So Linked Together
Treadmill
There's Glory for You!
Long Vacation
Things Less Noble
The Dividing Stone
The Brain
A Hansom to St James's

THE 'ROWCESTER' NOVELS
Higher Things
The House in Fishergate
Sinecure
The Darkened Room

BIOGRAPHY
Gambler's Glory (*John Law of Lauriston*)
Count Cagliostro
They would be King (*Lambert Simnel, King Theodore, Bernadotte, Henry Christophe*)
Prince of Hokum (*Peter Cheyney*)
Charles Dickens: A Sentimental Journey in search of an Unvarnished Portrait
Rosa (*Rosa Lewis of the Cavendish*)

TRAVEL COMMENTARY
Dawn Express
Reported Safe Arrival: The Journal of a Voyage to Port 'X'

HISTORICAL
Airborne at Kitty Hawk
The History of the Hat
London by Gaslight
London Growing: The Development of a Metropolis
Mulberry: The Return in Triumph

TOPOGRAPHICAL
In the Footsteps of Sherlock Holmes
The London that was Rome

PHILATELY
Mauritius 1847
A New Approach to Stamp Collecting (*with Douglas B. Armstrong*)

NUMISMATICS
The Coins of Great Britain

CUISINE
Beer Cookery

SHORT STORIES
Transit of Venus
Exploits of the Chevalier Dupin

ADVERTISING
Technical and Industrial Publicity

London Beneath The Pavement

MICHAEL HARRISON

PETER DAVIES : LONDON

Peter Davies Ltd
15 Queen Street, Mayfair, London W1X 8BE

LONDON MELBOURNE TORONTO
JOHANNESBURG AUCKLAND

FIRST PUBLISHED 1961
THIS EDITION 1971

432 06651 9

Made and printed Offset Litho in Great Britain for Peter Davies Ltd
by Cox & Wyman Ltd, London, Fakenham and Reading

DEO INVICTO
MICHAEL ERICIUS
VOTUM SOLVIT
LIBENS MERITO

Acknowledgements

In the writing of this, as in that of all my previous books of an historical nature, I have received much help from both those who knew me and from those who did not. In the writing of novels, an author is inclined to overlook the sources of his material; in the writing of history, he is so constantly aware of those sources that he may never be forgetful of them—though some authors are not sufficiently alive to the necessity of acknowledging the extent to which they have been dependent upon the research of their predecessors. I should not like to be guilty in that respect.

As far as possible, I have endeavoured to cite my references in the body of the text; and I have given, in the Bibliography at the end of this book, the principal sources consulted.

But I must make my proper acknowledgements, too, of help received in a far more personal fashion: such help, for instance, as was given to me by Mr C. A. Lyon, Press Officer of the London Transport Executive, who willingly and ungrudgingly undertook much research on my behalf.

I must thank, too, the Librarians and staff of the British Museum Reading Room, the Westminster Central Library, the Holborn Public Library, the London Library, the Guildhall Library; the Press Officers of the Gas Council, the Ministry of Public Building and Works, the Greater London Council, and many other public bodies.

Especially my thanks must go to Mr Landsley, Librarian of the Institution of Electrical Engineers, for help in this and previous works; Mr John Fraser, Press Officer of the Electrical Development Association; Mr J. Cooper, of the *News of the World*; the late Rev. Cyril Armitage, M.A., C.V.O., Rector of St Bride's; Miss Mabel S. Claye (for valuable information

viiiviii ACKNOWLEDGEMENTS

regarding Sir Hugh Myddelton); Mr W. D. Williams (for even more information on Sir Hugh); Mr E. Williams, Secretary of the Chancery Lane Safe Deposit; the Clerk of the Board, the Metropolitan Water Board; the Secretary, the Clothworkers' Company; Mr T. R. Blurton; Mr R. T. Clarke, Press Officer to the New Zealand High Commission in London; Messrs Giuseppe and Woods, of the Bank of England; Mr J. B. Cuthbertson, Assistant Manager of Drummond's Bank, London; Mr G. A. Bone, Secretary of the Sir Hugh Myddelton Lodge N.1602; Mr C. U. Mather, Managing Director and Secretary, Messrs Spiers and Pond Ltd.; and Messrs C. A. Johns, K. Benest, J. P. Bardsley and Stanley H. Miller, F.R.I.B.A., whose letters contained valuable information that I have used and acknowledged in this book.

A number of people have been kind enough to allow me to quote sizeable extracts from works in copyright: *The Wastes of Civilisation* by J. C. Wylie, published by Faber and Faber Ltd.; *The Water Supply of London*, published by the Metropolitan Water Board; *London and Londoners in the Eighteen Fifties and Sixties* by Alfred Rosling Bennett, published by Eveleigh Nash and Grayson Ltd.; *Town Gas: Its Manufacture and Distribution* by E. G. Stewart, published by Her Majesty's Stationery Office; *London's Natural History* by R. S. R. Fitter, published by William Collins Sons and Co., Ltd.; *Treasure in the Thames* by Ivor Hume and *The Vital Flame* by Sir Compton Mackenzie, both published by Frederick Muller Ltd.; *The Engineer; Reminiscences* by Col R. E. B. Crompton, published by Constable and Co., Ltd.; and an essay by Professor W. F. Grimes in *Recent Archaeological Excavations in Britain*, published by Routledge and Kegan Paul Ltd. I would like to express my thanks to all those who have given permission for my use of material from these works.

For all those whose help has not been acknowledged here—and they include many a London and Provincial Editor, who has given me access to the files of his newspaper or journal—I give here my blanket blessing: though I must single out one Editor, Mr R. H. Harris, of *The Engineer*, from the pages of whose esteemed journal I got much valuable information on Deep Shelters.

Nor must I close this list of deep-felt acknowledgements without mentioning my wife, who, day after day, and week after week, made it possible, by driving me overground, from Library to Roman Bath, from Carmelite Crypt to Sewer Entrance, for this book on *London Beneath The Pavement* to be written.

Contents

Contents

List of Illustrations

(inserted between pages 114–115)

1. The Mighty Heart

THIS is a book about London. But that simple remark, I feel, needs some qualification, if it is to be clearly understood.

The 'London' of today—'the largest aggregation of human beings ever recorded in the history of the world as living in a single community'—stretches from Hertford in the north to Reigate in the south, and from Tilbury in the east to Slough in the west: a vast, irregular oval whose major axis is over fifty miles in length. To many people besides the megalomaniac quill-drivers of County Hall, 'London is where the red buses run', and wherever there is a bus-stop with the familiar red-and-blue plimsoll-mark of London Transport's sovereignty, there is London.

Of course, London cannot be extended by bureaucratic ambition in this way, and for all that London Transport's motor-buses 'serve' (to use the jargonauts' own jargon) places as far distant from London Stone as Gravesend and St Albans, London is to me—and will be so treated in this book—as the London that men discussed up to the year 1888, when the Greater London Council was established. London, to me, is the City, with Westminster, and the ancient suburbs closest adjoining. I know what I mean when I talk of 'London'—and so will most people who read this book: it is the same London that Wordsworth meant when he described how it looked on a clear September morning in the year 1802.

'Earth,' said Wordsworth, still uplifted with the calm glory of that autumn morning, 'hath not anything to show more fair.'

The solitary traveller of today, stopping at dawn to rest his elbows on a Westminster Bridge rebuilt in cast-iron Victorian Gothic, would—provided that he were not moved on by the police—see little in common with the scene which so moved Wordsworth's heart.

The River, of course, is the same River, though it has been disciplined and narrowed since Bazalgette's Embankments. And even in this too-regulated age, it may still be said of the Thames that 'it glideth at its own sweet will'. But of all the buildings that Wordsworth saw, only Somerset House, St Paul's, the spires of the surviving City, Westminster and South-wark churches, and the old Shot Tower until recently pre-served, in the forecourt of the seedy Festival Hall, now remain.

As I walk through the London that I have known since the year when Blériot crossed the Channel, I confess that I feel like a wanderer in a waste land. Day by day, the visible physical links with the past are being swept away, to make place for the harsh angularities of a pauper culture: the only type of architecture with which—seeing that it has no traditions in Humanism—the alien, rootless New Men may feel really comfortable.

As I write, I have before me *The Builder* carrying an inter-view with the person responsible for the design of the new Royal College of Physicians in Regent's Park. Some splendid Nash houses have given place to the new R.C.P. headquarters. I recommend a close study of this interview to all who would learn perfectly to what grisly inevitabilities they had better resign themselves. (Looking at a photograph of the new Opera House at Tashkent in company with a Russian architect, I remarked on the fact that Russia had moved back, in taste, to the architecture of the Napoleonic Wars. 'Yes,' he said, with-out rancour, 'we too built, in Moscow and Leningrad, as you are building in London today. What else could we do? We, too, were poverty-stricken—in ideas as well as in money. But we are a rich nation now, and we build—as we think—in a manner becoming our wealth.')

Let us get back to London: to the new London, of flat, despairing façades, where the only sculpture is that commis-sioned by the G.L.C. to give otherwise jobless refugee 'artists' a living. The intention of those who rule us is to sweep away every vestige of the visible London which links us with a past that we are being urged to deprecate. The bombing of London revealed, on Tower Hill, a marvellously preserved length of London Wall: bureaucratic reaction to this find was as typical as it was immediate—the wall was demolished in order to make room for a workmen's urinal.

Soon—very soon—the only survival of Old England that we shall be able to offer our American visitors will be a ride in a British Railways train (preferably in a restaurant-car).

Yet for all the desolation and uprooting, the physical links which unite the London of today with the London of times past are numerous and abiding. Some of these links are immaterial—as, for instance, the pre-Celtic name of London River, and the names of many of London's streets. London Stone, the Palladium of Empire, is obviously marked for oblivion by the malign ambition of the Planners, who have already begun to demolish the church in whose wall this ancient and hallowed relic had been placed for safety; but the physical links with the past are still numerous—and many of them will be with us for a long time to come.

But to find them, we shall have to go beneath the asphalt and the paving-stones. We shall have to look, not to the London around us, but rather to the London beneath us, if we are to find the relics of London's vast antiquity.

It was to find and list those relics that I set out to write this book.

If we see, in a modern city, the macrocosmic analogue of the microcosm, Man, which dwells within it, we may compare the visible part of the city—the streets, the buildings, the bridges and wharves—with the skin and hair of the human being.

As with a human being, the 'important' parts of the city are hidden beneath its skin. With the true prescience of the poet, Wordsworth called London 'that mighty heart'—but the heart of London, as the heart of any other city, is hidden within the skin. So, too, are the liver, and the kidneys and the bowels of our modern London—and though they are not as old as some parts of the remaining skin, they will last longer, as we shall see.

For if what Wordsworth saw, as he leant on the parapet of Westminster Bridge more than a century and a half ago, has changed greatly, what lay beneath his feet has changed even more. Beneath the London of 1802 there were the ancient rocks, the relics of past cultures, crypts, tessellated pavements, caverns of immemorial antiquity, sewers old and new—but there were no mains for gas and water and electric light; there were no underground railways, safe deposits, cold stores, bonded warehouses, 'deep shelters' and a host of other sub-terraneous places. The London of 1802 was still very much a surface affair—to pursue our physiological analogy: still very much a body which was almost all skin. In the years which have elapsed since then, the skin has been filled with internal organs. Within that skin now the heart beats systole-diastole, to keep the blood circulating and regenerated; the lungs purify the blood, the kidneys separate what is waste from what is good, and the bowels—the immense and intricate sewerage-system—eliminate the body-wastes, which discharge, in a manner perfectly analogous to that of the human body, through the eliminatory portals, into the all-purifying sea.

But, side by side with the engineering intrusions into sub-surface London lie the still untouched relics of the more or less distant past. For every mammoth or rhinoceros which is uncovered as men excavate the foundations for a Drummond's Bank, an Admiralty Arch or a New Zealand House, the bones of countless others of these vast mammals still rest in the iniquity of oblivion, and there are still buildings which have found, as it were, shelter and harbourage beneath the surface which would long since have been denied to them only twenty feet higher up.

In *The Time Machine*, Wells imagined a London of the far distant future in which man had penetrated so deep into the soil of the city that Londoners had split into two distinct racial types: the surface-dwellers and the troglodytes—inhabitants of the subterraneous world that Wells extrapolated from the deep basements and sub-basements, the underground railways and the safe-deposit vaults, of the late nineteenth century.

Though, at present, man seems to be going Up, rather than Down, the social stresses of the lithium-hydride bomb may still see Wells's troglodyte world an inescapable reality. In the meantime, the sub-surface city is given over, not to living room so much as to the means by which surface living is possible.

And, since the vital mechanisms of the city occupy relatively little space compared with the 'skin and hair', the London beneath us is today far richer in the relics of antiquity than is the London that we see.

The oldest thing to be encountered in everyday London—and the most enduring link with its remote past—is its river's name.

In London's museums and beneath London's pavements and open spaces are, of course, much older things than the name that we, of all the millions who use it, have come to pronounce as a monosyllable: 'Thames'.

When, in 1925, the foundations of the only recently abandoned Lloyds building were being excavated in Leadenhall Street, the skull of a woman was found—'The Lady of Lloyds'. There were no bones with the skull, or perhaps the bones were not seen by the workmen who found the skull. In terms of geologic age, the level at which the skull was found is a recent one, and the woman herself belonged to the so-called Cro-Magnon type: the first true *Homo Sapiens*—people averaging 5 ft. 9 in. in height, with long heads and large skulls, and faces which, in their flatness (with high cheekbones), would appear to us Mongoloid were it not for the full and prominent chins. The racial type is still with us, though as a 'people' the Cro-Magnon seems to have died out. Those of my readers who are old enough to remember the popular film actor, Richard Dix, will have a good idea of what a Cro-Magnon face looked like.

Somewhere about a date between 100,000 and 50,000 B.C., the mutation which developed the Cro-Magnon type took place, and all over Europe, the vastly more intelligent Cro-Magnon displaced the then reigning Neanderthal Man: a humanoid creature who, though a tool-maker and fire-user, still used his knuckles to help him stand upright, like his still too-near cousins, the apes. Neanderthal Man had himself—again by reason of the intellectual advance that *he* represented—displaced the even more primitive Acheulean Man, at a time possibly some 235,000 years ago, the dominance of Neanderthal Man lasting some 150,000 years, when Cro-Magnon appeared.

But even the primitive Acheulean type was not the first man-like being to inhabit these isles: the relics of the first 'human' settlements take us back a million years, to a time when, it may be, no more than two hundred and fifty people represented the total population of the British Isles.

All these progressively more human types have left their traces in the various 'terraces' and 'levels' that the Thames, over a period of a million years, has left as it has cut its way through the chalk and gravel and clay and rock.

But, save for the student of ethnology, these Old Ones are no longer with us as we go to the City on the bus or in the Tube; and their laboriously and carefully worked flint weapons, with which they slew rhinoceros and cave-bear, mammoth and giant elk, hippopotamus and musk-ox—the remains of all of which have been found either in the gravel of the Middle Terrace or its brick-earth—are to be seen only on the Londoner's rare visits to his neglected museums.

But the name 'Thames' is a monument of antiquity which is of the current coin of everyday usage. It is older than Rome; it is older than the Celts who poured in from Europe possibly as early as the end of the second millennium before Christ, and certainly no later than the beginning of the first millennium. The name had already been given to London River before ever the first wave of Celts arrived: and it is possible that not even the so-called Beaker Folk, who finished their long journey from South Russia in Britain around 1800 B.C., were the first to give the Thames its present name.

There is a hint as to the identity of the namers in the structure of the present Welsh language, which, as Professor Maurice-Jones pointed out over fifty years ago, is a language using a Celtic vocabulary imposed upon a non-Celtic (and non-Aryan) syntax. It is a fact of philology that, when a new culture imposes itself upon an older culture by conquest, and the language of the conqueror displaces the language of the conquered, the second generation after the conquest will speak the conqueror's language with the grammar of the older tongue.

Professor Maurice-Jones looked around for another language or other languages whose structures presented the idiomatic peculiarities of Welsh Celtic—a language that he considered to be that derived from a non-Aryan people who had been conquered by a Celtic-speaking invader. Professor Maurice-Jones found striking parallelisms of syntactical idiom in a group of North African tongues: Tamashek, Tuareg, and so on, to which the generic name 'Berber' may be given.

From this—and because of the fact that the syllable 'Ber' is to be found, not only in North Africa ('Berber'), but in the ancient names of Spain ('Iberia') and Ireland ('Ibernia')—Professor Maurice-Jones put forward the theory that the Beaker Folk had come to Britain from the Black Sea by way of the North African coast, and so by way of Spain and Ireland and Cornwall. And that the names of our rivers and of certain places which are demonstrably not Celtic (or even Aryan) were given by this people which spoke a language allied to the present languages of North Africa.

From them, not only the Celts but the Anglo-Saxons, it may be, inherited certain pre-Aryan words; not only the names of such rivers as Thames, Tyne, Towy, Tees and so on, but even the word 'sea' and the name for that peculiarly marine activity, 'to sail'.

At any rate, the name 'Thames' dates back far beyond the coming of the Celts and, because of its patent antiquity, there is evidence that, until very recent times, the name had a quality of sacredness, of tabu, which made many people prefer not to call it by its 'real' name. The same avoidance of the 'real' name, for tabu reasons, so that a substitute descriptive phrase is employed instead, accounts for the fact that the Aryan *arctos*, 'bear', was known—'to be on the safe side'—as 'the Brown One' (*baer, bruin, bern*) among the Teutonic peoples, and as 'the Honey Eater' (*medvezh*) among the Slavs. So Mussolini, when he was feared, was always called, in Rome, 'Mr Smith'.

'Father Thames', too, seems to have inspired enough superstitious dread to be called, by prudent Londoners, 'the Flood'— in particular reference to his most mischievous practice.

There is still a Flood Street in Chelsea and, until 1836, there was an old street, about where Epstein's frightful caricature of General Smuts now stands in Parliament Square, which bore the same name.

And what of 'London' as an ancient name?

Well, if 'London' be a Celtic name, then it is by no means as ancient as 'Thames'. But it may not be a Celtic name: in which case, it may well be contemporaneous with the name of the River on which it stands.

But whether or not it be a Celtic name—and it has the *form* of a Celtic name—it shares its name with the great city which stands on the Seine. If we split the word 'London'—'Lon-don' —and assume that the latter syllable is the Celtic *dun*, 'fort', 'enclosure', 'settlement' (all words meaning the same among primitive communities), then we recognize the first syllable in the old name of Paris, Lut-etia (Parisiorum), for the name 'Lud' also crops up in London's history, and we are able to say that, originally, both 'Paris' and 'London' bore names which incorporated, as their main element, the syllable (or name) 'Lund', the 'n' of 'Lund' becoming nasalized among the Gallic Celts, and disappearing, as it so often did in Indo-European, before a dental (compare Latin *dent-* with English 'tooth').

Let me state firmly that I am no believer in the theory which holds that there was no London before the immediate pre-Roman period. The argument against a pre-Roman city seems to be an *argumentum ab nihilo*.

The Royal Commission on Historical Monuments has this to say:

'On all grounds, it must be admitted that, whilst the possibility of some pre-Claudian occupation of the site of London cannot yet be finally dismissed, there is at present no valid reason for supposing that London existed prior to A.D. 43.'

There is, in my opinion, at least one 'valid' reason for supposing that there was a 'pre-Claudian' London—a reason sixty miles long, and a reason, too, which caused Caesar, when he set out from Gaul, to choose a landing-place at Pevensey: the great road which ran, straight as an arrow, due north from Pevensey.

It is not denied that this great road, so well defended that Caesar was unable to proceed along it (so that he had to take the roundabout way through Canterbury, Rochester, Swanscombe and Dartford, with the crossing of the Stour, the Medway, the Swale and the Darenth), was built before the Romans arrived.

But *why* was it built? If it did not lead from the Channel to London, to what did it lead? The presence of such a road of such importance postulates the existence of a city—or settlement—of equal importance.

The arguments against the existence of a pre-Roman London are based on two 'facts': the first, that London is not mentioned earlier than the famous passage of Tacitus, referring to events in A.D. 61. But how many writings of earlier date have we not lost, which may well have mentioned London? The second 'fact' is that the remains of pre-Roman date, recovered from the bed of the Thames and from under built-upon London, are so scanty as to deny the possibility that such a pre-Roman London could have existed. Where are the buildings? Where, even, are the midden-heaps, the discarded pottery, the dropped coins, the bones of the dead?

Perhaps in the name 'London' a clue may be found and, though I think that I am the first to advance this theory, there are hints—and more than hints—even in the much-quoted

Tacitus, that I may be right in contending, not only that London was here long before the Romans came to Rye, but that its structure was of such a nature as to leave only scanty remains.

If the name 'London' be truly a Celtic name, then it must mean something like 'lake-fort'; and this is an accurate description of the Neolithic 'lake dwellings' or settlements of the so-called Terramara type: villages which were built upon piles driven into the bed of a lake. A causeway, joining the village to the shore, could be raised at night or when hostile forces appeared upon the shore—and though the Terramara type of settlement disappeared in the face of the Roman advance through Western Europe, we know that it survived in at least one place in Britain: Glastonbury.

It is possible that the pre-Roman London was a Terramara town, built—literally—*on* the Thames, not merely alongside of it.

Because it does not suit the theories of those who hold that the further limits of London are co-terminous with the Roman invasion, the very plain statement of Cassius Dio has been challenged. Talking of the place at which Aulus Plautius (complete with his war-elephants) found himself at the Thames, Cassius Dio refers to the Britons retiring 'at a point near where [the River] empties in the ocean and at flood-time forms a lake'.

Commenting upon this passage, and the ideas it has engendered in other minds, Mr R. S. R. Fitter observes:

'There is a widespread impression that Roman London was a kind of island in a marsh or lagoon that stretched over wide areas of modern Central London, wherever alluvium is now shewn on the geological map. Recent research, however, suggests that this idea, so assiduously preached by Sir Walter Besant and others, is wide of the mark.'

My own theory calls for the lake, but rejects the idea of an island-city—at least a city on a natural island. I suggest that there was an island-city, in a lake, but that the island was

man-made: a township on a platform of wood, laid on piles
driven into the Thames, such as may be seen today in hundreds
of places throughout Malaya and Indonesia and Polynesia.

Mr Fitter himself, while rejecting Besant's theory, lends support to mine. 'In fact, it is doubtful if the Thames were nor-
mally tidal above the present site of London Bridge in the first
century B.C., so that Caesar, wherever he forded the Thames,
most likely did so above the tidal limit, and the lagoon referred
to by Cassius Dio must have been some miles downstream.'

This makes very little sense to me: but that the Thames has
become more tidal as the years have passed is a known fact.

Even as recently as 1858, the report of Bidder, Hawksley and
Bazalgette to the Government on the Metropolitan Main Drainage scheme notes the fact that 'the removal of Old London
Bridge has greatly augmented the tidal scour', and all through
the period since the Romans came, one factor after another
has successively 'augmented the tidal scour'.

The answer seems to be that the Celtic pre-Roman Londoners
lived in a Terramara township, built on piles above the then
wide, shallow, non-tidal Thames, that the Celtic London was
destroyed—perhaps just burnt—and that its remains have been
swept away along a Thames which has become progressively
more tidal.

Whatever may be said about the Romans, this may be stated
with certainty: they were consistent in behaviour. Now, one
of the practices of the Romans was, when conquering a country,
not to take over an existing town, but to build a Roman town—
a typically Roman *civitas quadrata* or 'gridiron-plan-town'—
near by, and either to destroy the indigenous town or to allow
it to decay. They did this everywhere else in Europe, so why
not in the case of London?

And this, I think, is what they did: they set up a new
London on the banks of a little river, the Walbrook, which
flowed into the Thames near the then existing built-on-piles
London, 'the lake fort'. This would account for everything: the
absence of the remains of pre-Roman buildings, the absence of
the relics of pre-Roman Londoners, for the tides and the

dredgers would have carted all away long, long ago, before there was ever such a profitless, fascinating, educative, worthwhile science as that of archaeology. . . .

Millions of years ago, southern England lay under the sea: at this period, the death of countless myriads of minute sea-creatures deposited the chalk. Then a land movement raised the level high above the water—see the account in Genesis of a similar up-and-down land-movement—while a further perturbation of our planet's extremely thin skin folded the plain so as to form what is now known as the London Basin.

This depression between two regions of higher altitude was for long submerged beneath a warm and shallow sea, which deposited upon the chalk bed layers of clay and sand. Then a further sinking took place—the London Basin still being beneath the sea—and in this period, that we called the Eocene, the London clay was laid down.

Again there were movements—though, indeed, they have never ceased: 'The Lytle Booke with a Crucifixe' [see the author's article in *The Illustrated London News*, 1953] contains a couple of sheets of a London diary of 1381, which quaintly records: 'Magno tremore in London'—and in these next convulsions the London Basin rose again, the sea drained away, a valley was formed, and through that valley flowed a great river, going eastwards to join the primordial Rhine. This appearance of the Thames marks the end of the Eocene period; and these events took place perhaps a million years ago.

The Eocene was followed by that period that geologists call the Pleistocene, and it is in this period that our remotest ancestors first appeared. Whence they came, no one knows as yet; but we know this about the men who made a settlement in the lower Thames Valley in the Old Stone Age—perhaps 500,000 years ago: they were of an incredible toughness. That they seem to us to be creatures nearer to the brute beast than to man may be the just observation of the truth; perhaps Nature had to keep them close to the unthinking endurance of the animal, since they were about to be put to a test that the more delicate organism of *Homo Sapiens* almost certainly would have been unable to withstand: the terrible, millennia-long Ice Age.

> 'Vast glaciers and ice-sheets [says Mr Fitter] spread at different times and from different directions over practically the whole of England north of the Thames. Once a tongue of ice came as far as Finchley, bringing with it boulders of rock far from the north, as well as clay and finely crushed rock from the lands over which it had travelled. When the ice melted, the boulders embedded in clay were left behind in the deposit we know as boulder clay. So it is that we find large lumps of chalk from Lincolnshire in the tongue of boulder clay that today stretches from Whetstone to East Finchley Station.'

So that the mixture of races that modern London's population represents is matched by a mixture of earths from many parts in the land upon which the modern city has been built.

Before and during the Ice Age, the Thames cut its bed down to lower levels, but, like that Greek river whose winding course has given us the verb 'meander', this ancient Thames wandered about as it passed through the valley, and it cut, as it flowed, terraces of gravel, which now remain to mark the successive stages in that proto-Thames's history.

Man, too, in this Ice Age, was not standing still. The intense cold gave way, at times, to the relatively warm climates of the inter-glacial periods, and in one of these Man of the next-step-up—Chellean Man—appeared. With him comes the Old Stone Age proper, and we have found the crude weapons that he fashioned so patiently out of the flint. His neighbours included the straight-tusked elephant and the woolly mammoth, and that the former, a sub-tropical beast, should be found in the same Boyne Hill gravel deposits as the latter, a sub-arctic beast, shows well the unsettled state of the climate in those far-off days.

Chellean Man was succeeded by Acheulean Man and, somewhere about 235,000 years ago, the Acheulean culture was displaced by the greatly more advanced Mousterian, whose flint implements have been found in enormous numbers in the Taplow gravels of Middlesex, particularly at Acton and Stoke Newington. If Mousterian Man was not a dweller in Central London, then he was at least a Suburban Londoner.

Mousterian Man—generally called 'Neanderthal'—lasted about 150,000 years, until, as I have said, he in turn was superseded by the first 'modern' Man of whom we have any knowledge: Cro-Magnon.

There is such a jump from Neanderthal to Cro-Magnon that one would expect to find some intermediary types: that they have not yet been discovered does not argue against their existence.

Cro-Magnon was not merely 'a man'; he was a man of advanced type—physically, intellectually developed to a high degree.

With him, for the first time, appears Art, and though he himself vanished as a racial type, the development that he represented was maintained. There were no more apemen after Cro-Magnon appeared, even though Cro-Magnon himself went.

The Old Stone Age gave way to the Middle Stone Age—the so-called Mesolithic—and it is to this period that the earliest known Londoner, the 'Lady of Lloyds', belonged.

Then, somewhere about a date between 9,000 and 7,000 B.C. —curiously enough, at about the time that Plato dates the collapse of Atlantis—the weather began to change from subarctic to sub-tropical, and a world-wide intellectual advance is to be noticed, accompanied with the familiar phenomenon of the extensive movement of peoples. The New Stone Age had arrived.

The Neolithic culture was not confined to a single country, or even a single continent; but then, it was not demonstrated within a single century, or even a single millennium. Asia shared in the Neolithic 'renascence' as well as Europe; and America and Australia shared it, too, though it is almost certain that the first men to migrate to Australia wandered there from Europe, through southern India, taking their Neolithic culture with them. (The argument in favour of this theory is in the fact that the Neolithic first-settlers in Australia took with them the domesticated dog.)

We are now almost into historical times, and in this warm, wet so-called 'Atlantic' period the fauna and flora of Britain began to take on their present character. Reindeer, mammoth and woolly rhinoceros had long since vanished from the scene, and the animals which were to be hunted as late as Plantagenet times were already established in the great forest of Middlesex: red deer, wild oxen, wolves and wild boar. 'The Thames must still have been broader and faster than it is today, with extensive mudflats at low tide, and innumerable small osier-covered eyots' [R. S. R. Fitter: *London's Natural History*].

This warm, wet 'Atlantic' period was succeeded by a drier, colder—the so-called sub-Boreal—period, which so closely coincides in date with another great social ferment in Western Europe that it is impossible not to assign the social ferment to the pronounced climatic change.

Irrupting into the peaceful pastoral existence of the British New Stone Age, in which many animals were domesticated, land cultivated and men settled in communities (the town and city are results of the invention of agriculture), came the Beaker Folk, irresistible in their knowledge of how to work and use bronze. They came from South Russia, as, two thousand years later, the Angles, Jutes and Saxons were to come.

Who the Beaker Folk were, we do not know; they seem not to have been Aryans at all, though their wanderings were part of that vast movement of peoples in which the Aryans were mixed up, and which took the Indo-European speech from a small district in the Lithuanian marshes, and eventually carried it to Ireland in the west, India in the south, Norway in the north and even as far east as the extreme limits of the Gobi Desert.

In the Mediterranean, the ferment had fundamental results; and it is in this period that the proto-Greeks crossed the Danube and advanced into the Hellenic Peninsula, there to subjugate

and absorb the original inhabitants, who are remembered
today by no more than a few non-Greek words in the Greek
language: such as the words for 'king', 'mouse', 'mouth',
'brick' and 'sea'.

Doubtless the reason anciently given for the irruption of the
bronze-working Beaker Folk is the correct one: they scoured
the Mediterranean coast-line and then proceeded up the coast
of Spain and Portugal and western France, and so to Ireland
and Britain, looking for tin and copper with which to make
bronze.

In Britain, especially in Cornwall, they found both. But that
they came to us by way of the Mediterranean, though long
suspected, has now been proved by carvings recently revealed
(by modern scientific photography) on the trilithons of Stone-
henge; these carvings belong to the same 'school' as those
which adorn the megalithic structures of Malta, Sardinia and
Ireland. The ancient legend which connects the Stone of
Scone with migrants from Egypt has more than a mere kernel
of truth in it.

Then, after Bronze, came Iron, whose working calls for a
much more developed technology, and so represents a major
scientific step ahead in man's technological progress.

Iron caused another world-shaking revolution, accompanied
by the usual movement of peoples, though this time the movement is associated with the Celts, a people—or a confederation
of peoples—speaking an Indo-European tongue, and powerful
because of their 'secret weapon'—scientific exploitation of the
horse (especially of the horse drawing a vehicle) as an instrument of war. Just as most of our military terms are of French
origin, so the Latin names of almost all specialized two- and
four-wheeled vehicles are of Celtic origin. The Celts were the
great horse-breeders and horse-tamers of the West, and their
empire, though destined to be consumed in the blaze of its own
undisciplined enthusiasm, extended from the Crimea to Asia
Minor, from Scandinavia to France, Ireland and Britain.

They worshipped the horse and the pig, as their descendants

in Ireland do to this day (the pig being, perhaps, held in the greater respect as 'the jintleman who pays the rent').

They were superb artists, unchallenged, before or since, for their mastery of the abstract design, built upon a repeat pattern (based usually on a group of three elements) using variations of the ancient 'classic volute' or so-called 'Vitruvian scroll'.

They were cunning workers in metal, they were persuasive talkers (as they still are), and their philosophical concepts made them an influence in Western thought long after the glory of their arms had begun to fade.

Successive waves of Celts crossed the Channel into Britain, though not all came from Gaul; what is now Belgium and Holland was a favourite jumping-off place for several of the immigrant bands. From Britain, they colonized Denmark in the first century B.C., but that they came to Britain at all was an event which, later taking on a political significance, was fundamentally to affect the whole history of these islands in general and that of its most famous city in particular.

For, in the fourth century B.C., the Celts had invaded the Italian Peninsula; had reached Rome, and sacked it. The Romans never forgot, and when they had imposed their rule on all Italy, and had moved out to 'pacify' the adjacent lands of the Middle East, they turned their attention to their old enemies, the Celts, whose empire had now shifted its centre to the lands of the Atlantic seaboard.

In crossing the Channel and the Irish Sea, the Celts had retained their original tribal divisions. Thus there was a settlement of the Parisii tribe on the Sequana (Seine) and another on the shores of the Humber; there were Brigantes in Switzerland, Yorkshire and Ireland; there were Belgae in the Low Countries and in South-west Britain; there were Menapii on the banks of the Scheldt and in southern Ireland, and so on.

They kept in contact, tribe with tribe, and the Celts in Britain and Ireland sent assistance to, and gave refuge to, those of their compatriots on the Continent who were hard-pressed by Roman arms.

There was, as the Romans well saw, no question of conquering Gaul unless Britain (and eventually Ireland and Scotland) were conquered, too.

Gaul itself being conquered, Caesar set out, in 55 B.C., to conquer the 'other Gaul'—Britain. The Belgae were then on both sides of the Channel; they held London, and it was they who had built the great arterial road which connected Pevensey with London.

The foolish legend that these Belgae were a pack of tattooed, fur-loin-clothed semi-savages should have died long ago. The Celts spoke a language not very different from that of the Romans; they had superb arms and armour; they had a gold coinage (something that a savage does not even need, let alone has the capacity to organize), and their missionary schools received pupils from the almost too-civilized lands of the Levant. A day which knew the Celts better thought it only proper to represent the boy Christ having served His apprenticeship as a ship's carpenter on a big cargo-vessel belonging to His uncle, Joseph, which traded between Palestine and Britain, and to represent Him as having spent some of the formative years of His youth among those Celts who still, today, are to be counted His most faithful supporters.

Caesar well knew what he was tackling when he landed at Pevensey: if he did not, the swift and enforced alteration of his plans must soon have persuaded him that it was against no undisciplined savage that he had brought his Eagles.

The arrow-straight way to the North—to London—was barred to him. Within the thick forest of Anderida, through which the road ran, the Celts were there, with a 'secret weapon' that they themselves had inherited from the dark little Neolithic people whom they had conquered: tiny 'pyramids' of flint, with four sharp points—the so-called 'fairy bolts'—which, poisoned with aconite, and 'spanged' with deadly accuracy with thumb and forefinger, bred panic among even the tough legionaries.

Caesar abandoned the road and set out by the long route

through Canterbury and Rochester, where, though there were at least four rivers to cross, there were not so many woods in which the snipers could hide.

He reached London—though he does not mention it. But for what else was he heading? He advanced to Wheathampstead, sacked it, made terms with Cassivelaunus, and called it a day. Then he went back to Rome, and Britain enjoyed an uneasy peace for another century, until, in A.D. 43, Claudius arrived, got a foothold in Britain, and brought the country under a Roman rule which was to endure for nearly four centuries. The evidence for all this history lies beneath our feet: some of the evidence has been found, some is yet to be found.

But no period, however brief, however 'uneventful', passes without its leaving some relic, however small, of itself. A skull here, a shard of pottery there; a mammoth's tusk here, the fossilized branch of some Arctic shrub there; a beautiful drinking-cup from fifth-century Greece (no London, four centuries before Caesar?); a bronze Celtic shield, bright with coral-pink enamel; a ship; an openwork leather shoe; a coin; a sword. . . . There's history for the reading in every cubic inch of the ground beneath us.

The earth gathers up and preserves the small indices of history. But, in recent years, those treasures, hoarded so long ago, have been given up at a novel and greatly accelerated rate.

We have begun to dig down, not to find out more about those remote ancestors of ours who fought Woolly Rhinoceros and Sabre-toothed Tiger, or even the hoplites of Achilles or the war-elephants of Aulus Plautius, but to get ourselves more room for living: for the higher the building, the deeper must the foundation be.

As London has soared skyward, so has it tunnelled downward. To maintain the ever-increasing London above street-level, a subterranean London has developed, whose main function it is to carry away the wastes from the towering city above, to provide that city with light and water and the means of communication and travel. Beneath the upper city is another almost as extensive, so that we may think of London—as we may think of any other modern city—as a two-storied affair, the lower story being the more important, since it is the lower story which makes it possible for the upper to stay up. It is with this lower story that this book is concerned.

2. London enters History

THERE are mysteries everywhere, when we come to the subject of London. What exactly does the name 'London' mean? Who named the River—and what did the original of 'Thames' mean?

Was there a town on the small tributary river, Walbrook, before the Romans came? Or did the original London, as I suggest, stand out, on piles, over the River itself? After having won a series of running battles, Caesar eventually reached the Thames, and there, he tells us, he found the Britons awaiting him, 'on the north bank', behind a palisade of sharpened wooden stakes, some of which stuck out from the bank itself, while others, driven into the river bed, were hidden beneath the water. Is this the 'lake fort' that I suggest?

Unfortunately Caesar not only does not say that the encounter on the Thames took place at London, but—if we assume that it *was* at London—does not say at which point he forded the Thames to attack the Britons behind their complicated *chevaux-de-frise*.

Lord Noel-Buxton has shown, in the only practical way, that the Thames may be forded, even today, at Westminster—he has walked across; though, if it be true that the London of today is some fifteen feet *lower* than it was in Caesar's day, then the 'proof' that Lord Noel-Buxton has given of the Thames's fordability is hardly proof at all. Yet Caesar says that he forded the Thames—the question is: where?

Now the Thames has yielded traces of armed conflict at two points: Chelsea and Brentford, the latter name clearly indicating that, in the past, the Thames was fordable at this point. At Chelsea, too, the River was fordable until recent times, and the termination of the name, 'Chelsea'—'ey', an island—may indicate that a small eyot obstructed the River at this point, providing a 'stepping stone' across the water.

It was at Brentford that part of a hut, floored with wattles—a typical building of the type found in the Iron Age 'B' settlement at Glastonbury—was found; and another was discovered, by Mr Ivor Noel Hume, at Isleworth, as he was on his way to photograph the 'lake village' remains at Brentford.

When Chelsea Bridge was being erected in 1854, the workmen uncovered a quantity of relics of a martial nature: iron spearheads of Roman type, a number of human skulls and what was described, in the *Journal of the British Archaeological Association*, as a Roman military boot. The fact that a number of other objects were found at the same time—domestic objects, many of which date from other periods than that of the Roman invasion of 55 B.C.—need not be held to argue against the theory that it was here that Caesar forded the Thames, for the presence of other objects, ranging over a long period of time, shows that this was a much-frequented spot—just the sort at which we should expect to find a ford.

At Westminster, too, then an island surrounded by small, marshy tributaries of the Thames, other weapons and skulls have been found and, indeed, it was at Westminster, when digging the foundations of County Hall, that one of the most exciting of all Roman relics was found in the mud of the foreshore: a Roman ship. True, the ship is dated as of the late third century; but its presence so far up the River from Walbrook—the ship sank at anchor, apparently—seems to argue that at Westminster, no less than at London, was some centre of activity, where one would expect, not only to find a commonly-used crossing, but also (is this what the discovered weapons argue?) some effective means of defending it.

Now, whether Caesar crossed the Thames at Westminster or Chelsea, at Brentford or—very far to the west, this suggestion—Halliford, at the ford known since Saxon times as Cowey Stakes, cross it he did and, having crossed it, he pursued the Britons as far as the capital city of Cassivelaunus, Wheathampstead, that Caesar, having captured, sacked.

London has yet not entered history here, save by surmise: it is, indeed, not until the return of the Romans in A.D. 43 that the written history of our city begins.

The events of those first decades of the Roman occupation are well known: the story of Boadicea has been singled out from the mass of historical event, as have the stories of King Alfred and the Cakes, King Canute and the Disobedient Waves, King Henry and the White Ship ('He never smiled again') and the Duke of Clarence and the Butt of Malmsey Wine. 'Everybody' knows how Boadicea's husband, Prasutagus, King of the Iceni, had stood aside during the Claudian invasion of Britain, and been rewarded for his 'neutrality' by being permitted to hold on to his kingdom, though as a vassal-monarch.

His capital, Camulodunum (which may be Colchester, but may not), had been adopted by the Roman authorities as a provincial administrative centre, and outside of the Icenian city a *colonia* had been established, populated by time-served Roman veterans granted land on condition that they became settlers in the conquered country.

Prasutagus had no male heir; and in order to guard against the displacement of his family from the throne he bequeathed half his estate to the emperor Nero, as a sort of 'peace offering'.

When Prasutagus died, in A.D. 61, the Roman authorities did not honour the agreement—if agreement there had been—and declared the royal Icenian line extinct. The half of Prasutagus's wealth which had not been left to the emperor was seized, the royal palace was sacked, and—for good measure—the king's widow was stripped and flogged, and her daughters stripped and raped by, it is said, a squad of *peditiones*.

'Everybody' knows what happened then. Wholesale confiscation of the property of the Icenian nobility having been ordered by the Procurator, Decianus Catus, Boadicea now had powerful allies among her own people. Calling the Iceni to arms, she turned first on the *Colonia*, massacred the Roman settlers, and set out on the road to London.

Decianus Catus had raised a 'home guard' among the unwilling Londoners: Boadicea met them, and slaughtered them.

Ordered south from Lincoln, to overtake and stop Boadicea, the Ninth Legion, *Hispania*, brave in their uniforms of purple and white, were, in their turn, wiped out.

The other legions were too far away to be able to halt the Queen; and not until after she had sacked London and St Albans did Suetonius, who had hurried back from Anglesey, meet her with the Second, Fourteenth and Twentieth Legions, and defeat her. As 'everybody' knows, she poisoned herself, rather than fall into the hands of the savage Romans.

Writing soon after these stirring events, Tacitus mentions London, both in his *Agricola* and in his *Annals*—and very curious mentions they are; not at all the sort that we should expect of a city which, according to some of our historians, was a little over twenty years old.

For one thing, he gives the total number of the pro-Roman population massacred by Boadicea in the three cities of Camulodunum, London and St Albans (Verulamium) as seventy thousand; and though scorn has been poured on this large number, it accords very well with the tone in which Tacitus speaks of the London of A.D. 61: '(a city which) although not designated by the title of *colonia*, was crowded with merchants and greatly celebrated for its commerce'.

Well, cities hardly grow to that magnitude in a couple of decades; and what probably happened is that the Romans, following their usual custom, set up a 'new London' on the river-bank not far from the spot in which the already famed and important lake-built London had stood.

Now we know where they chose to establish the new city: across the banks of a small river which flowed into the Thames between two modest hills. Those two hills are today called Ludgate Hill (significant name!) and Cornhill, and the river which flowed between them, and which, indeed flows, though underground, is the Walbrook.

Contrary to former theory, the entrance to the Walbrook was not the main port of Londinium; this was probably Bil-

lingsgate, on the east side of the present London Bridge; but
that there were several other Thames-side ports, even at any
early date, is certain.

But here, on the Walbrook, where the Temple of Mithras
was found a few years ago, was the first Roman settlement in
London. With this as a centre, the Romans laid out one of
their typical 'grid-iron' city plans, and though, as the centuries
passed, another street-plan was overlaid upon that of the
original *civitas quadrata*, the square Roman city can still be
traced on the modern maps, and there is at least one street
which maintains almost precisely its original location and
direction: Cheapside.

This street, the main east-west thoroughfare upon which all
the Roman square-cities were based—the *decumanus maximus*
—has at least one Roman official building still on it: the crypt
of St Mary-le-Bow, while, at the eastern end, is the Guildhall,
successor to the palace of the Imperial Prefect, whose successor,
the Lord Mayor of London, rules the City from it.

The western of the two hills was crowned with a Temple of
Diana—its successor is St Paul's Cathedral; the eastern with
the basilica-flanked Forum of Londinium, extensive traces of
which have been found during the past and the present century.

Only recently, a part of the basilica was found when the
workmen were digging the foundations for Messrs T. R.
Blurton's new shop in Gracechurch Street, and Mr
T. R. Blurton kindly invited me to inspect the find, as I shall
describe later in this book.

The bombing of the last war revealed much which caused
earlier theories concerning Roman London to be scrapped;
and we now know that the Romans first built their London,
and only after a considerable time had passed did they encircle
the city with a wall, traces of which still remain.

The gradual development of this wall was revealed by the
teams of archaeologists probing the 'bomb sites' after the end
of the war, and it is now clear that the fortification of Londinium began with the construction of a small, almost-nearly-
square fort, with sides 200 yards in length, the other side of
what we now call Cheapside, and thus to the north-west of the

Walbrook-based settlement. From the lower western corner and the upper eastern corner of this fort, a wall was built out, which eventually enclosed the area of 330 acres which made up London-within-the-Wall. The south-eastern angle of the Wall is marked by the Tower of London, the south-west angle at Blackfriars, and between these angles the old River line of the Wall may be traced by Upper Thames Street, a relatively straight line on which the remainder of the Wall arches in an irregular bow to enclose the extent of Roman London.

Early in the history of Roman London, there were settlements without the Wall: the strict Roman municipal laws against burials within the walls of a city made the establishment of cemeteries essential and, for safety, these cemeteries were as near to the protection of the city as the urban regulations would permit. There was a Roman cemetery about where St Clement Danes church—the 'Oranges and Lemons' church —now stands; and the street which ran from the bridge across the Fleet River to the cemetery is Fleet Street.

The date at which Christianity arrived in this country has been so hotly—and ineffectually—debated that I should wish to raise the topic here; but if there were Christian churches in London before the Imperial Rescript of Constantine, in the third century, made Christianity the state-religion, then we should expect to find these churches near to the city, but beyond its wall. Now to the north-west of Roman London, about 300 yards from 'New Gate', the flanking bastion of which (No. 19) can be visited beneath the General Post Office in Newgate Street, is the church of St Etheldreda, in Ely Place, the crypt of which, if not probably a surviving Roman structure, is certainly built of Roman materials. Just outside the walls is where we should expect to find two Christian churches of early date: and the locations of both St Etheldreda's and St Bride's satisfy the requirements in this respect.

It must not be forgotten that Roman rule lasted in Britain for four centuries: a space of time equal to that which separates us from the beginning of Elizabeth I's reign. It is plain—and it is principally to archaeology that we owe the knowledge— that Roman control, and—worse—Roman culture, had begun to decay perhaps as much as a century and a half before the Rescript of Honorius, in A.D. 410, recalled the legions and marked the official end of Roman suzerainty.

Even before the end of the third century, building was being carried out by 'cannibalizing' existing structures, which had been permitted to fall into a ruinous condition. The Wall was repaired not only by using building materials from crumbled houses and public offices, but by using statues, inscribed monuments and the tombstones and sarcophagi of those notable soldiers and administrators who had gained their renown in the Golden Age of Roman Britain. It is true that an apparent parallel may be found in today's use of old tombstones for the paving of those 'playgrounds' into which Progress has converted our churchyards; but, with our rulers, the desecration is intentional; it is plain to see that, with the Roman Londoners of the third and fourth centuries, there was real—and too obviously, at times, desperate—need for the desecration. Something had happened throughout the Empire; happened, not only in Britain but in Rome itself, where the debased craftsmanship of the Arch of Constantine is embellished with sculptures filched from an arch of two centuries earlier—there was no one living in Constantine's day who could have worked to such a standard.

In the relics of the latter period of Roman London that excavation has revealed, the progressive decline of the culture is saddeningly plain to see: two-storied cottages, such as now command so very excessive a price in Chelsea, built out of material rescued from the decayed grander buildings that no one would—or could—keep in repair.

The 'stately homes' of Londinium Augusta were 'too big', 'too inconvenient', 'too costly to run'—haven't we heard all those phrases ourselves?

Out of their rubble, the degenerate later Roman Londoners built themselves a seedy shanty-town which served well enough, one supposes, for their simple purposes.

When I was a boy, I was given a book about King Arthur and his Knights, illustrated in colour by Walter Crane. The 'reason' for Crane's inability to live up to his ambitions has often been sought; but, looking back at that book, I think that I can suggest the reason: his romanticism and his common sense clashed—to his inevitable loss.

I mention that because, though King Arthur and his Knights were dressed by Crane in a sort of fourteenth-century plate-armour (as I recall), Crane, remembering the supposed date of the King's exploits—say, about A.D. 500—filled in the background of the pictures with the still intact Roman buildings of classical cut, liberally marked with the S.P.Q.R. of the Imperium. Archaeology does not confirm that picture. Long before the legions were recalled, the passing of the Imperial Idea had been reflected in the passing of the Imperial standards of living.

When, in 1852, a large section of the Roman Wall was being demolished, the antiquary, Charles Roach Smith, noticed that this part of the Wall had been repaired with a large number of worked stones, among which were not only the drums and cornices of columns which had formed part of some imposing building or buildings, but the half of a Roman funerary monument, the other half of which was found embedded in the remains of the same part of the Wall when, in 1935, the London Transport Authority was building an electricity sub-station.

The two halves, now in the British Museum, bear the following inscription:

DIS
(M)ANIBVS
(C. IVLI. F)AB. ALPINI CLASSICIANI
PROC. PROVINC. BRIT(ANN.)
IVLIA INDI FILIA PACATA I(NFELIX)
UXOR

TO THE GODS
OF THE UNDERWORLD
(IN MEMORY OF) CAIUS JULIUS ALPINUS CLASSICIANUS
PROCURATOR OF THE PROVINCE OF BRITAIN
(THIS STONE HAS BEEN PUT UP BY)
JULIA PACATA, DAUGHTER OF JULIUS INDUS,
HIS SORROWING WIFE

The important fact to observe here is that the memorial stone, torn up, mutilated and used as building material to repair a wall, was one of the Founding Fathers of the Roman City—a place once so important that it boasted the second largest basilica in the whole Empire.

What was it like, this Roman London, to which, in the third century—doubtless at the apogee of its wealth and importance —was granted the honorific title of 'Augusta'?

By chance a representation of part of it exists, though we cannot say that the representation is an exact one. Still, for what it is worth, there is a picture of late third-century London to be found on a gold medallion of Constantius Chlorus, part of the hoard which was found at Beaurains, near Arras, just after the first world war. This medallion was struck at Trèves to commemorate the liberation of London from the rule of the usurper, Allectus, and the (alas, only temporary) restoration of Roman rule over the Province of Britain. Constantius Chlorus repaired the Wall, and doubtless erected a monument or two, possibly even a triumphal arch. But let us see what the gold medallion shows.

Riding a horse, Constantius Chlorus is being greeted at the main river-gate of London—outside which an oared galley waits—by the kneeling figure of what has been described as a 'citizen', but which is more probably the personification of London herself. The legend around the design refers to Constantius as 'Restorer of Light'—and here, in this most obscure phrase, the interpretation of which has defied scholars for the past forty years, may be another hint as to the origin and meaning of the name 'London'.

The Celtic God of Light was *Lugh*, an Indo-European word cognate with the Latin *lux* (>*lug-s*), and the name of this Celtic deity may form the first syllable of London. It may be remarked here that the traditional Londoner's pronunciation of 'Ludgate' is 'Luggid'—listen to any London bus-conductor, whose speech has not been corrupted by 'education'.

On the medallion, the river-gate of Londinium is shown as flanked with two tall, somewhat narrow towers, with domed or conical roofs. The towers are many-storied, the divisions between stories being clearly marked with string-courses, such as may be seen today in the still existing 'Black Gate' at Trèves, where this medallion was struck.

Unless the artist was merely assuming that the river-gate at London—he has marked 'Lon' under the gate—was the same as the Porta Nigra at Trèves, this is what the main gate of London looked like as the third century drew to a close.

If the reference on the medallion to 'the Restorer of Light' is a reference to the still-understood meaning of the name 'London', then it hints at the fact that London was not yet completely Romanized, and that part, at least, of the population would understand and appreciate the reference to 'Lughdun'.

Constantius Chlorus restored the Wall—he had intended to land his troops in Kent, had lost his way in the fog (yes, even in those days!) and, finding himself in the Thames Estuary, had sailed up to London where, entering the city through the tumbled Wall, he routed the troops of the already-slain usurper, Allectus, and made himself master of the capital of Britannia Prima.

It is thought that the Roman ship, uncovered from the black river silt when, in 1910, work began on the building of County Hall, belongs to this date. The remains are thirty-eight feet in length and sixteen in beam, part of a ship estimated to have been originally sixty feet by eighteen. The ship appears to have been sunk by a large stone 'cannon ball' shot from a ballista. Four coins found aboard are contemporary with the trouble; one bears the head of the usurper, Carausius, another of Allectus himself.

We shall see later what treasures, besides this ship, which is now in the London Museum, have been found in the River, but here I should mention one object which bears impressive testimony to the splendour of Roman London in the first centuries of its existence, before the still inexplicable world-weariness which sapped the imaginative vitality of the Empire's heart had done no less for its most northern Province—and especially the capital of that Province.

This object is a colossal head of the Emperor Hadrian, builder of the still-existing Wall which bears his immortal name: the greatest triumph of Roman engineering of which we have knowledge.

This head, which was found in the River close by London Bridge—one account says, during dredging work to the east of the third arch, in 1834; another says that it was found two years earlier—belonged to a statue of heroic proportions, which may have stood at the entrance to the Roman bridge, or in some River-side forum near by. That there were more than one such statue is proved by the fact that no fewer than three hands have been found, as well as a foot: all of the proper proportions to have formed part of this or comparable figures.

A similar bronze head of heroic size was found at Saxmundham by a small boy, who fished it out of the River Alde. This head—it is of the Emperor Claudius—is thought to have been looted from the temple of Claudius at Colchester. To have found the evidence of two such statues at such great divide argues that in Britain, as in other Roman Provinces, the setting up of these colossal figures was a commonplace.

Taken in conjunction with the remains of at least three religions—that of Mithras, that of Cybele and that of Christ—the evidence of these colossal statues (no less than the size of the Basilica of Londinium) more than suggests a city whose standing and wealth drew to it the highly cosmopolitan population that all great cities have always attracted.

London's decline, so the archaeological evidence suggests, was a long-drawn-out affair: it is now known that 'the Saxons' began to make their irritating presence felt quite two centuries before the date that school history-books assign to the coming of 'Hengist and Horsa'; and some unrecorded beleaguering of Londinium by the 'Saxons' may account for the certain evidences of London's progressive decline.

In the surviving written records, the last date at which London is mentioned is A.D. 429, when St Germain, Bishop of

Auxerre, paid it a visit. The legions had been officially recalled just on twenty years earlier and, though a deputation of the British had later gone to Rome to plead for help against the Saxons, Rome was unable to give it. There was, even in those days, probably the equivalent of a League of Empire Loyalists; but Rome had grown tired of imperialism, and the envoys from stricken Britain were sent away with the blunt advice to look after themselves.

According to St Germain, all was peaceful in Britain or, at least, in London: though Roman rule had ceased, Roman order still survived. Perhaps the Wall had been kept in repair: at the other side of Europe, the carefully-tended fortifications of Constantinople kept the city safe from the Turks for centuries.

After that date, A.D. 429, the written record is silent upon the subject of London. Not until A.D. 604, nearly two centuries later, does the name of the city return to the record, when Mellitus was consecrated its Bishop in what may well have been the first Christian church to be built on Thorney Island, on which Westminster Abbey now stands.

Archaeology has failed signally to describe the London of the period between the passing of Roman rule and the re-establishment of the Roman Christian Church in Britain.

Was London—as the scantiness of the remains seems to hint —unoccupied during these two centuries while the Anglo-Saxons were forging the links which were to bind them to Europe, civilization and Christianity? Had the city, after being sacked, been abandoned by the primitively superstitious, still pagan Teutons? Did what was left of the Imperial splendour crumble away: its houses and temples, its baths and administrative offices affording shelter only to vagrants and outlaws, and its empty streets knowing the tread only of the bear and the wolf, passing unchallenged from the depths of the great Middlesex Forest?

There has been, in fact, no find which can be definitely assigned to a date between these two limits—the end of Roman civil rule and the beginning of Roman ecclesiastical rule.

On this subject of a probable break in the continuity of life in London, the Royal Commission has this to say:

'There is no substantial reason why the few remaining walled cities should not have remained as islands in the flood [*i.e.: of the Anglo-Saxon invasion*]. . . . The walled towns of the south-east, out of reach of the Picts and out of mind of the Saxons, may thus be thought to have lingered on almost as "reservations" for the second Romano-British population. The silence of history in regard to them is probably just; London in the year 500 can have mattered little to anyone save a few decivilized sub-Roman Londoners.'

On the other hand, the curious standing of the Lord Mayor, with his unique rights and privileges; the existence of 'London law', which continued in force until 1729; the fact that London has never formed part of the county of Middlesex (though, up to 1857, the County of Middlesex was ruled by the Lord Mayor and the Court of Common Council), the traces of a Celtic dialect—neither Welsh nor Cumbrian, neither Lincolnshire nor Pictish—in Cockney English, all seem to hint at a time and condition in which London was a completely autonomous city-state, and London could have achieved this condition only by an inviolate isolation following the departure of the Legions and until the coming of Augustine. There is nothing in the Anglo-Saxon Chronicle to suggest that London's independent position developed after the Anglo-Saxon conquest of the whole country—it must have developed before that; and, whether or not the Londoners within the walls were few and 'decivilized' in A.D. 500, there seems little reason to suppose that they had not maintained their defences in a sufficiently strong condition to repel the Anglo-Saxon invader and to maintain the independence of the City.

The defences, indeed, must have been remarkably strong, or the city-dwellers remarkably adept at repulsing attack. So much so that, even more than four centuries after London had 'come back within' the Anglo-Saxon England, London could still demand, and get, from William the Conqueror, a promise to

respect 'London law', in return for his being permitted to enter
the City.

This moral dominance can have rested only upon a tradition
of independence, of autonomy, developed during the two centuries between, say, A.D. 400 and A.D. 600.

Of course, between the enthronement of Mellitus as Bishop
of London and the coming of Duke William, the walls had
been damaged often, and as often rebuilt. After the Danes had
sacked the City in 851, much of its three hundred and thirty
acres lay waste, so that, when the Danes returned again in
872, it is said that they entered freely and encamped in the
ruins. This sentence would have astonished a pre-1939 reader
more than it will astonish anyone today, who has only got to
go out to see waste places in the heart of London, which have
been permitted to remain so for the past twenty years.

Alfred it was who rebuilt the city and renewed the walls.
He also confirmed those ancient rights and privileges upon
which London stood firm in her dealings with William.

London, in early times, was peculiarly vulnerable to fires—
as, indeed, were all cities in the past. Disastrous fires burnt a
great part of the city in 982, 1077, 1087 and 1136, and as most
of the houses burnt were of a flimsy nature, much must have
been entirely destroyed which, had it been allowed to crumble
away and be buried under the soil, would have remained as
relics of the age when London was changing from Old English
to Norman-French.

What we are doing here is to lay down what, later, we shall
endeavour to dig up; and a word must be said here about the
formation of that underpart of London which will yield us
our sought treasure.

First of all, the London of up to late mediaeval times was a
city of rivers—or, rather, of streams. Not until the end of the
twelfth century was a part of Walbrook paved over, giving
London its first sewer since Roman days; and the other London
rivers and streams—the Tyborne, the Hole Borne, the Fleet,
the West Borne, and many others (no fewer than seven are
channelled in iron conduits beneath the present Bank of

England)—remained open until very much later; the Fleet, until the middle of the eighteenth century.

All these rivers and streams were, practically, open sewers, into which Londoners, for centuries, cast their refuse. The beginnings of urban sanitation can be traced far back beyond the time when the open streams of London were last used as refuse-dumps by the citizens: in Chaucer's day, twelve refuse carts patrolled the city to collect the rubbish that the citizens were invited to put out for collection before their houses. Each London ward had its officially-employed 'rakyer'; but twelve carts could hardly be expected to cope with a city's refuse, and the rivers still received much more than the dung-carts, which, in any case, tipped their loads into the Thames.

The mention of Walbrook becoming London's first modern sewer reminds us that a Roman London could not have been without an extensive system of Roman sewers. The Romans of Rome had inherited their sewers—'big enough to drive through in a cart, or, when they carried sufficient sewage, to boat down them to see that they discharged freely into the Tiber'—from the Etruscans. These gigantic sewers, indeed, served the needs of Rome so well that it was not until 1913 that it was necessary to add to them.

But what the Romans adopted they made their own; and every town and city throughout the vast Imperium was given its characteristic Roman shape, both above-ground and below: grid-iron street-plan above, network of sewers below.

As the Roman buildings—what was left of them—crumbled away, to be buried under the accumulating detritus which has left them twenty to thirty feet below modern London, the sewers beneath them must have crumbled far more slowly. They must have become choked at an early period; for sewers need constant flushing and sweeping if they are to remain usable, and, lacking a central civic sanitary authority, old London may be assumed to have disregarded and soon forgotten its valuable subterranean Roman legacy. While the open rivers served as sewers, those underground would have been left to rot.

Wells, too, though of vital necessity to Londoners, were early put out of use by being used as sewers and rubbish-pits and, in most cases, their location is proved only by the names of the streets in which they were to be found. The well which gave Holywell Street its name is still marked on the Ordnance Survey map—Holywell Street is now covered by Australia House, and the well lies just within the small garden plot on the east side of Clement's Inn—but the well itself must have stopped being both holy and a well long before the beginning of the fourteenth century. And it was the same with London's other wells, especially those in close proximity to the Thames.

Just a century ago, *Punch* was campaigning week after week against the pollution of the Thames; but, five hundred years before that, the Thames must already have been one of the filthiest rivers known to man. In 1307 the first stone bridge to span the Thames was built: a strange structure, half bridge and half street, whose houses were not removed until the latter part of the eighteenth century.

From the windows of the houses on London Bridge, and from the backs of the shops beneath those houses, rubbish was cast into the River for five full centuries, while the Bridge-dwellers got their water by letting down buckets into a Thames that they were constantly polluting from latrines which projected over the River. They must have been a hardy race, those early inhabitants of Cockayne!

So, of course, the River, like the bricked-over streams and the rubbish-choked wells, has yielded much treasure. For things fell into the River by accident, as well as by design: we shall see later what some of those intentional and accidental discards were. A few—a very few—were fished out: among them, the infant daughter of a London merchant; and, by rescuing her, a City apprentice made the fortune of a present ducal family; but that, as Kipling said, is another story.

Perhaps, though, it is to the rubbish which was *not* thrown into wells and rivers and the River—to rubbish which was cast out into the street and there trodden underfoot—that we owe the preservation of what remains beneath the surface of the city.

Not all the dung dropped in the streets was collected for the market-gardens of London—there were too few market-gardens and too much dung. Horse, cow, pig, kite and pigeon droppings, in the course of a generation or two, can soon raise the street level to the first floor, which then becomes street level; and street-level rooms become basements, and basements become cellars, and cellars become the foundations of later buildings—all within no more than a few decades, when rubbish is not collected.

Nor is the accumulation of rubbish in towering piles a phenomenon of the remote past: King's Cross was built on the site of such a dump—a veritable mountain of ordure, that legend says was bought by the Russian Government for shipment to Petersburg, to provide foundations for a dock on the Neva. That dump at King's Cross vanished in the 1820s, but a similar dump remained until many years afterwards at Mile End—as high as a tall house. A regiment of rag-pickers was constantly swarming about its lower parts, while small boys danced and shouted, 'I'm the King of the Castle!' on its summit. One may imagine why the ritual response to this cry was always: 'Get down, you dirty rascal!' It was a habit of Londoners walking eastward from Aldgate to make the 'Whitechapel Mount' their turning-point; and old pictures show the Sunday strollers looking at, or slowly passing by, this abomination as Romans might saunter about the tomb of Cecilia Metella.

Refuse-heaps—middens—have been, to archaeologists, the most fruitful source of 'finds'; but it is incorrect to suppose, as even some of the more amateur archaeologists do, that the house-midden was always *outside* the house. It is probably correct to say that, right up to the reign of Charles II, when the Great Fire swept away many an old social custom along with many an old building, only the larger refuse was thrown out: the table-scraps and smaller pieces of refuse were thrown, as modern 'patrons' throw their burning cigarette-ends, cigarette-packets and potato-crisp envelopes in the Wilton-carpeted pubs—on the floor. Read the letter on the subject written by Erasmus to Wolsey's physician.

But, until the end of the seventeenth century, floors were not carpeted. Indeed, until 1634, it was still illegal for the floors of houses to be tiled or paved—the refuse-filled earth, covered at intervals with a fresh strowing of reeds, was so rich in nitrogen that it provided the nation's most important source of saltpetre, essential ingredient of gunpowder. 'So vital to the safety of the country,' says Mr J. C. Wylie, 'was the nitrate-rich litter that "saltpetremen" could go in and dig without obtaining permission from the householder.'

Of course, there were many houses, even at the beginning of the seventeenth century, where the homely old customs of scraping the plates on to the rush-strewn floor and urinating and defaecating in the corner had long since been abandoned: but the remains of past voidings were still in the floors themselves; and the cleanlier inhabitants, their floors uprooted by the 'saltpetremen', were thus the unlucky inheritors of an old tradition.

That many people had ceased to use the floors of their houses as middens is evident from the debate which took place in the House of Commons in 1601, two years before Elizabeth I's death. One angry Member complained, concerning the activities of the 'saltpetremen', that 'they digge in dovecotes when the doves are nesting; cast up malting floors when the malt be green; in bedchambers, in sick-rooms, not even sparing women in child-bed; yea, even in God's house, the church'. But it was explained that the right of entry into private houses could not yet be forbidden to the 'saltpetremen', since 'the kingdom is not so well placed for powder as it should be'.

Gunpowder was introduced into English warfare towards the end of the thirteenth century—its use, though, not being recorded until some fifty years later. Quite apart from its effect on war, so succinctly and beautifully described by Shakespeare, gunpowder had a profound effect upon social custom and human mortality away from the field of battle. Its availability created a need for it; and men sought it where they could find it. The filthy floors provided a rich supply, and so the floors were prevented by law from becoming less filthy, so that the supply of saltpetre (and so of gunpowder) should not be imperilled. It really was a vicious circle: the gunpowder industry depended upon the continuance of a barbaric custom, and the barbaric custom was rendered permanent because of the nation's need for gunpowder.

The connection between endemic and epidemic diseases and filthy surroundings may be plain to us—but it was only as recently as the middle of the last century that the connection was detected, established and proved. Before that, men had no idea that they were, in keeping their refuse near them, sowing the seeds of the plagues which affected humanity with disastrous regularity. The persistence of germs in infected soil is, I think, greater than even the scientists concede; and here I must recall an experience of my early childhood which, to me at any rate, seems to hint at a great longevity for disease.

My father had moved into a pretty little Regency villa on the south-eastern outskirts of London. It was splendidly isolated —a half mile from a village of tiny shops and thatched cottages —and all around were orchards and farms and hop-gardens. We were happy there; but, from the moment of our arrival, we children were never well. Even the dogs and cats were affected; and one Sealyham, which had gone mad, was destroyed before his snarls could turn to bites. The fact is that we were covered with sores: even a small scratch, hardly enough to draw blood, would turn septic. The doctors could do nothing: we were in a constant condition of bandaged fester.

We moved to another house, on the south coast, and our skins instantly recovered the texture of health. Then my father came across an old map and, on it, at a place marked 'Black Fen', he read this: 'Where those dyed of the Plague were buried'. An unlikely tale? Yes, but I have never suffered from any affection of the skin, however slight, since.

Under the sites of houses then, as well as under the sites of their gardens and outbuildings, the traces of their long-dead inhabitants have been, and will be, found.

And now, before we turn to the object of our search—the London which lies beneath us—one word on what is meant, in this book, by 'London'.

I have already said that I do not accept as 'London' that vast irregular oval which is 'served' by the London Transport trains and buses. All the same, it is a good many centuries since 'London' meant something greater than London-within-the-Walls.

The city itself was probably ringed with villages since its very beginning; and, as early as the reign of Henry III, legal recognition was given to a fact which must have happened a good while previously—the extension of the City's jurisdiction to take in the nearer suburbs.

In the following century—the fourteenth—there was such an increase of population that the City authorities incorporated into their territory those beyond-the-Wall parts of the county of Middlesex which are now the City wards of Aldersgate Without (i.e.: the Wall), Bishopsgate Without, Cripplegate Without and Farringdon Without.

In the early fourteenth century, the building of a stone bridge over the Thames between Southwark and the City linked the two indissolubly: from 1307, Southwark was no longer a mere suburb, but part of London itself.

The wells, too, extended London. All were outside the City proper—Clerkenwell, Holywell (that I have already mentioned), St Clement's Well, Shadwell, and others. But small villages grew up around them, and roads linked them with the City even before the villages arose. It was inevitable that the well-villages should have become incorporated into London.

Southwark was linked up with—and so became a part of— London by means of the Bridge; Westminster was linked up with the City by the continuous line of houses which bordered the Thames.

A great Abbey had arisen on Thorney Island as early as the seventh century; after the Norman conquest, the lands between Thorney Island (West Minster) and the City were granted to the great religious Orders which had begun to spring up even before the final collapse of the Empire and, in large measure, inherited its power, as they assumed its duties.

There were religious foundations within the City—the church and small street named Austin Friars recall such a foundation—but, generally speaking, the religious foundations were outside the walls of London. The Benedictines, living under the reformed rule of Cluny, had their vast Abbey at Bermondsey, traces of which may still be seen in the wall of a warehouse. In 1371, Sir Walter Manny established the Carthusian monastery at Smithfield, while, at nearby Clerkenwell, the still existing Priory of the Knights of St John of Jerusalem had been founded as early as 1100. All these religious foundations provided refreshment and lodging for the traveller, and their gatehouses had developed into taverns (hence the old and new meaning of the word 'inn') centuries before the dissolution of the monasteries under Henry VIII. The present-day Fleet Street tavern, Ye Olde Cheshire Cheese is, in fact, the north gate-house of the Whitefriars monastery.

All these great religious foundations helped to extend London to its present limits: for the mediaeval monasteries were not only houses of prayer and monastic discipline, they were market-gardens ('Convent Garden'), hotels and the mediaeval equivalent of the A.B.C. and Lyons and Express Dairy Company restaurants.

London then, for our purposes, is the London from about Putney to Bow, and from about Pentonville and Stoke Newington and Canonbury to Bermondsey and Vauxhall and Clapham.

Purley and Sidcup and Barnet may be 'London' to the quill-driving Caligulas of County Hall—they are not London to me.

3. The Beginnings of Archaeology

ARCHAEOLOGY, to be understood as regarding something dug up as valuable rather than as rubbish, may be said to date from the time when laymen, as well as clerics, began to learn Latin. (Greek, as a common accomplishment of the cleric, was not encountered before the Reformation in England.)

Looking for the relics of the past in order to grace the palaces of the present had begun in Italy as early as the fourteenth century; it was not until the first muffled shock-wave of the Renascence reached England at the end of the fifteenth century that men in England became aware that Latin was a language spoken not only by Cicero and Seneca and Horace, but by men who had walked the cobbles of Cheapside, moored their ships at Dowgate and patrolled the parapets of the same Wall which then still girded the ancient city.

The Londoner's first archaeological awakening came through reading: once again, after ten centuries, men in England became aware that something more than religion linked them with Rome; and now, as workmen, digging the foundations of buildings, turned up a coin or a ring, the volute of a classic capital or a lettered tombstone, men found that they could recognize these things for what they were, read the inscription on coin and tombstone, and recall, thereby, the severed link that the New Learning was re-forging.

This early archaeology was, at best, an amateur and haphazard affair. Things found were—and for long remained—in that amateur's classification of 'curiosities'. Recognition of an object's nature was too often wide of the mark; recognition itself was twisted by prejudice and pre-conceived opinion, so that the bones of mammoth and hippopotamus were 'recognized' as the 'Bones of Gyants'—it may be, even the bones of Gog and Magog themselves.

On the other hand, there was no mistaking the nature and the identity of coinage; and cabinets of Roman coins were to be found in the mansions of London gentlemen even before the beginning of Elizabeth the First's reign.

More, if the evidence of the Cheapside Hoard—to which we shall come later—is not to be misinterpreted, not only Roman intaglii but Egyptian faience scarabs were valued in the sixteenth century.

And if it be hard to maintain that there were already archaeologists before the end of Elizabeth I's reign, there were certainly antiquaries. The limits of their interests may have been narrow, but within those narrow limits the learning was deep. To such antiquaries as William Lambarde, whose copy of *The Black Book of Arundel* I described in an article in the London *Daily Telegraph* in the last Coronation Year, we owe not only the collection of ancient abbey rolls and other manuscripts, but also the restoration of the Anglo-Saxon language. Indeed, with Selden and Camden, Lambarde makes up a trio of antiquarian learning which would honour any age. It is true that the interest of such antiquaries was concentrated mainly on manuscripts, but in their collections were to be found Anglo-Saxon jewels, mediaeval reliquaries, Celtic leaf-swords and torques, as well as Egyptian mummies and Roman and Greek statuary. Their taste in relics was as eclectic as it was unformed: but they did collect, and by collecting put a value on what had hitherto (save when it was of gold or silver) been thrown back again as rubbish a moment after discovery.

Yet there was one class of find that these early collectors sought which, for all that they misread the evidence of these particular finds, does put them into the class of 'archaeologist', rather than into that of mere 'treasure-seeker', or even 'curiosity collector'.

Mr Cuthbertson, the Assistant Manager of Drummond's Bank at Charing Cross, very kindly showed me the Bank's collection of bones and other finds which were made when the present premises were erected. Here are the bones of extinct creatures, which once roamed this part of London when the world was very much younger: there are the bones of mammoth and rhinoceros, hippopotamus and many another animal that changing climate has either banished to more tropic climes or exiled altogether from the tally of the world's fauna.

Bones of the same class have also been found only a few hundred yards away, as the workmen have cleared the site of the old Carlton Hotel, to make way for the new London headquarters of the New Zealand Government.

Now men were finding this sort of bone all during the period which stretches backward from the present: the only difference between their discovering them and our discovering them is that we say that they are the bones of mammoth and rhinoceros, while such sixteenth-century antiquaries—archaeologists, if you prefer—as Reyne Wolf, Holinshed, Harrison and Stow, called them 'Bones of Gyants'.

And so they were 'Gyants', but not, as the men of the sixteenth-century thought, human giants, but giant animals.

Many of these 'Gyants' bones' had been found, indeed, long before the sixteenth century: and Stow writes of one such: the Giant of St Mary Aldermary. It was said to have been brought to St Mary Aldermary—where it was exhibited to public view in the cloister—in a parcel of bones brought from the charnel-house at St Paul's, but Stow doubts this story. It seems that the bone was known long before.

Thus Stow describes it:

The shankbone of a man (as is said) very great, for it is in length 28 inches and a half of assize, light and somewhat porie (*i.e. porous*) and spongy.... True it is that this bone (from whensoever it came) being of a man, as the form sheweth, must needs be monstrous, and more than after the proportion of five shank bones of any man now living amongst us.'

The man, Stow tells us, who claimed to have found this monstrous shankbone among the rubble of St Paul's charnel-house was Reyne Wolf, Stationer—'the greatest preserver of antiquities in these parts', Stow calls him.

Reyne Wolf was not only a great antiquary, but the inspirer of antiquarianism in others. He was the employer and patron of the chronicler Holinshed, himself a noted antiquary; and the inspirer of Shakespeare, in one respect. William Harrison, another sixteenth-century antiquary drew copiously upon the store of Holinshed's learning; and Stow, too, was indebted to all three.

Reyne Wolf curiously anticipated a modern practice (not altogether approved now among the best archaeologists, palaeologists and palaeozoologists) in 'reconstructing' the 'giant' of which the shankbone was displayed. He commissioned an artist to prepare a scale drawing of the 'giant', which drawing was fastened to the east wall of St Mary Aldermary, close to the shankbone itself. The drawing, Harrison tells us, 'sheweth the person of a man full ten or twelve feet high'.

Several London churches had these 'giants' bones', which had been dug up when the churches' foundations were being made.

St Laurence Jewry had a fine collection of bones.

'I myself, more than seventy years since, have seen in this church the shank bone of a man (as it is taken), and also a tooth of a very great bigness hanged up for show in chains of iron, upon a pillar of stone, the tooth (being about the bigness of a man's fist) is long since conveyed from thence: the thigh or shank bone of 25 inches in length by rule remaineth yet fastened to a post of timber, and is not so much to be noted for the length, as for the thickness, hardness and strength thereof.'

In one important respect, Stow may be claimed as our first antiquary; not because he found more, and wrote more on what he found, but because he doubted more. In him, for the first time in modern history, we find that constructive doubt which is the beginning of learning.

He utterly rejected Harrison's description of the giant that

he had seen—'on the 10th day of March in the year 1564'—
28 feet high, with a mouth, 16 feet wide, filled with teeth each
weighing ten ounces troy, and with a skull big enough to hold
five pecks of wheat.

But even what Stow had himself seen he could have his own
views about. Giants? Everybody said so: no one doubted that
these were the bones of giants.

Stow made a marginal note on the tooth and the 'shank
bone'.

The tooth, he suggests, might be that of 'some monstrous
fish, as I take it'; 'the shank bone', he cautiously argues, 'might
be that of an Oliphant'.

Stow, you perceive, was remembering that Aulus Plautius
had brought his 'oliphants' to London—and there is no record
that he had ever taken them back (such as survived the ham-
stringing axle-scythes of the Britons).

But, though he came to the truth without exactly knowing
it, Stow was correct in his surmise that the 'shank bone' of
St Laurence Jewry 'might be of an Oliphant'. It was. It was
the thigh bone of a mammoth (*Elephas primigenius*) or of a
straight-tusked elephant (*Elephas antiquus*).

Stow, too, though an antiquary more concerned with history
and—when it came to material relics of the past—ancient buildings, still had an eye for a Roman London coin or a Roman
London tessellated pavement. But it is not until we get to Ash-
mole and Bodley and Sir Thomas Browne in the seventeenth
century that we arrive at the dawnings of our modern interest
in the buried remains of the past.

Though he was writing about the discovery of Roman burials
in Norfolk, Sir Thomas Browne's *Hydriotaphia* gave, as it
were, the cachet of learning to 'digging'; and it is interesting to
note that when, in 1678, workmen excavating foundations in
Goodman's Fields, Whitechapel, dug up a copper urn and
several pottery urns, together with silver coins and 'bars'
(probably ingots), the remains were not only recognized as
Roman, but the sure evidence of the finds was fully appreciated,

and it was well realized that Goodman's Fields had, indeed, been a Roman burial-place.

Archaeology is not just either seeking or finding what is buried by time: it is reading the evidence both of the buried thing and the circumstances of its burial. If we accept this as the standard of archaeology, then we may say that archaeology certainly dates from a time prior to 1700.

The eagerness with which, during the digging and widening of the Fleet Ditch in 1676, search was made in the river-bed for the relics of past times, as well as the care with which such finds as were made were recorded and preserved, indicate that archaeology had made a decided step forward.

'There, at a depth of fifteen feet, was found the stray rubbish, bones and refuse of Roman London. The coins were of silver, copper and brass, but none of gold. The silver was ring-money, of several sizes, the largest as big as a crown, the smallest about the size of a silver twopence, every one having a snip in its edge. At Holborn Bridge, thrown away by spoilers or dropped by thieves, were two brass Lares (about four inches high), one a Ceres, the other a Bacchus, both covered with a petrified crust, but the stream had washed much of the oxydizing matter from the coins, "thrown away on the approach of Boadicea," says the vivacious and imaginative Pennant, his mind, like a true antiquary, of course reverting to the one special crisis of interest in ancient London story. The excavators also discovered in the miserly river various British and Saxon antiquities of interest—arrowheads, broad spur rowels, keys, daggers, scales, seals with Saxon names, ships' counters with Saxon characters, and medals, crosses, and crucifixes, of a later date.'

One memento of this late seventeenth-century interest in our Roman past is not only still with us, but is daily handled by tens of millions of us: our British penny. It was a Roman-British denarius, recently dug up, which provided the model for the penny-piece of the new coinage ordered by Charles II. Frances Stuart—'the Maid Charles never Made'—sat as the model for the engraver preparing the die: most people know that. What fewer people realise is the extent of the interest in Roman relics—extending even to the King—which made it seem the most natural thing that, in designing a new coinage, a Roman original should provide the pattern.

But there were other—and older—reasons for digging into the historic soil of London. People dug both to find buried treasure and to conceal their own.

The legends of buried treasure multiplied in the period immediately after the dissolution of the monasteries by Henry VIII, but they did not begin at that time. For one thing, monasteries and other religious foundations had been 'dissolved' by kings many centuries earlier than Henry VIII: to take one example, Edward II, though with great reluctance, had submitted to the pressure of the Pope and of the French King, and had suppressed the Order of the Temple in England. (The Scots King refused to do this: and the 'Scottish Rite' of Freemasonry is supposed to be in direct line of inheritance from the Order of the Temple in Scotland.)

Much of the Templars' wealth was seized, but it consisted mostly in its lands and great ecclesiastical and monastic buildings. The amount of actual coin and jewels found in the various 'Temples' scattered throughout the English and French dominions of the Plantagenet king was very small—astonishingly, disappointingly so. How the Templars—adequately warned of the impending attack upon them by the Pope and his money-mad French master, Philip the Fair—managed to get their treasure away is less hard to understand than how they managed to hide it so successfully that neither torture nor search revealed it.

For years—centuries—it was believed to be hidden under or in the vicinity of the Round Church of the Temple, one of the few relics of mediaeval London that the disturbing Oriental 'development' of modern London has permitted us to retain.

When, during the last war, a high explosive bomb, followed by a score of thermite bombs, first shattered and then set fire to Temple Church, it was hoped that reconstruction would

THE BEGINNINGS OF ARCHAEOLOGY

give a centuries-sought opportunity of exploring beneath the foundations. The search was made, but neither treasure nor any likely hiding-place was found.

Yet, in seeking such probable or even improbable treasures, the treasure-hunters of other days must have found many an unsought and unexpected trove.

And not everything, even in those non-antiquarian times, would have been thrown away, if intrinsically worthless, or melted down, if of monetary value. I was shown, in Paris, a small bronze casting: it is the forepart of a capricorn—the half ending in a round-sectioned screw-joint. I was told that it was 'found in the Thames', but when, or in which part of the Thames, my friend who owns it did not know.

If it was found in the Thames, it is an interesting piece, for it appears to be the regimental badge of the crack Legion XX *Augusta*, and to handle it is to have recalled for me some of the most exciting, as well as some of the most critical, weeks in the always troubled history of our Island.

When Boadicea was hurrying from Camulodunum to London, she was overtaken by the Legion IX, *Hispania*, brave in its uniforms of purple and white. The Queen of the Iceni halted, turned, and wiped out *Hispania*. Legion IX had been hurrying south from Lindum. Legion II, *Victoria Victrix*, had left Glevum with orders to make all speed for London, where it was to join Legions XIV and XX, that Suetonius was rushing from Mona.

The Legion coming from Glevum never reached London: its Imperator, Poenius Postumus, dared not risk the fate which had overtaken Legion IX. He halted his troops, and let Suetonius, with the cavalry and practically no infantry of Legions XIV and XX, enter London alone.

Prudence at that moment seemed to have affected the entire Roman strategy. Suetonius, like Poenius Postumus, decided that he would not face Boadicea—at least, not in a London choked with panic-stricken refugees and as yet undefended by walls.

Suetonius stayed in London only long enough to decide that

he would not stay, and hurried away from the city, leaving it
to be sacked and burnt by Boadicea. That she did so is no invention of the Roman propagandist historians: twenty feet
down from the surface of modern London, workmen digging
the foundations of buildings at various points between Walbrook and London Bridge invariably come across, at a level
only a little higher than that represented by the very first
occupation of London, a layer of bright red ash: relic of the
flames that Boadicea lit.

There are several other such red streaks, at higher levels: for
London burned many times before 1940—and may well burn
again. But that first red streak is the immortal testimony to a
more-than-human hatred: a memorial far more permanent
than that statue of the Queen which stands at the northern end
of Westminster Bridge, crowning, with incongruous splendour,
the Ladies' Convenience.

Suetonius cunningly let Boadicea and her men exhaust themselves in the sack of London, and when the Queen, sated with
plunder and murder, turned north again to put Verulamium
to the flames, the Roman, his troops rested, if apprehensive,
was ready for her.

The Queen missed the traditional Roman punishment of
execution: her followers were not so lucky. With his two
Legions, Suetonius returned to London, and there, perhaps,
some careless legionary of the Twentieth—may be in the
excitement of victory—dropped his regimental badge in the
Thames.

It is usual, in talking of the treasures of London which
have been unearthed, to assume that the finding of them is a
matter only of the last three centuries—the implication being
that, before, say, the Restoration, nothing was ever found by
men digging in the earth of the city. This is, of course, not true:
what is true is that, until archaeology arose to put a price upon
'rubbish', or a greater-than-intrinsic price upon objects of
obvious value, then the numerous finds were never reported.
For this state of affairs we have the ancient law of Treasure
Trove to thank.

Britton, the legal commentator of the thirteenth century, lays down what is essentially the law today regarding 'things found'.

Concerning treasure found concealed in the earth, and concerning wrecks and waifs belonging to Us (*i.e.: the Crown*), and sturgeons and whales, and other things found, which of right belong to and are detained from Us, let careful enquiry be made, and of the names of those who found them. . . . For treasure hid in the earth and found shall belong to Us, but if found in the sea, it shall belong to the finder.

It was long a debatable point whether or not the term 'sea' meant also 'river'; but the prudent man never put the interpretation to the test, and always concealed what he had found.

Britton lays it down that a dutiful subject, on finding anything 'hid', 'shall forthwith inform the Coroner of the district, or the bailiffs thereof'. To this day, it is one of the duties of the Coroner (i.e. the 'Crowner') to hold an inquest upon treasure trove, and this has been among his duties from just after the Conquest.

These early Coroners, in the days of chronically impecunious Kings, had not only to 'sit' on buried treasure, but to act in some sort the part of detectives, in order to see that the treasure was reported.

A Coroner ought to enquire of Treasure that is found, who were the Finders, and likewise who is suspected thereof; and that may well be perceived when one liveth riotously, haunting Taverns, and hath done so of a long time.

Bracton, another legal writer, elaborates on the evidence by which a Coroner, on the look-out for concealed treasure trove, may happen on the dishonest finder: 'if he carry himself more richly than usual in clothing and other ornaments, food and drinks, and the like'.

Today, in England at least, the Coroner has to be both a registered medical practitioner with a medical degree, and a barrister-at-law. His social position makes him above this hanging around bars to see who's diddling the Crown. That seedy job is now left to the undercover boys of the Inland Revenue who, as status-seekers, haven't had quite the success of Mr Coroner.

How much treasure was found until about 1800, when archaeology had at last established itself, not only as a more-or-less-exact science, but as the legitimate hobby of well-to-do gentlemen, cannot, of course, even be estimated. Those who found kept their mouths shut. But what has been discovered since, on the sites of Roman villas in Northumberland, Norfolk, Suffolk, Hampshire and elsewhere, must give us some hint of what must have been found by the methodical seekers of the middle ages; for they, as well as we, were aware that the Romans had once lived here.

'Treasure hidden in the earth', says Blackstone, 'belongs to the King; the punishment of such as concealed from the King the finding of treasure was no less than death; but now [late eighteenth century] it is only fine and imprisonment.'

Not until archaeologists were prepared to buy and say nothing did treasure trove have a chance of survival against the Draconian laws which governed both its finding and its finders.

Archaeology, in its simple beginnings, may perhaps first be detected in the passion for opening up the tombs of kings, notably in Westminster Abbey. It is true that it was in the hope of finding treasure that this desecration was permitted; but, nevertheless, the accounts of the opening of the tombs indicate that those who opened them were not insensible to the interest of ancient clothing—even to the interest of the mouldered corpses themselves. This embryo archaeology will be dealt with in the chapter which treats of the subterraneous parts of Westminster Abbey and the Royal Palace of St Stephen.

We have seen how, more or less contemporaneously with the founding of the Royal Society, there arose an interest in ancient things, based rather on what they were than on what they were worth. Though that interest first showed itself in relation to the evidences of Britain's classical past: the 'tear-bottles' and the cinerary urns, the wine-vessels and the coins, the funerary inscriptions and the tessellated pavements, the relics of our 'Gothick' ancestors, though held in less esteem, were not altogether rejected. The sixteenth- and seventeenth-century antiquaries still prized Saxon *sceat* and *scramasax*; and, as we have seen, 'Gyant's Bones' were valued as curiosities worth the preserving, long before Cuvier, Buffon and Lamarck laid down the foundations of a system of experimental zoology.

It is, though, not until the eighteenth century, and then mostly in the pages of *Archaeologia* and *The Gentleman's Magazine*, that the development and formalizing of our modern archaeology are recorded; and remember that the Society of Antiquaries was an eighteenth-century foundation.

Every man who had had a grammar-school education could, in those times, read a Latin inscription, and the London of the eighteenth century was expanding at a more rapid pace than is even the London of today. There was building on a vast scale, especially within the limits of the City of London; and though the workmen, digging foundations, did not go as deep as they do today, they still went deep enough to uncover the remains of the Roman bath-houses and private dwellings, offices, storehouses, and military and municipal buildings. Rooms were rarely, if ever, found intact: but often the tessellated floors were as good as new, and towards the end of the eighteenth century, when the taste for classic architecture was still dominant, many of these floors were not only lifted up to be preserved, but lifted up to be incorporated into modern buildings. One such floor was found when digging the foundations for the last East India House in 1799, and was laid in the new building. It is now in the British Museum.

But if the archaeologists of London ever seek a Founder—or a Patron Saint—they should look no farther than Sir Christopher Wren. With him—and not even with Sir Thomas Browne—we find archaeology first developed.

There was a legend, current in Wren's time, that St Paul's

Cathedral—or, rather, the earliest Christian church at that place—had been built upon the remains of a demolished temple of Diana. (This legend is curious, because the cathedral of Notre Dame in Paris is certainly built over a temple of Cernunnos, the Celtic Horned God; and a small altar, bearing what appears to be an inscription to Diana, was found, not far from the site of St Paul's, in nearby Godliman Street.)

Now Wren refused to accept this legend; but, like a good archaeologist, he took the trouble to disprove it (at least to his own satisfaction) by practical research. When digging the foundations for his new cathedral, he instructed the workmen to go carefully, and to report to him what they found.

Wren, says Strype, 'gave but little Credit to the common Story, that a Temple had been here to Diana . . . meeting with no such Indications in his Searches.' But, in fact, Wren not only gave little credit to the story before he began to dig; he dug, we may say, to put the legend to the test.

What Wren did find, however, when digging the foundations of the Bell (or north-west) Tower were pretty clear evidences of a Roman burial-ground and a Roman pottery, in which the lamps, bottles, urns and dishes that Wren found had been made.

'The first discoveries were of Saxon graves lined with chalk-stone, and Saxon coffins hollowed out of the same material. Beneath this layer were the remains of the ancient Britons [Sc. Roman Britons], the abundance of the ivory and wooden pins that had fastened their shrouds showing that the bodies had been laid in rows. Below these were Roman sacrificial and ceremonial remains, and portions of Roman pavements.'

But, once started on his archaeological quest, the thorough Sir Christopher (Mr Wren, as he was still), dug down in time to a point far beyond that at which even Mousterian Man had his settlements on the low hills overlooking the Thames lagoon. Wren found 'clay, sand, sea-shells and, eventually, a beach, suggesting pretty clearly that the hill where St Paul's stands was once under the sea'. The evidence was read aright: Ludgate Hill was once under the sea—about one million years ago.

There is a story of buried treasure which is intimately connected with a man who is buried in St Paul's crypt, alongside Sir Christopher Wren. This story of Mr Mylne, who was Surveyor of St Paul's until his death in 1811, does not really belong in this book at all; so that here, in this chapter, is as good a place as any to tell it.

One of England's most famous 'stately houses' is King's Weston, on the borders of Somerset and Gloucestershire. The mansion was designed by Vanbrugh, but at the beginning of the last century, the then owner, a Mr Southwell, decided to extend and 'improve' the property. Southwell had met Mylne in Rome; had admired his architectural work; and now invited him to carry out the alterations at King's Weston. During the preliminary surveys, Mylne uncovered a secret room, which, when opened, was found to contain a mass of old parchments. One of these recorded the grant of a barony, by Henry III, to one of Mr Southwell's ancestors. In consequence of this find, Mr Southwell petitioned that the barony be called out of abeyance, and the Committee for Privileges of the House of Lords recommend to the King that the title of Baron de Clifford be restored.

A later Lord de Clifford married a daughter of Mrs Meyrick, the 'Night Club Queen' of the 1920s, and since her most famous 'club', the *Forty-three*, was partially underground, her story, at least, belongs in this book, and will be told at its proper place.

4. London goes to Ground

LONDON, like any other great city, has always had sewers, which were large, extensive and underground in Roman times, and few and small until we approach the modern period.

Perhaps we can date this 'modern period'—at least in its modest beginnings—at about the end of the sixteenth century, when Sir John Harington published a discourse on, and his design for, a water-closet; the book having the punning title, *Metamorphosis of Ajax: A Cloacinean Satire.*

Now flush-privies call for two necessities: a constant supply of water and either sewers or deep cess-pits to receive the waste. The water was not available when Harington published his book (which, it is said, both shocked and delighted Queen Elizabeth): but the water was on its way—from Ware, forty miles distant from London; and as digging was an art long, long before Harington's time, there was no trouble in supplying the cess-pits—300,000 of which were serving London's needs when the first of the modern sewerage schemes was begun a little more than a century ago.

Let us take the water first, which called for the first real opening-up of London's subterraneous parts since the Romans had laid their sewers beneath Londinium Augusta.

In the early part of the seventeenth century, London was running short of water—not merely to flush water closets, but to provide people with drink. The city, little larger than a provincial market town at the end of the fifteenth century, had grown during the adventurously expansive reigns of Henry VIII and Elizabeth I into a metropolis housing nearly half-a-million people. As far as Government was concerned, the problem of providing them with water for drinking, let alone for washing themselves or their clothes, was not only pressing but, apparently, insoluble.

The man who came to the rescue was Hugh Myddelton, son of Richard Myddelton, a powerful super-squire, who was a Member of Parliament and Governor of Denbigh Castle. Hugh came to London, was apprenticed to a goldsmith, and before he was forty had become a wealthy man.

Some modest attempts to supply London with water had already been made whilst Hugh Myddelton was piling up his fortune as a banker. In 1581, Peter Morris, a German, was granted by the City Corporation the right to erect a water-wheel under the 'first arch' of London Bridge. This produced the power for machinery which pumped water from the Thames, through wooden pipes, to the City conduits.

A similar undertaking, at Broken Wharf, by St Paul's, was originated in 1584 by Bevis Bulmer. The two undertakings were eventually united in the London Bridge Waterworks, with a capital of £150,000 divided into three hundred shares of £500 each. The continuity which marks the development of these primitive municipal services into the present Metropolitan Water Board is well demonstrated by the fact that the Board still pays annuities in respect of these early ventures to a total of £3,750 a year, and will continue to do so until 2082! The Morris undertaking was large enough for his grandson, in 1701, to be able to sell his rights to Richard Soames for £38,000.

Nevertheless, the waterworks at London Bridge could not provide for the needs of more than a small London district—most of London's water being provided by the 'water carriers', a powerful public-utility corporation which raised loud voices against the 'new-fangled' methods of supplying water.

If London was really to get an adequate supply of drinking-water, then thinking, planning and execution on a large scale were required. The answer forced itself on the numerous Parliamentary and City committees which met to discuss the problem: to link the water-rich parts of Hertfordshire with water-starved London by means of an artificial river.

In only one of those books dealing with the planning and construction of this 'New River' have I seen it mentioned that a similar ambitious undertaking had already been successfully carried out by Sir Francis Drake, when he brought the water to Plymouth, so that, to this day, the people of Plymouth celebrate, each year, the memory of Sir Francis.

To take nothing away from Hugh Myddelton's achievement, it may be stated as a fact that it was the successful bringing of water to Plymouth, over a distance of twenty-five miles, which persuaded the authorities that something similar could be done for London. It was done. And it was Hugh Myddelton who did it.

Parliamentary sanction for the construction of a 'New River' was easily obtained, and two enabling Acts were passed with hardly a dissentient voice. And there, but for the enterprise and energy of Hugh Myddelton, the matter might well have remained for a century more. Well aware, since he had served on most of the numerous committees, that neither Government nor City Corporation intended to pass beyond pious resolutions, Myddelton volunteered to cut the New River at his own expense, provided that any profits should belong to him. This offer was gratefully accepted by the City Corporation which transferred to Myddelton the rights of construction conferred on it by Parliament.

The final plan, as carried out by Myddelton, was to construct an aqueduct, ten feet wide and about four feet deep, from the springs at Chadwell and Amwell, in Hertfordshire, to Islington, following a winding course of just under forty miles. Even with modern mechanical excavators and other labour-saving devices, the cutting of such an artificial river would be no small undertaking. Yet, in 1609, Myddelton undertook to cut the New River within four years—at a rate, say, of a little over one mile a month.

Into the project, Hugh Myddelton poured his immense fortune, but it was not the actual excavation of 8,500,000 cubic feet of earth which was his main difficulty. Like the builders of London's first underground railway, two hundred and fifty years later, Myddelton found that he was driving his aqueduct through a succession of law-suits brought against him by land-lords who claimed that the 'overflow of water' would impair the value of their property. A powerful Parliamentary opposition—its collective palm well-greased by the Honourable Company of Water Tankard Bearers, who had the right to sell water under charter—continuously sniped at Myddelton, until, within sight of success, his capital ran out.

A word here on the systems that Myddelton's threatened to displace. The pollution of the Thames had rendered its water unsuitable for drinking as early as the beginning of the thirteenth century, if we must give that pollution's obviousness a starting date. So much so that, no later than 1236, a Royal Patent was granted for the construction of a leathern conduit, to bring water from Tyburn Brook (about where Derby House now stands, in Stratford Place, Oxford Street) to the City. The two principal conduit-heads in the City were at the two ends of Cheapside, and at the west end of Eastcheap. They have not been forgotten by modern historians of the fourth-form class, for it was the custom, during the later Middle Ages, to cause these conduits to run with wine, to celebrate some notable event.

The system of piping which carried the water to the conduit-heads was of mixed timber, stone and lead—even, as in the case of the conduit of 1236, leather. Leather piping, at least as far as fire-fighting appliances were concerned, survived until the present century.

Nevertheless, by the beginning of the seventeenth century, the majority of Londoners living at some distance from the wells were entirely dependent upon the house-to-house services of the Honourable Company of Water Tankard Bearers. Seeing their monopoly threatened by the New River, the powerful financial interests behind the Water Tankard Bearers ganged up to impede Myddelton's work—and, if possible, to make it useless for him to continue. But, to save both the scheme and London's hopes of fresh water, unexpected and all-powerful assistance came forward. James I offered to 'go halves' in the cost—past and future—of the New River, in return for a half-share in all the profits: the Royal Moiety, as it was called.

To anticipate a little: in 1631, King Charles I sold back the Royal Moiety to Sir Hugh (as he had then become) for a perpetual rent charge of £500. This charge, known as the King's or Royal Clog, though now subject to deduction by Land Tax, is still paid by the Metropolitan Water Board as successors to the New River Company.

With the King's backing, Myddelton could now secure an extension of the time-limit from the City Corporation and, by pressing on with the work, Myddelton completed the New River on September 28th, 1613, only seven months later than the date fixed in the contract for the termination of the task.

The Water House at Islington, on which the offices of the Metropolitan Water Board now stand, was built on the site of the round pond in the parish of Clerkenwell into which the waters of the New River discharged.

In the history of underground London, the construction of the New River is important in that it brought water to London by an open channel; but, on arrival in London, that water was distributed, by means of buried pipes, to various conduits and even to private houses.

There was no novelty in this—only in the scale of the supply. Water-pipes to private houses had been laid already, in connection with the bringing of water from Hampstead and other places to the city in 1543 (note here that four reservoirs were constructed on Hampstead Heath in 1589), from the Thames, at Dowgate, in 1568—machinery being used here to raise the water from the river; and in connection, too, with the schemes of Morris and Bulmer, that we have already noted.

Permission to 'tap' the water from the City conduits by means of pipes to private houses was granted to certain of the citizens—the authorizing document being known as a 'quill'.

Myddelton's New River rather supplemented than displaced the various waterworks on the Thames, which, at the height of their capacity, in the eighteenth century, were furnishing a daily supply of four million gallons.

The London Bridge Waterworks, into which the various smaller undertakings had been amalgamated, lost their principal pumping-station through the Great Fire of 1666, but rebuilt it in the following year, acquired a lease of the third arch of London Bridge in 1761, and of two further arches in 1767. Eminent engineers, including Brindley and Smeaton, were consulted on the effect that the additional machinery would have on the structure of the bridge and on the navigability of the river; and Smeaton himself designed an improved wheel to operate under the fifth arch. These waterworks were demolished only when Old London Bridge was replaced by the present structure in 1831.

As for the New River, the supply from Amwell and Chadwell was early supplemented with water drawn from the River Lea, and in 1768, after a century and a half of successful development, the Company introduced steam power to the works at New River Head.

In the last century, the principal pumping-station was established at Stoke Newington—only a short while after Edgar Allan Poe had attended the Manor House School in that then rural village—and two subsidiary reservoirs were completed at Stoke Newington in 1831 and 1833. From the Stoke Newington station, the greater part of the water was eventually distributed to London's northern parts, the remainder of the water being passed on to New River Head for distribution to the City and the adjoining districts.

Following the passing of the Metropolis Water Act, 1852, filtration works were built at Stoke Newington, Hornsey and New River Head. The ancient Round Pond at New River Head was abolished only as late as 1914, the adjacent filter beds being finally abandoned only as recently as 1945. Today, the New River ends at Stoke Newington.

Through many other companies, Londoners were assured of more and more water—more or less 'fresh'—as the eighteenth and nineteenth centuries progressed. The principal companies in the water-supply business were the Hampstead Water Company, originating in the granting by the City of the lease of its Hampstead undertakings to certain 'projectors', including William Paterson, founder of the Bank of England; the York Buildings Waterworks, the first in London to make use of steam-power for pumping—Thomas Savery, in 1712, having installed a machine 'for raising water by fire'; the Chelsea Waterworks Company, the first (in 1829) to introduce sand-filtration to London, after experiments carried out by their chief engineer, James Simpson; the Lambeth, West Middlesex, East London, Kent, Grand Junction, Southwark and Vauxhall, and some others. All these were finally absorbed into the Metropolitan Water Board in 1902.

5. The Pipers are Coming!

THE supply of water need not—but usually does—involve the use of pipes, mostly buried, for convenience and safety, below ground. Even the members of the Brotherhood of St Christopher of the Waterbearers, who carried the water from house to house in metal-bound oaken pitchers, drew their water from conduits to which it had been piped.

Peter Morris 'laid on' water to consumers' houses by means of lead pipes but, as the number of his customers grew, bigger pipes were needed—'mains'—and these were constructed out of either timber or stone.

The conduit at Aldersgate, opened in 1610, used pipes of wood and stone, and the New River Company used wooden pipes from the beginning of its career; wooden pipes not being superseded by cast-iron pipes until the coming of gas made a substance less porous than either wood or stone imperative.

Thus that familiar condition of the London street—'dug up' —was already becoming a commonplace before the end of Elizabeth I's reign. But, even allowing for the exaggeration of the contemporary or 'eye-witness' commentator, the main London streets at the beginning of the Gas Period—which coincided with the stepping up of competition among the Water Companies—must have been open to traffic only a very few days in the year.

'Despite high death rates,' says Mr Wylie, 'fortunes were made out of the supply of poisonous water. Eight private companies supplied London. Some streets had three separate pipe lines with three sets of labourers, selected for their belligerence, all looking after the interests of their separate companies. Plumbers made fortunes by persuading customers

to change from one supply to another, and streets were virtually closed to traffic as they were torn open to allow connections to be transferred. Frequent changes of allegiance could
pay the consumer as well as the plumber, for in the resulting
confusion he was often not charged for the water he used.
During one year the Vauxhall Company spent £24,000 on
new piping in one street, and had the barren satisfaction of
collecting £81. So fierce was the competition that directors
of water companies spent most of their time in their offices
sending scurrilous letters to each other, while their workmen
fought in the streets.'

And though the story of Gas belongs to a later chapter, this
quotation from Sir Compton Mackenzie's *The Vital Flame* is
apposite at this point:

'Cut-throat competition among the various coal-gas companies was persistent. During the 'forties, Oxford Street and
Tottenham Court Road were supplied by four different companies, and from five distinct stations. As late as 1857, half
a century after the first gas-lighted street lamps were erected
by Winsor in Pall-Mall, there were eighty gas-joints and
treble sets of mains in a sixteen-yard frontage in Cockspur
Street.'

We see, then, that progress in the supply of lighting, heating,
water and sewers to London has inevitably led to a deeper and
more extensive carving out of London's below-pavement parts.
Let us now look at the earliest piping: that for which London
was first excavated on a grand and systematic scale.

We have seen that Peter Morris used lead piping to carry
water to his customers' houses; but against the use of lead there
are today, and there were even then, many practical objections,
besides that of lead's toxicity—a fact which was hardly
appreciated four centuries ago.

Lead's useful ductility, together with a low-melting point
which enabled welding to be carried out at a very low temperature, made it the ideal metal for working with the primitive
tools and techniques of the late Middle Ages; but what are

advantages to the workmen are advantages, no less, to the spoiler and the thief.

Lead is so soft that it can be cut with a pocket-knife or broken with the hands, and as it has always been a relatively costly metal (useful, too, for adulterating silver), it has always been the special prey of the sneak-thief.

Lead, then, for piping, was soon replaced, on prudential and economical grounds, by the material that the Romans had used: wood.

The earthenware pipes—*tubuli*—that the Romans also used had to wait until the eighteenth century before being re-introduced.

Tree-trunks were bored—usually by a water-powered machine—so that a socket was cut at one end, the other end being tapered. The tapered end of one pipe fitted into the socket of the next, the pipes being driven into each other to form a joint, which became water-tight as the water passing through swelled the wood.

It was the common practice to slide an iron hoop over the socketed end of each pipe as a precaution against the splitting of the wood.

To cut out the middleman, some of the water-companies maintained their own boring-mills and permanent staff of borers. Tree-trunks were delivered by the timber-merchants direct to these mills.

The New River Company's horse-mill was at Dorset Stairs, on the Thames at the back of Fleet Street.

These wooden pipes, which continued in use for more than two centuries, could be produced cheaply: the raw material was not costly, transport (mostly, as in the case of the New River Company's mill at Dorset Stairs) was by water, and cheap, too; while the labour, itself cheapened by mechanical aid, was certainly no expensive item. On the other hand, wooden pipes did not last. The wastage was heavy.

Today, wherever men dig in the older parts of London, they come across the remains of these old wooden pipes, and no harm is done when the local newspaper, trying desperately hard to add some romantic gloss to the plain story of another Kliptiko shack's erection, tells its readers of the discovery of 'Ancient Roman pipes'.

Save in the most exceptional circumstances, wooden pipes laid in London's damp soil do not last very long: for practical purposes the 'life' of a wooden pipe was from four to twenty-five years, the pipes lasting longer in clay. Decay set in almost at once, and soon the pipes had become so porous that leakage was serious. Again, even a wooden pipe in sound condition could not stand anything like a high pressure: either the pipe itself would burst or, more likely, the joint would 'give'. So that, to carry a pressure which is now handled by one cast-iron pipe, it was not uncommon to lay half a dozen of the wooden pipes. It is a wonder that the roads were ever free from the attentions of the pipe-layers—it is almost certain that there can hardly have been a road in London which was not frequently 'up'.

Two developments abolished the use of the wooden pipe: the rising pressures consequent upon the introduction of mechanically-powered pumping-stations—especially the intro-duction of the intermediate, 'booster' station—and the discovery that wooden pipes permitted the water within to absorb the smell and taste of gas from leaking gas-mains.

Fortunately, there was a remedy to both these problems in the cast-iron pipe which, employed on a small scale since the beginning of the eighteenth century (the introduction of machinery had called both for its invention and its production), came into general use with Thomas Simpson's inventing the spigot-and-socket joint, which made the cast-iron pipe's large-scale employment practicable.

All the water-companies founded at the beginning of the nineteenth century were using cast-iron pipes within a decade of their establishment; and, in 1811, the New River Company adopted the policy of replacing its wooden pipes by pipes of cast-iron.

The change-over was greatly accelerated by the passing of the Metropolis Paving Act in 1817, which enacted that all the water-companies, when laying new pipes, should use cast-iron; but the Act, in permitting the repair of existing wooden pipes, provided that loophole that experienced wide-boys know will be written into every Act, and enabled those who wished to use wooden pipes to continue to use them until well after 1850. It is these last survivors which turn up, in such large quantities, as the 'Ancient Roman water-pipes' to be seen in glass cases in the entrance halls of the new office buildings.

Today, the use of cast-iron has been supplemented by that of drawn steel; but there is another widely employed material: glazed earthenware, the modern history of which dates back to the year 1729.

In that year, Switzer successfully tested earthenware pipes of small bore at the York Buildings Waterworks—the waterworks at which Savery's steam-engine was installed—and pipes of this material were in use at the beginning of the last century. But it was not until the development of the tough 'stoneware' pottery at Lambeth—a development notably associated with the name of Henry Doulton—that pipes could be made both strong and impermeable enough to carry water through the earth. The development of this 'stoneware' extended over the second quarter of the last century; though it was not until the latter part of the nineteenth century that the earthenware pipe was used on a large scale.

Occasionally workmen find pipes made of stone—and these, to the uninstructed, seem even more 'Ancient Roman' than the rotted wooden pipes unearthed in excavation.

Patents for the manufacture of stone pipes as a substitute for those of wood or iron were granted in 1805 and 1811, but extensive practical tests by the Grand Union Company in 1812 proved that the pipes were useless, and their employment was discontinued.

The necessity of laying pipes in large numbers and at frequent intervals involved the frequent tearing-up of the road surface. Attempts to find a practical remedy for this constant disruption of the traffic were made almost as soon as the need for a remedy became obvious; and the most reasonable proposition was that which has now, to a large extent, supplied the desired remedy.

The title of a book published in 1828 states the problem clearly and suggests the answer. The author, John Williams, advocated the provision of 'subways' capable of housing gas and water mains and sewers. Williams had taken out a patent in 1822 and, like so many of the vigorous propagandists of the last century, was an indefatigable letter-writer to Authority. In a series of letters to the Commissioners for Metropolitan Improvements and the Commissioners for the Health of Towns, written during 1844 and 1845, and published in the latter year, Williams urged the adoption of his scheme of 'subways' by cogent arguments not hindered by unattractive prose.

In the part of this book which deals with the sewers of London, attention will be called to another advocate of pipe-carrying 'subways': W. Austin.

In their book, *The Rise of the Gas Industry in Britain*, the authors, Dean Chandler and A. Douglas Lacey, make the very odd remark that 'the cost of such schemes must, however, have proved prohibitive, and no attempt to carry them out seems to have been made'. A remark such as this, in a work of such patent scholarship, seems extraordinary. Not only are twenty-four of these subways carrying London's gas, water, light, power and even television—nine miles of subway altogether—but the oldest still in use, that under Garrick Street, was built as long ago as 1861, only eight years after Austin's scheme had been 'approved by the Metropolitan and City Sewer Commissioners and the engineers'.

The London Beneath Us need not lie so very far down. Go to Piccadilly Circus, and note the manholes and iron gratings set in the pavement over which so many thousands pass each day.

Sometimes, when the sad, grey, tired English sun is in a certain part of the shallow sky, a beam of pale sunlight will strike down through the iron bars of the grating and light up what lies below: a tunnel which leads to a deeper tunnel, which runs below the booking-hall of the Underground Station.

Access to this tunnel is gained through a manhole set flush with the pavement. One climbs down a steel ladder fixed to the side of a brick shaft; through the wide gratings the pipes are hauled in or taken out.

Climb down the steel ladder, and you find yourself in a wide brick tunnel: this is one of the subways which carries the 'life lines' of London. This tunnel is near the surface, and carries not only electric cables and a water-main, but the six-inch high-pressure main, carrying water at 700 lb. to the square inch, to keep London's hydraulic lifts and hoists running.

Murdoch, the man who gave us gas-lighting, was the inventor of a 'pneumatic' lift; but around the middle of the last century, the steam-powered lift was introduced, to serve the new blocks of flats which were going up, particularly in brand-new Victoria Street. However, the steam lifts were unreliable: so much so that their further use was forbidden by law, and the hydraulic lift (which had been used by genuine Ancient Romans in the warehouses at Ostia) was re-introduced to London. In spite of the development of the electric lift— the automatic, self-levelling electric lift dates from 1892—the hydraulic lift has not yet been entirely displaced; and the high-pressure mains upon which it depends still run beneath our city.

If one walks along the tunnel which runs beneath Piccadilly Circus, one will come across a steel-lined pit, some forty feet deep; and, at the bottom of this pit another tunnel branches out. Here, under Piccadilly Circus Underground Station is a most impressive collection of pipes and cables, all neatly laid along the walls of the tunnel, so that any one of them can be got at, for repair or replacement, with the minimum of trouble.

The Post Office cables, colour-coded, are borne on heavy brackets, and the cable coloured a bright scarlet carries the vitally important fire-brigade calls.

Branch tunnels lead off the main tunnels in this central part of London, and as one walks under the pavements, catching an occasional glimpse of the pedestrians' hurrying feet, and—above the foreshortened bodies—the parapets of the buildings against the sombre sky, one realizes that, beneath the visible Circus is a hidden Circus, no less extensive, and hardly less busy.

As the new Underground Stations are built, or older ones reconstructed, a subway to carry mains and cables is built to run beneath the stations, though these tunnels are not as deep as some excavations that we shall consider later.

This mains-carrying tunnelling is not all on one level: one goes up and down, as well as forward and back, and sideways, too. There are stairways but, as 'short cuts', there are vertical ladders, fixed to the sides of circular brick shafts. In an emergency, the repair men can move from point to point of this vast subterranean complex in the quickest possible time.

There are few parts of London—especially the 'landmarks'—under which it is not possible to walk, following the course of the pipes and cables which supply London with heat, light, sound and water. One can stand under the statue of Boadicea, on the Victoria Embankment, or under busy Commercial Road, Whitechapel, in which the famous thriller-writer, Peter Cheyney, was born, and see there the two four-foot-diameter pipes which supply the busy, ambitious and hardworking East Londoners with gas.

One may walk from Cambridge Circus to Trafalgar Square —underground—and, as the rebuilding of London progresses in all its hopeless dreariness, the existing public-utility subways will be linked, to form a network of subterranean passages no less extensive than the sewers which carry away London's wastes.

It need hardly be said that, *on paper*, the most strict precautions are taken to secure these subways against unauthorized visits, and Londoners against the damage and disruption which would come through inattention to the many pipes and cables which are carried through these subways. 'Officially', whenever a blowlamp has to be used for some repair in these subways, the place at which the torch is to be used is first tested by an inspector of the London County Council to see that no gas is leaking there.

All the same, accidents will happen, and just before the war some panic was caused—('Do you think Hitler has begun *already*?')—when two Georgian houses at the back of Queen Victoria Street blew up with a mighty bang. It was not Hitler —it was only gas.

There is a newcomer to London's underground pipe-population: the hot-water pipe.

The old Guards' Barracks at the corner of Pimlico Road and Chelsea Bridge Road have just, as I write, been pulled down; but some new barracks, for civilians, are nearing completion, a little to the east of the Guards' Barracks.

Named 'Churchill Gardens', the new civilian barracks are supplied with hot water from Battersea Power Station, just across the River.

There is a tunnel under the Thames at this point—we shall talk about the numerous Thames tunnels in detail later—which carries the cables from Battersea Power Station. There is also another tunnel, built since the war, which plays its part in supplying Churchill Gardens with hot water.

Water for the boilers of the power-house is drawn from the Thames and, after having been heated to boiling point, is eventually discharged into the River.

When a new wing had to be built on to the power-station, it was necessary to build a tunnel to the opposite bank of the Thames, so as to ensure that the water taken in would be cool. It occurred to someone—after this tunnel had been built—that one way of getting rid of the hot water, without raising the temperature of the Thames, would be to 'pipe' it to the barracks going up on the other side of the River.

Dolphin Square, a vast block of flats that journalists, for some whimsical reason of their own, always call 'luxury flats', is also supplied with hot water from the Battersea Power Station—and the 'piping' of hot water to blocks of flats as they go up is a development which, to use the fashionable jargon, is 'Number One Priority in Planning'. In other words, more and more blocks of flats will use the hot water from the power-stations.

In this book, I intend to treat separately the sewers and the water-mains of London; but there was a time when reasonable people had to think of them together—and for good cause. There was an intimate link between them; and the name of that link was—Death.

The connection between impure drinking water and the epidemic visitations of cholera and typhoid fever which used to carry off so many thousands of Londoners was something which not only had to be discovered, but had to be brought home as a scientific fact, by the unceasing propagandist efforts of a handful of public-spirited men, the chief of whom was Edwin Chadwick. Like the man, Charles Pearson, who gave London—and so the world—underground railways, Edwin Chadwick, who gave London—and so the world—clean water, was a lawyer, and an indefatigable publicist. Both Pearson and Chadwick wrote innumerable letters, both published their letters in pamphlet form; and both had the happiness, after years of self-sacrificing effort, of seeing their plans come to fruition.

Edwin Chadwick had become Secretary to the Poor Law Commissioners and, in 1842, he published his historic *Report of the Sanitary Conditions of the Labouring Population*, a report based upon the evidence collected by Drs Southwood, Smith, Arnott and Kay, and upon the impressive statistic-backed evidence adduced by Farr in the preceding year.

Chadwick's *Report* led directly to the appointment of the Royal Commission on the Health of Towns, and to the eventual passing of the Public Health Acts of 1848 and 1875, and the Sanitary Act of 1866. Our generally efficient Public Health services are directly attributable to Chadwick's work; and my American readers will recall the great Chicago scandal, when inefficient control of the public health services permitted the infection of the city's drinking water by overflow from the sewage pipes. Many died in Chicago, as many more died in

London, from the same cause, before the work of Chadwick brought the underground piping of London under proper control. It says much for the efficiency of our Water and Sewer authorities that even with the heavy bombing of the last war, deaths due to 'seepage' of the underground-piped wastes were few indeed; and that, throughout the war, Londoners could count upon the purity of their drinking water.

It was not always so. In 1849, eighteen thousand Londoners died from cholera; in 1854, the deaths numbered twenty thousand. Yet, in 1853, the private water-companies were still supplying 'drinking' water from the Thames to their customers.

This year of 1853 is an important one, for it was in that year that the Lambeth Water Company moved its intake farther up the River, to a point where the water was less polluted.

Within one year, the death-rate within the area of the Lambeth Company's supply dropped to 37 per thousand, as against the 130 per thousand in those districts where the sources of supply had not been changed. These were figures to impress ordinary people—not merely scientists. But once 'the penny had dropped', the scientists had a chance to back up the argument with their figures and facts.

For over a year, I was in correspondence with Sir Howard Roberts, the then Chairman of the London County Council. The result of our correspondence was that Sir Howard regretfully decided against putting up one of the G.L.C.'s blue-and-white plaques to mark the house in Sloane Street at which Edgar Allan Poe had attended school. A number of plaques commemorate persons whose claim on our recollection is hard to justify—'George Odger, Labour Leader' (who the devil was *he*?)—but no one will find fault that an old house in Sackville Street bears a plaque noting the fact that in this elegant little house once lived Dr John Snow, a Yorkshire physician, who first proved that the germs of cholera are water-borne. How Snow discovered a fact so vital to human happiness makes one of the great romances of pathological detection—and detection of the sort which glorifies the Scotland Yard man as well as the laboratory technician.

In 1849, Snow had published a pamphlet, *On the Mode of Communication of Cholera*. In this pamphlet, he had sought to show that cholera was caused by 'a poison extracted from a diseased body, and passed on through drinking water which had been polluted with sewage'. When the next epidemic visitation of cholera came in 1854, Snow seized his opportunity to prove his arguments.

Looking for evidence, he noted that, during the first fortnight of September, 1854, no fewer than six hundred persons had been carried off by cholera in an area which appeared to be centred about the junction of Broad Street and Cambridge Street, Golden Square.

Snow—just like Sherlock Holmes—'hailed a hansom', and drove down to Broad Street, where he found a public pump. By patient house-to-house inquiry—what a lesson in fact-finding these nineteenth-century professional men could show our reporters!—he established the fact that, *without exception*, every one of the persons who had died from cholera within the Broad Street area had drunk water from this particular pump.

After that, it was no difficulty for Snow to demonstrate, first that the well supplying the pump was filled with infected water, and that, second, that it was sewage, seeping through cracks in the brick wall of the well, which was contaminating the water.

Of course, to apply the reasoning, energy and practical discoveries of such men as Snow and Chadwick to the improvement of the general human condition was no simple matter. Ever since the first handful of parasitic workshies ganged together in Sumer to form a 'Civil Service', the bureaucrat has always been more concerned with saving his face than saving the mob on which he battens.

It was so in 1854. Snow, by the way, had already 'shocked decent people', by his willingness (as well as his ability) to administer chloroform to Queen Victoria at the birth of Prince

Leopold; and the opposition of the private water-companies to Chadwick's scheme to bring water in great quantity from the Surrey hills had got Chadwick the sack, only a few weeks before the cholera epidemic hit London again. Nevertheless, though Chadwick was dismissed from his post, vested interest had already begun to lose the battle.

The Metropolitan Water Act of 1852 had made filtration compulsory, and though Londoners had to wait a further fifty years—exactly—until the establishment of the Metropolitan Water Board practically guaranteed them water supplied by a system in which quality was not controlled by cost (as Mr J. C. Wylie so well puts it), the history of the water-supplies of London during the latter part of the nineteenth century is a history of progress against which vested interest in disease and death fought a constantly losing action.

Still, though it seems obvious to us that the work of such men as Snow and Chadwick removed the threat of cholera in particular and the pathogenic qualities of our drinking-water in general, there are those who—like the directors of some of the private water-companies—refused to accept the connection between unfiltered drinking-water and disease as proven. These people point to the fact that cholera, though it carried off a quarter of a million people (mostly in London) between 1848 and 1854, made its appearance only in 1831. Granted, they say, that the work of Snow and Chadwick may take the credit for the disease's virtual disappearance after 1868: what of the centuries before 1831, when London's water was, if anything, even filthier than it was in the first year of William IV's reign?

The answer is not easy to give. It seems to be true that cholera was imported from the East—but, then, trade had been carried on with the East for centuries before cholera first appeared in London. Why the people of London should have been immune before 1831, when they ceased to be immune afterwards, is something that medical science is still unable to explain.

But the mortality-figures have established, beyond doubt, the role of the public water-supplies as originators and disseminators of disease: purify the water, and the incidence of water-borne diseases, such as cholera and typhoid (which was killing 390 people in a million in 1868), drops. Allow the water-supplies to become tainted—as in Chicago, forty years ago—and the close connection between impure water and disease is demonstrated beyond contradiction.

In spite of noise, hypertension, rock-and-roll, agene in our bread and strontium-90 in our air, we have added, in the thirty years which have included the most devastating war in history, a life expectancy of no less than eleven years to a woman's, and just under ten to a man's, life.

This has happened, not by making life 'easier', but by making existence cleaner. In eliminating lice, we have eliminated typhus; in eliminating the fly, we have eliminated a host of diseases, including spotted fever; in cleansing water, we have eliminated cholera and typhoid fever.

The mechanisation of the water-supply system is a process which has been continuous over the last four centuries; and, about one hundred and fifty years after water-driven machinery had been installed to power the waterworks at Dowgate on the Thames, steam-power was introduced at the York Buildings Waterworks, as we have seen.

The development of the steam-engine throughout the last century went hand-in-hand with the development of the steam-engine's use in supplying Londoners with more and more (and better and better) water. Today, both electricity and the internal-combustion engine of the Diesel type have almost ousted steam-power.

The need for power is simply explained—it is a need which has been felt from the beginning of the water-supply industry. In the first place, it is rare indeed to find a water-source *above* a town; in which case it must be drawn up either from a well or a river—in both cases, some mechanical contrivance is necessary to raise the water.

Very simple mechanical devices can handle the problem of getting water up from a river or well. It is when water has to be brought over long distances, and forced up to levels higher than the source of supply, that considerable power is needed: and this is power in the sort of quantities for which the human muscles make totally inadequate provision.

Water, as we learnt at school, finds its own level. Water coming down from a hill will rise in a pipe to the level—and not an inch higher than the level—of the hill-top reservoir.

It is not always easy to provide hill-top reservoirs or high water-towers to supply the needed pressure to take the water to the taps of a tall building—and, in any case, the water must be taken, in the first place, up to the top of the hill or water-tower. Yet the upper stories of houses, no less than the ground floors, must be supplied—and it was to do this that the elaborate system of main and subsidiary ('booster') pumps, powered by steam, was developed.

As, generally speaking, the pumping-stations are above ground, the details of their development and present condition do not enter into this story; but there are underground, as well as surface, pumps; and a word must be said about these underground pumps. The Metropolitan Water Board has forty-seven well stations; and pumping machinery is installed in forty-two walls and eighteen boreholes. With the exception of two wells in the Upper Greensand and two boreholes in the Lower Greensand, all the wells and boreholes are in the chalk.

In the early days, underground pumps were usually beam- or bell-crank-driven of the bucket type, first having flap-valve, and later of the double-beat design, and culminating in the multiannular Perins model. Drive from Diesel engines was generally by means of step-down gearing, the pumps being usually of the three-throw type, having a steady rate of output and absorption of power.

Centrifugal pumps for wells and boreholes were introduced about 1925, the vertical-spindle driving motor (or, in certain cases, the bevel-gearing for drive from Diesel engines) being placed at the surface but, just after the beginning of the last war, the submersible centrifugal pump was introduced, in which both motor and pump are located below water level.

'Since', says *The Water Supply of London*, 'all the Board's water is either river-derived or obtained from below ground, maintenance of the supply is entirely dependent upon continuous pumping.'

One of the principal duties of this continuous pumping is 'raising water from below ground to the surface, and forcing it into supply'.

'Owing', the Board says, 'to the pressure needed to impel the water along the miles of main between station and consumer, and to deliver it at a head sufficient for his requirements whatever the elevation of his dwelling or factory, by far the greater part of the water-horse-power put out by the Board's pumping plant is required for forcing filtered water into supply. Further, the distribution of the consumers is such that some of the water pumped to a head sufficient for a part of the population has to be repumped for those more remote and lying on higher ground. In a number of cases, water is pumped as many as three times after filtration. As a result, the nature and size of the filtered water-pumping machinery vary greatly.'

The annual cost of pumping London's water is about £1,320,000—or about ten guineas per million gallons supplied. And how is it distributed?

The length of the trunk, distribution and service mains— mostly buried in the ground beneath us—is no less than 8,500 miles; and practically all of these mains are of cast-iron. Except in the case of certain clay areas, the soil of London has no damaging effect upon either cast-iron or lead; nor has London's water. This means that many of the cast-iron mains carrying drinking-water of a purity unrivalled throughout the world are well over a century old—as good today as they were when they were laid.

The largest size of the pipe laid in the street is 4 feet in diameter; and, for all that some 2-inch and 3-inch mains are still in use, no mains of smaller diameter than 4 inches are now laid.

Altogether, there are 569 miles of mains having a diameter of 24 inches and over, but the greater part of the piping making up the distribution system is of 4-inch diameter. The 4-inch piping accounts for about 50 per cent of the total mileage, or 4,230 miles.

When the Metropolitan Water Board was established in 1902, it took over eight separate water-supply systems, and these were connected at only a few points. During the sixty years that the Board has been supplying London's water, these systems have been merged by elaborate interlocking, so that, today, every area, in a time of temporary shortage, can draw upon one or more alternative sources of supply.

We have seen that cast-iron pipes—some of them more than a century old—carry London's water beneath its streets and houses and, sometimes, across its railway stations (though not its drinking-water). Some of the iron pipes have been centrifugally cast—or 'spun'—a method of manufacture which makes for greater strength. Where iron pipes have to be laid in clay areas, the iron is protected against corrosion by a sheathing of bituminous material.

Steel is used in conditions where excessive corrosion is threatened, and here the steel is both lined and sheathed with the bituminous composition; today it is the practice to use pipes of this nature for all trunk mains of 24 inches in diameter and over.

London's water is still supplied, in the greater part, by London's River. Of the total of the water gathered, filtered and distributed by the Metropolitan Water Board, the Thames contributes no less than two-thirds.

6. They Hadn't got no Noses!

WHEN I was a small boy, and the air became suddenly vibrant with the ripe odour from some drain, I was bidden sternly to 'hold my nose'—for the simple people of my childhood still held the view that a 'smell' was not only the evidence of corruption, but actual air-borne corruption itself. 'You catch typhoid,' said Nanny who, at another time, told me that the thunder was 'God speaking'. There are, of course, aerobiotic germs, but that of typhoid is not among them.

All the same, when one considers with what importance our ancestors—simple and learned—credited mere 'smells', one wonders how it was that they suffered this, to them, deadly contagion so long. Or couldn't they smell it? It hardly seems possible; and, in fact, the eighteenth-century novelists make it clear that the eighteenth-century man was highly conscious of London's many and disagreeable odours.

What, I think, may be said of the past is this: they could stand assaults upon their nose to a greater degree than can we. It is simple: they had either—albeit under protest—to bear the stench with patience, or go mad. Perhaps a lot of them did go mad.

But, as a start was made on the reduction of the overall decay and consequent stink, so did noses grow more delicate. Until there came a time when, whatever else had survived from the eighteenth century into the nineteenth, the tolerant eighteenth-century nose was not among the survivals.

It is often said that tolerance of foul odours, as 'one of those things', came to an end when the Members of the Houses of Parliament found that the stink within Barry's new buildings was threatening a total abandonment of the Commons and the Lords—the alternative to being gassed (as well as gassing) at

Westminster being nothing but a move up-river to Hampton Court.

It is my opinion that the loudly-voiced objections to the stink of the Thames (it was only later that the honourable Members discovered that the new buildings had been erected over a drain closed only with a covering of thin and permeable stone slabs) were both voiced and loud simply because remedial measures were already under way. It was the knowledge that they would have to bear the stink very little longer which made so many people cry out against the delay in getting rid of the abomination.

Before the stinks went, they grew worse—as though, in some derisively valedictory way, the smell of the Past was bidding a prima donna's farewell. And the stepping-up of the stench was caused, paradoxically—and amusingly—enough, by a burst of energy in the interests of cleanliness and sanitation. In this way: Lord John Russell, then Prime Minister, had set up a Sanitary Commission to investigate the possibility of improving the nation's sanitation, and (at Dickens's request) had appointed Henry Austin, Dickens's brother-in-law, Secretary.

Henry Austin, no enemy of nepotism, then appointed his wife's brother, Alf, to an Inspectorate under the Commission. Alfred Lamert Dickens—that 'Alf' who had sponged on Chapman and Hall in earlier days—found himself in the first near-honest job he had ever had; and gratitude and officiousness combined in both Alf Dickens and his boss to produce some horrible results from Russell's well-intentioned plan.

Both Henry Austin and Alfred Dickens were artists *manqués*: Austin having originally shown promise as a musician (it was while studying at the Royal Academy of Music that he had met Fanny Dickens, whom he afterwards married), while Alf, had he stuck to his drawing and painting, could have made something of a name for himself as a water-colourist. It was a curious fate which condemned these two artistic spirits to end their days as sanitary engineers!

The chief result of the Commission was the passing of a Bill which made it compulsory to provide at least one water-closet for every house, in place of the cess-pit which was traditional.

The installation of the water-closets called for the provision of main drainage; but this main drainage carried the sewage no farther than the Thames, 'with the result that the waterways of London', as a contemporary observed, 'became a vast open sewer which, when the tide rose, closed the outlets and sent the sewage pouring back on the low-lying ground, where it lay stagnant for many hours of the day, causing in 1849 a serious cholera outbreak.'

It probably did not cause the cholera outbreak: what it did cause was a revolt amongst the M.P.s and the editorial staff of *Punch*. Together, these two powerful forces gave London, for the first time since the Romans had left, efficient sanitation.

Even in Roman days, when the sewers ran under the streets of London, the rivers and streams which meandered through the city had served as open sewers; and the practice was continued just so long as those rivers remained open, as is attested by the discovery of rubbish in the bed of the Walbrook; this rubbish dating back to Roman times.

In the course of time, most of London's rivers were covered over, the Fleet alone remaining uncovered until the second half of the eighteenth century. It was doubtless the frequent and sudden rising of the water in the Fleet—the river being fed by several wells and a small tributary brook, the Oldbourne—which caused its roofing-over to be so long deferred; Londoners preferring to cross it by six bridges, the main crossings being at Holborn, Fleet Lane, Fleet Street and Bridewell.

After the Great Fire, the Fleet was converted into a dock, with creeks forty feet wide, at a cost of £28,000. Following the old English custom, still with us, of covering up an unsavoury past with an engaging new name, the Fleet Ditch was rechristened 'the New Canal', but that the erection of handsome buildings around 'the New Canal' did nothing to alter the traditional character of the Fleet Ditch may be gathered from any account in early eighteenth-century writings.

That the thick waters of the Fleet—enriched by the scour-

ings from the dyers', soap-makers' and slaughterers' establish-
ments which lined its malodorous banks—had a nutritive value
to certain types of creation seems to be proved by this odd
account from *The Gentleman's Magazine* (1736).

'A fatter boar was hardly ever seen than one taken up this
day (August 14th, 1736), coming out of the Fleet Ditch into
the Thames. It proved to be a butcher's near Smithfield
Bars, who had missed him five months, all which time he
(*that is, the boar, not the butcher*) had been in the common
sewer, and was improved in price from ten shillings to two
guineas.'

In 1734, so pestilential had the Fleet Ditch become, even by
eighteenth-century standards, that the Lord Mayor and Cor-
poration caused it to be arched over from Holborn Bridge to
Fleet Street; and in 1763, when Blackfriars Bridge and Bridge
Street were being built, the remainder of the Fleet Ditch, from
Fleet Street to the Thames, was covered.

The Fleet is the chief of London's now covered-up rivers,
but it is in no sense a forgotten one. As we shall see, the Fleet
overflowed into the cuttings during the construction of the
Metropolitan Railway, in 1860 and succeeding years, the water
rising in the cuttings to a depth of ten feet; and a description
of what happened during the cold January of 1809 hints at
what might well happen today, were adequate precautions not
constantly taken against flooding:

'The snow being deep on the ground, there came a rapid
thaw, and the arches not affording sufficient passage for the
increased current or storm-waters, the whole space between
Pancras (*sic*), Somers Town and the bottom of the hill at
Pentonville was covered with water. The flood was three
feet deep in the middle of the highway, and the ground
floors of houses were flooded.'

Today, the Fleet is still London's principal underground
river—and it is still London's principal sewer, for all that it is
now covered over with substantially-constructed brick arches,

wide enough to drive, as they drove through the sewers of King Tarquin, a chariot through.

Even jacketed within its brick tunnel, the Fleet is a river capricious in its turbulence, as well as turbulent in its caprice. The marée which threatens the slow-moving walker on the sands outside Mont St Michel, the bore which comes sweeping up the Bristol Channel: these sudden heapings-up of water do not come more suddenly, move more quickly, and advance more dangerously, than the torrent which boils up within the Fleet Sewer. Heavy rainfall on the hills of North London will swell the Fleet River within a few minutes. The men who work in the sewer, hearing the noise of oncoming water, leap for the nearest manhole, and scramble up out of harm's way.

Into the Fleet Sewer come tributary tunnels in large numbers and, where the Fleet Sewer reaches the Thames, its height increases from ten feet to eighteen feet. With its solid granite pier dividing the Fleet at a point not far from Ludgate Circus, London's principal underground river is still an impressive river indeed.

Some blocks of Portland stone embedded in the brickwork of the tunnel take us back to the eighteenth century: for these are stones from one of the six bridges—the Bridewell—which spanned the Fleet. The Fleet no longer discharges directly into the Thames, for it now forms part of the network of main and subsidiary drainage by which London's rainfall and sewage are carried away from beneath the surface of the city.

There are more than four hundred miles of pipes in the Greater London Council's main drainage system, and some two thousand, five hundred miles of subsidiary piping.

Two great outfall works—at Beckton, serving London north of the Thames; and at Crossness, serving South London—receive the four hundred million gallons of rainwater and sewage which, every day, pour into London's drains.

This network of drains does not connect directly with the River. What are called 'intercepting sewers' have been constructed to run parallel with the Thames, and it is these into which the sewage drains, being then carried to the outfall works. But, should the rainfall prove excessive, so that the sewers overflow, the excess water discharges into the Thames, which thus acts as a relief-sewer.

In the days before Bazalgette built his great system of 'intercepting sewers', the sewer-mouths opened directly on to the River, whose waters, entering the sewer-mouths at high-tide, performed a flushing action which, however much it might have polluted the River, did at least keep the drains reasonably clear. The sewer-mouths were tall, wide brick arches, each protected from unauthorized entry by an iron portcullis which, however, was raised just when the outrush of water from the sewer was expected.

There was a hazardous occupation—one of the many riverside vocations—known as 'tosh-faking'; mostly carried on by spry and not-easily-frightened small boys. As the portcullis was opened, these lads entered the mouth of the sewer, and hunted around for such treasures as might have been swept down by the water. Adventuring farther and farther up the sewer, in search of 'trove', they risked being caught by the return of the water, which could—and often did—dash them against the crumbling brickwork of the tunnel's sides. Many a lad was lost in this way—but the profession of 'tosh-faking' went on until the construction of the 'intercepting sewers' did away with sewers discharging directly on to the River.

There was a special treasure that these 'tosh-fakers' sought; and, when they found it, the discovery was the cause of no ordinary rejoicing. This was a ball, sometimes as much as two feet in diameter, which had grown through the fusing together of coins and odd pieces of metal; the fusing being the result of the backwards and forwards surge of the sewer-currents. Year after year, the ball would grow, as it picked up fresh substance; and to find one of these balls was the ambition of every 'tosh-faker', whose joy was complete when a gold coin was found embedded in the (mostly) copper mass.

Running between Rupert Street and Macclesfield Street, south of Shaftesbury Avenue, is a narrow alley, named Dansey

Yard. Until recently, this straight and noisome passage was lit at night with an old-fashioned gas-lamp: but a gas-lamp of a most unusual pattern. A squat, cast-iron lamp-post, ornamented with the debased, but still classically debased, Classic of the Regency, supported the lamp proper; and on the base of the lamp-post was this legend: WEBB'S PATENT SEWER GAS DESTRUCTOR.

Nothing sums up the attitude of the Early Victorians to the Sewer better than did this modest lamp-post, one of several scattered over the breadth of London. Like the woman who was so ugly that no man could resist looking at her, the Sewer —or, rather, Sewage—at once violently repelled and irresistibly attracted the Early Victorians. Even where they did not see in it what, later, Snow and others demonstrated to be the fact—a fertile breeding-ground of pestilence—they could see in it a means by which 'one of the noblest of rivers had been turned into a cesspool'.

But one of Chadwick's remarks—that the houses containing the domestic cesspools were no more than 'inverted containers of the gases of putrefaction'—draws attention to the other aspect that sewage presented to Victorian eyes.

For, to the Waste-Not-Want-Not basis of Victorian political and commercial economy, sewage had a marketable value, and the very 'gases of putrefaction' that Chadwick so bitterly condemned could be fed into a burner, and made to provide light and heat, as Webb's Patent Sewer Gas Destructor was demonstrating until only the other day.

We saw, just now, that the Fleet Ditch, from Holborn to the Thames, had been covered in by the beginning of the eighteenth century's second half; but this covering-in applied only to the part which runs through the City proper. At its upper part—Farringdon, St Pancras—the Fleet remained open (and, of course, a sewer) until almost a century later. The coming of the Metropolitan Railway in 1860 had an important tidy-up effect on some of London's smaller rivers, for, in order to keep them under control, and prevent the flooding, by these rivers, of the 'cut-and-cover' tunnels ('archways', the designers called them), the builders of the Metropolitan Railway had to enclose the rivers within large cylinders of cast-iron.

But, before schemes for utilizing the sewage for farming, the sewage itself had to be got under control; even the most commercially-minded saw that. And if the progress of 'the Sanitary Idea' seems to us to have been a slow one, we must remember that the tax-payer has to be 'sold' those progressive ideas which, however much they may offer in comfort and hygiene, are still going to put something on the rates or the income-tax. The nurturing of an idea; the making it, first acceptable to, and then demanded by, the tax-payer: these take time.

People are 'used to' certain inconveniences and, when it is suggested that they will have to pay for the suggested changes, they protest—not, when one considers the rise in the income-tax since 1842, without reason.

Then again, the practical means have to be ready in order to put some desired improvement across. Most of our important modern inventions—the telephone, the internal-combustion engine, the electric lamp, even television—were evolved, in theory, long ago. Hooke was experimenting with the internal-combustion engine in the reign of Charles II. But none of these ideas could be realized practically, because of the absence, not only of some essential material or tool, but of 'public acceptance'—what we call a 'market'.

Fortunately for those struggling hard to give London an adequate drainage system, the practical means were to hand. Where gentlemen of private means had taken up mathematics as a hobby in the seventeenth century, and architecture in the eighteenth, they took up engineering—notably sanitary engineering—in the nineteenth.

Associations of the prosperous upper- and middle-class men and women busied themselves with Improving the Condition of the Working Class; and their efforts were not only, for the most part, practical, but generally successful. The industrial exhibitions which were so characteristic a feature of the mid- and late-Victorian periods were supported by the enthusiasm, not of the manufacturer or the professional civil engineer, but by that of the 'scientifically minded' layman, with time and money to back up his enthusiasm.

Prince Albert himself prepared the design, and brought down to a little over £400 the cost, of a two-dwelling house, complete with interior bathroom and water-closet—the house may be seen in the park at Camberwell today—and humbler men were no less industrious in seeking to ameliorate the lot of the under-privileged.

The most significant testimony to the role played by the amateur in the practical realization of the 'Sanitary Idea' is the fact that some of the most striking improvements in sewers and their accessories originated in competitions set by the Royal Society of Arts.

We have noted that it was the invention of the salt-glaze pipe at the Lambeth potteries—particularly that of Mr (later Sir) Henry Doulton—which gave the sewer-improvers what may be called the 'raw material' of their work. With the name of Doulton must be coupled that of John Loe, engineer to the Holborn Commission, who introduced an ingenious modification to the Doulton glazed pipe by giving it an ovoid section. This egg-outlined sewer pipe concentrated the flow of the sewage into a narrow channel at the bottom of the sewer, so that, even in the driest weather, though there might have been only a trickle of water, that water was not only at the bottom of the sewer, but constantly on the move. In other words, there was always sufficient flow to keep the solid parts of the sewage from 'silting up'.

Loe also showed that a sewer laid in a straight line or, at most, with very shallow curves, would carry a greater proportion of sewage than a sewer laid with sharp curves. He showed too, that, by his system, a four-inch pipe could carry more sewage than a six-inch pipe; with a consequent saving in cost.

It has often been asked: why this intense interest in sewers, lavatories, water-closets, and so on, shown by the comfortably-off amateur of the mid-nineteenth century? The answer is that only too much of the evidence for the sewers' necessity was—literally—staring him in the face.

Even those sewers which had already been laid were incompetent to cope with the bulk of London's sewage: but much of that sewage never reached the sewers—let alone the Thames. Apart from the noisome condition of the cesspools in the 360,000 houses which contained them, there were districts in the heart of London where the sanitary conditions and social manners differed nothing from those of the Middle Ages; and there were no kites or pariah dogs to act as scavengers, as there had been centuries before.

In 1847, New Oxford Street was constructed, so as to join Holborn with Oxford Street. To make this new street, many of the old houses of the notorious St Giles's rookery had to be demolished, the then Duke of Bedford being compensated in the sum of £114,000 for the freehold sites of the houses over which the new road ran.

Other houses in the rookery were also demolished, to 'improve' the property; but, as the houses were pulled down, the tenants were forced to move into those still standing; so that, by 1849, all that remained of old St Giles were ninety-five houses, in which no fewer than 2,850 persons were living.

A large water-tower supplied the rookery with water for drinking and such washing as it did; and the Society for Improving the Conditions of the Labouring Classes had erected a 'model lodging house', six stories high, in George Street. But there were no sewers and refuse-collecting services. The inhabitants of St Giles, in the fifth decade of the nineteenth century, were throwing their refuse into the street, as their ancestors had done five hundred years before.

John Hollingshead, theatrically famous as the licensee of the Alhambra and the Gaiety, wrote, in 1861 or 1862, what is now a rare little book: *Underground London*. If one cannot imagine any of the great London impresarios of today writing a book on London's sewers, that is because we can now afford to take sewers for granted.

There is a quotation in this book of Hollingshead's, taken from Ellis's *History of Shoreditch*, which indicates that before the modern improvements of the drainage system came along, there had been a lamentable falling-away from a standard almost as high as our own.

The water-pipes [says Ellis] used in old times were not always imbedded in the earth as they are now, but enclosed within a capacious arch of brickwork, into which the workmen could descend to repair any decay or accident.

Pouring scorn on the 'romantic' view of old cellars and passage-ways, Hollingshead says:

Next to the romantic way of regarding sewers, there is the scientific or half-scientific way, which is not always wanting in the imaginative element. I remember attending an exhibition, about four years ago [i.e.: 1858 or 1859], at the Society of Arts, which, although it consisted only of engineering plans for the improvement of London's subways, was amusing from the impractical character of the schemes proposed.

A number of designs were submitted to the Metropolitan Board of Works for the total sub-surface reconstruction of the Metropolitan streets, and these designs—about forty in number—were referred to a committee of eminent engineers, whose task it was to give away certain money prizes. Nearly all the designs, as far as I can recollect, exhibited the same features: a centre tunnel under the roadway, accessible by traps from the street, and containing the different pipes for gas, water, telegraphic wires and sewage.

The plan that got a prize of one hundred guineas proposed to have arched brick vaults, extending from the houses on each side of the tunnel, giving a solidity to the roadway, and increasing to a great extent the cellar accommodation of houses and warehouses. Another plan, which got fifty guineas, had a central tunnel under the roadway, but provided for the same purpose two side tunnels running parallel to each other, and connected with houses on either side. The difference in estimate of the cost of the two plans was very great; the central tunnel scheme requiring something like thirty-six pounds sterling the linear yard to carry it out; and the side tunnel scheme being estimated to cost only fifteen pounds for each linear yard. As the latter plan had two tunnels to construct in the place of one, the great difference in cost must have arisen, if the calculations were correct, in the great area which the tunnel projector proposed to build over with vaults.

Many of the schemes exhibited were enlivened with pictures of the father of a family going down under the roadway in front of his house to see that the gas and water pipes were in proper order, and that no one had run away with the main sewer. A little more fancy on the part of the draughtsman might have represented whole parties of visitors inspecting the underground labyrinth as they would a conservatory at an evening party.

Both the prize plans were regarded as very ornamental and excellent as pictures, but too expensive for practical application. The short central tunnel in King Street, Covent Garden, a pure experiment on the part of the Metropolitan Board of Works, undertaken, perhaps, to silence theorists, may appear to have been copied from the first plan; but copied or not, it will probably be the only piece of fancy subway that London will see during the present century. The handling together of gas and water pipes and telegraphic wires on each side of the New Road, to make way for the Metropolitan Railway, is some approximation to the second plan, though very hurriedly and rudely carried out.

Hollingshead, as a prophet, was correct only in that cost would prevent these subways being built for a long time. He was wrong in thinking that they would never be built. They had been built in the past, and the twentieth century was to see them return.

On the plans for London's drainage generally, Hollingshead is much more reliable:

The two great plans that have occupied public attention for many years have been the purification of the Thames and the utilizing of the sewage. It is easy to talk about the noble river being made the floating cesspool of some *three hundred and sixty-three thousand inhabited houses* (according to the census of 1861) and of some two million eight hundred thousand inhabitants. It is easy to talk largely of ninety millions of gallons of sewage washed away every day through costly sub-ways by two hundred millions of gallons of rain-fall, when they contain a daily fertilizing value of three hundred and sixty pounds sterling, or a sum that would reach more than one million pounds sterling by the end of a year.

It is this muddy stream, trickling from innumerable house-taps, rushing down thousands of gullies, oozing through beds of gravel, draining off marshy meadows and ploughed land or flowing from thousands of dwellings, that helps to wash out the hundreds of downwards sewers and their miles of tributary channels.

This process of washing scatters and dilutes the valuable elements of fertility, until they are said to be lost beyond all hope of recovery. Men of science, capitalists and social reformers, have consumed many years and much money in trying to restore this lost mass of valuable sewage to the hungry land, but nothing practical or remunerative, in a commercial sense, has ever been put before the public.

'Considerable works', says Mr Austin, 'of the most expensive kind were constructed for distributing liquid, very nearly worthless as manure, over a district obtaining the valuable stable manure of the metropolis, at the most economical rate, by means of the return carts which convey to London the produce of the market-gardens, and which would otherwise return empty.

'In fact, practically, this was little more than a company for supplying the market-gardens of Fulham with water during periods of drought; and although, no doubt, a beneficial service, it will readily be imagined that the saving of labourers of hand-watering over a limited district of ground would produce no adequate return for so costly an establishment.'

Hoffmann and Will, the 'eminent chemists' who were commissioned to examine the problem for the Government in 1857, gave no very favourable opinion about the utilizing of sewage.

'Everybody', they reported, 'admits the necessity of removing the daily excreta of so vast a population as that of the metropolis; of removing them rapidly, completely; and beyond the limits within which their decomposition would spread discomfort and disease.

'All admit, moreover, that the excreta of which we have to rid ourselves possess a very considerable value in an agricultural point of view, and that it would be highly desirable to recover the valuable matter.

'These points being granted, the question resolves itself into this: Have we the means of accomplishing the latter desideratum, while satisfying the former condition?'

After having argued against it, the writers conclude:

'Nevertheless, on considering the immense value of the matter thus annually lost, and remembering that it nearly equals that of the whole quantity of guano imported annually [at £10 per ton—M.H.] into the United Kingdom, it would be unwise rashly to abandon this source of wealth without the most strenuous efforts to save at least a portion of it.'

Hoffmann and Will suggested that it might be possible to employ 'the whole or a part of the London sewage for the purposes of irrigation'.

Strenuous efforts were, and have since been, made—but, on the whole, most disappointingly, to convert the sewage into manure. So long as commercial values exercised some influence upon the problem, it was cheaper to dispose of the waste than to collect, deodorize, desiccate and deliver it to the farmers.

Of course, when a modern war puts 'commercial values' aside, then a use can be found for London sewage, as for every other kind of waste. The 'gases of putrefaction' of which Chadwick talked are the gas, methane—CH_4—which is finding a use on more than one thousand French farms for driving agricultural machinery. It is estimated that it takes only the dung of one cow to provide the domestic power for a family of three, and that the dung from a small farm would give enough power completely to 'mechanize' the farm.

We have made little use of methane in Britain, though some internal-combustion engines were fuelled with methane during the last war. Possibly the most interesting use of sewage-methane was in the construction of incendiary bombs, used with disastrous effect on Stettin, Kiel, Stuttgart, Berlin, Hamburg and Koenigsberg, the old East Prussian capital being almost completely destroyed by them. These thirty-pound bombs were filled with petrol in which methane had been dissolved under pressure. On exploding, the methane-petrol sent out flames twenty feet long. It took the diabolically humourless ingenuity of the war-mentality to convert a negligently dropped human turd into so fearsome a lethal weapon!

'Sewage', remarks Hollingshead, 'whether fluid or solid, mixed or unmixed, is very much like our convicts: everybody wants to get rid of it, and no one consents to have it.' One use for it has been in the construction of the so-called 'sewage farms': fertile no doubt, but highly offensive to the nose, and only possible where the inhabitants cannot raise any effective opposition.

Today, all sewage, before being taken out to sea by the 'hoppers'—which now cost £250,000 apiece—or used to recover the marshy areas of such places as Pitsea, and turn it into arable and building land, is 'purified', that is, the process of decomposition is arrested, the liquid part of the sewage separated from the solid—or 'sludge'—and the liquid and the solid disposed of differently: the sludge being loaded on to the 'hoppers' or sewage-ships, and taken far away. (But not far enough: the tides wash it back, and we have the sort of newspaper agitation against 'foul beaches' which is a nine-days'-scandal as I write.)

A new problem has arisen since the last war: the increasing use of the so-called 'detergents', which are made from a gas collected in the process of refining petroleum. In its 'natural' state, the detergent is non-foaming; but as the manufacturers swear that they could not sell a non-foaming cleanser to a woman as a soap-substitute, soap's traditional foaming property has to be added to the detergent, in order to sell it.

Choked drains, especially the runaways from domestic baths, sinks and lavatory basins, rivers piled high with froth, and mountains of stagnant foam over each gutter exit—these are what we have following the using of 250,000 tons of detergent manufactured annually in Great Britain alone.

Sludge in sewage is produced at the rate of from one-quarter to one half-gallon a day per head of the population; and many means have been tried either to handle it with benefit to the community or simply to handle it. It has been dried and pulverized, it has been burnt. Only the city of Bradford has processed it and made money out of the job.

During the last war, it was worth while to recover the fat from sewage-sludge; they *said* that the nutritious grease was either given to the pigs (notoriously easy-going in the matter of their food) or used to grease the axles of British Railways rolling stock.

Today, in London, whether one urinates or defaecates, washes a dish or one's hands, empties the bath or hoses down the car, a drainage system as efficient as it is elaborate takes the water away. It was not always so; and it has been so only within the last forty years. I remember, as a boy, the overflowing of the gutters which followed any considerable rainfall as the night follows the day—little 'street-arabs' used to delight to walk through the black stream, feeling it trickle between the toes of feet hardly whiter.

Today, only litter fouls the streets; not 'drain-water'. And, beneath us, the sewers, though necessarily smelly, are cleaner (in their absence of disposable refuse) than are the streets above.

No such incrustations of nitre—'distilling a ghastly dew'—such as Montresor and Fortunato found in the cellar, as Fortunato was lured to his death, are to be found on the brick and stone walls of London's sewers. Regularly hosed down with high-pressure pumps, the walls are thoroughly scrubbed with stiff brooms, so as to ensure perfect cleanliness. Nor is this attention to cleanliness paid simply from a desire to see things 'bright and shining'; matter allowed to remain and decompose will soon generate a respectable head of methane gas, and when this mixes with the fumes of the petrol and Diesel oil which seep into the sewers, a violent explosion may well occur, such as wrecked a New York street some while ago, destroying neighbouring houses and killing or wounding several persons.

The sewer-men of London—those tireless, valuable and never-remembered public servants—have to be constantly on the alert for danger. We have mentioned the water which comes rushing down the main sewers after a heavy rainfall. There is a danger of a similar sort when the Thames overflows, and the river-water threatens the men within the sewers.

The sewer-cleaners are known as 'flushers', and they work in parties, under the orders of a head man or 'ganger', one of whose principal duties it is to be on the watch for any unusual hazards.

Throughout the many miles of London's streets, there is a man-hole at about every hundred yards. At whatever point a gang of 'flushers' is working, a watchman is posted above ground and, should rain begin to fall, he sounds a warning by the simple method of raising the man-hole cover and dropping it. The booming sound travels far within the sewers, and calls effective attention to possible danger. Three clangs of a man-hole cover are peremptory, and mean 'Get out at once!'

Part of the training given to men of the London Fire Brigade deals with accidents in the sewers and subways of London; and special life-saving equipment, including oxygen-masks, is always to hand when a call comes through from beneath London. Mention of oxygen-masks recalls the fact that noxious gases will asphyxiate as well as explode. Tests are carried out when the presence of such gases is suspected, before the 'flushers' are sent in. Tests are made by dropping a wire-basket into the drain, the basket carrying a gas-detecting paper which changes colour in the presence of gas. All men working 'below' carry a safety-lamp which glows red at any contamination of the air.

Yet, working in the gloom of the tunnels, often thigh-deep

in water, brushed by rats and constantly inhaling the far-from-sweet air of the sewers, the 'flushers' and their gangers are healthy and, if tradition may be believed, have always been so.

Indeed, there is a somewhat ribald little song, composed in their honour, that I heard as a boy:

> Dan, Dan, the lavatory man;
> Underneath the ground all day:
> Sweeping out urinals,
> Cleaning up the finals—
> Happy as the birds and the bees in May!

Earlier, it was mentioned that much of London's 90,000 miles of water-piping is over a century old, and still in excellent condition. The same thing may be said of London's sewers, which were constructed, in so far as the central parts of the metropolis are concerned, just about a century ago.

With the building of the new main drainage system, the modern ideals of practical cleanliness were established as a permanent working factor in the system; but what those drains replaced!

In almost precisely the same terms with which the scatophile Swift described the London sewers of Queen Anne's time, the no less strong-stomached Mayhew has described those of a century and more later:

The deposit [i.e.: of the old sewers] has been found to comprise all the ingredients from the breweries, the gas-works, and the several chemical and mineral manufactories; dead dogs, cats, kittens and rats; offal from slaughter-houses, sometimes even including the entrails of the animals [an article of food]; street-pavement dirt of every variety; vegetable refuse; stable-dung; the refuse of pig-styes; night-soil; ashes; tin kettles and pans (pansherds); broken stoneware, as jars, pitchers, flower-pots, &c.; pieces of wood; rotten mortar and rubbish of different kinds; and even rags.

This, if the world last that long, should bring tears to the eyes of an archaeologist of the year 3960! What a haul of nineteenth-century artifacts! But Mayhew, though he constantly astonishes us with his courage in penetrating into the most noisome parts of the City, can rarely have given himself an 'assignment' more nauseating than this visit to the old sewers of London.

That phrase, 'and even rags', needs comment. In Mayhew's day, and for long afterwards, rags, being the staple of the paper-making industry, were an article of trade; and their collection by the street barrow-man, with his traditional cry of 'Rags, Bottles and Bones!', ensured that none was wasted. Hence Mayhew's astonishment to find something as valuable as rags included in the refuse. But there was worse to come.

Hundreds of old buildings, and dozens of old streets, were being swept away to make room for the new road, Victoria Street, which was to connect Pimlico (at Victoria Station) with Westminster (at the Sanctuary). Along, and at the back of each side of, this wide, straight street, were to rise the first flats in London, many of which are still standing. Two great hotels were to go up and, for a short while, the steam-tram of an American projector, Street, was to run along it.

The demolition involved houses—especially in Tothill Street —dating back even beyond the fifteenth century—William Caxton's house among them—and more modern buildings swept away included the old Westminster Workhouse, Elliott's Brewery, the Tothill Fields Bridewell for Women. It was necessary, too, to fill in the canal basin, the memory of which was preserved, until its demolition only a few months ago, in the name of a public-house opposite Victoria Station: 'The Grosvenor Basin'.

Victoria Street, the more so now that the new Esso and Monsanto offices have been erected, may strike others, as it has struck me, as being one of the most dreary streets in London. When the Westminster Palace and Windsor hotels were still hotels, there was some life, some *humanity*, in this street; but since these two great hotels (the first built in 1861) have been 'converted to offices', the grey catatonia of office existence has fallen upon this wide thoroughfare.

Mayhew went to see the old sewers of Westminster, which

were being replaced by those being laid under the Bazalgette scheme: for, though dreary now, Victoria Street is one of the few London main-thoroughfares which was designed and made *complete*. Above, it has straightness and width; its flats were of six and even eight stories, and they had lifts. But, beneath ground, it was no less up-to-the-minute in design. The upper parts of this ambitious new street have not entirely survived; the under parts have.

Hear Mayhew on a typical pre-Victoria Street Westminster sewer:

A sewer from the Westminster Workhouse ... was in so wretched a condition that the leveller could scarcely work for the thick scum that covered the glasses of the spirit-level in a few minutes after being wiped ... a chamber is reached about 30 feet in length, from the roof of which hangings of putrid matter like stalactites descend three feet in length. At the end of this chamber, the sewer passes under the public privies, the ceilings of which can be seen from it. Beyond this it is not possible to go.

In all journalism, there can never have been another man quite like Mayhew, whose results, impressive though they are, seem unimportant, compared with the *means* by which those results were secured. I find the *thought*—the *idea*—of Henry Mayhew himself perennially more fascinating even than the nightmare world that he displayed in print, even as Doré displayed it in picture.

Henry Mayhew, the London solicitor; professionally neat in his cutaway and stove-pipe hat, notebook in hand and spectacles on nose; venturing into slums where even parties of the police dared not go; interviewing whores and their bullies; wharf-rats, criminals of every sort; taking it all down in his notebook, in circumstances where even the production of a notebook, let alone the persistent asking of intimate questions, would have been enough to get any other man's throat slit....
What a man!

There is poetry, too, in his descriptions of this Ultharian

night that he alone had the wish and the courage to penetrate. Since he is the lone venturer, a sort of patron's possessiveness develops in him, and this begets, first a tolerance which both astonishes and emprides him, and then what is clearly an affection based on what he realizes is a unique understanding of the world which is open to no one, in this city of three millions, but him.

There is never any fear on Mayhew's part. He does not turn away in fright even from the giant rats, 'as big as good-sized kittens'. No: he stays and turns that keen eye, that keener ear, upon them. He watches them as intently as, not so very far above, he would watch a doxy of the most depraved kind in her cellar-brothel in Seven Dials. Then, going back to his office, Mayhew notes that the rats were 'fighting and squeaking there like a parcel of drunken Irishmen'.

A handful of men gave London its modern drainage system and all the benefits, not least to health, which have derived from the system. This handful of planners and executors were not Master Men—a few of them, indeed, were rather the opposite: but, as a group, they found themselves in that rare condition in which almost any man, not quite an imbecile, can not only be inspired to get things done, but can actually achieve them: they had a solid body of public opinion behind them. They employed no high-powered pressure-group- or public-relations-executives to make their ideas acceptable to public opinion: the pressure-group voluntarily banded itself into powerful being; and the P.R.O.'s stepped forward, eager to get to work, at no fee. With the voluntary support of such editors as Mark Lemon, of *Punch*, such popular artists as John Tenniel and Dicky Doyle, of the same influential journal, of such novelists as Dickens, and such journalists as Sala, the main-drainage scheme did not lack for a powerful press-backing.

But persistent agitation by the leading journals and the most popular writers would not have got any Bill for providing London with adequate drainage past the Committee stage, had there not been available the practical men to carry practical schemes into effect. And the man at the head of the body of practical men was one of the greatest civil engineers who have ever lived: Joseph Bazalgette, Engineer of the Metropolitan Board of Works. While enthusiastic amateurs of the Art of Drainage were submitting their ingenious ideas, all based upon the fact that no fewer than one hundred and eighty-five sewers were discharging into the Thames, Bazalgette was quietly planning the one adequate solution to the problem of London's drainage.

All the same, some of the proposals make interesting reading today.

Another gentleman proposed to bring half the southern sewage across the river at the Thames Tunnel, and the other half across the river in iron pipes, at some higher spot not specified, the material, when delivered, to be filtered, deodorized and utilized. The peculiarity of the scheme was the bold proposal to defile the Thames Tunnel, and wake up this wonder of joint-stock credulity from its long sleep of idleness.

Another suggestion was to carry the whole mass to New-haven-on-Sea, and throw it in the sea.

Another gentleman suggested that the sewage should be collected from the houses and streets in large portable cisterns floating up the river, and that at stated times steam tugs should call at each station, and tow this unsightly fleet far out to sea and get rid of its contents.

One gentleman wished to take the sewage away in iron vessels, and drop it quietly, when no one was looking, into the sea; while another gentleman, evidently thinking that criminals ought to suffer a little sewage infliction for their sins, proposed to form great deodorizing caverns from Black-friars Bridge to the House of Commons.

All the above suggestions have been adapted, in part, to the general drainage problem: and such sludge-ships—'hoppers'—

as the S.S. *Henry Ward* or S.S. *John Perring* testify to the fact that some of these amateurs came up with the right idea.

Others, of course, did not.

Another projector, more fanciful than any of his competitors, proposed to carry the sewage through the air by vast atmospheric tubes on both sides of the river, beginning somewhere about Putney, and terminating, as usual, in a great deodorizing reservoir on the South Coast.

Another projector proposed to construct two great sewers under the Thames, a favourite but costly plan; and another gentleman thought he could deodorize sewage and ventilate the sewers by passing all the smoke of London into them.

Hollingshead, who lists close on fifty of these ideas—*all of which he considers impractical*—ends with the simple statement:

The plan which Mr Bazalgette is now carrying out, as the engineer of the Metropolitan Board of Works, is certainly framed to divert this sewage by a system of intercepting and outfall sewers.

This was the final scheme, and this is the scheme that London is using today—more than a century later.

It had taken a long time to decide that the stink of London was not inevitable—Mayhew had remarked upon the stench from the cesspools 'throughout the new Paddington district, the neighbourhood of Hyde Park Gardens, and the costly squares and streets adjacent'—but, once the decision was taken to deodorize London, the Victorians set about it in a characteristically practical way.

In 1857—spurred on as much by the nidor in the House itself as by the weekly jibes of *Punch*—the Government called for a Report on the Metropolitan Main Drainage Scheme. The Government appointed, as referees, Galton, Simpson and Blackwell. The Metropolitan Board of Works appointed Bidder, Hawksley and Bazalgette.

The Report, a masterpiece of lucid reasoning, clear exposition and practical suggestion, was accepted without opposition, and the proposals that it made were given the force of Law.

One aspect of Bazalgette's practical genius was apparent in his decision to ask for everything at once—to obtain for himself statutory powers (in the name of the Board) to carry through the whole scheme, even for those parts of London still half rural. So the Main Drainage Scheme dealt not only with the sewers, but with that vast sewer, the Thames; and when the time came for passing the Thames Embankment Bill in 1862, it passed in the face of strong opposition, simply because most of its provisions had already been anticipated in the Bill empowering the construction of the new sewers.

In 1857, the Report on the Metropolitan Main Drainage Scheme had remarked, in commenting upon the foul condition of the Thames, especially in the central part of London:

> Several causes have contributed to the present condition of the river and its banks.
>
> The removal of old London Bridge has greatly augmented the tidal scour; the improved land drainage brings down upland waters with increased expedition after rainfall, thereby diminishing the quantity of water in the river in hot weather, and adding to the quantity of earthy matter conveyed by the flood.
>
> The agitation of the water, by the action of steam-boats, and the augmented velocity of the current, induced by the removal of obstacles to the tidal flow: these operate to retain the mud in a state of suspension.

The answer was to regulate the tidal flow by means of two constricting embankments. And that these embankments—proposed by Wren in 1667—were in Bazalgette's mind when he was preparing his main-drainage scheme is shown by the fact that he allowed for the presence of these roadways in the siting of his sewers and (more particularly) the subways carrying the sewers. The subway carrying sewers, gas mains, electricity cables and so forth, which runs under the Victoria

Embankment is over a mile long; and Bazalgette saw to it that the new streets which were being driven through London were new underneath as well as above. So that, when Southwark Street, linking the Borough High Street and the Blackfriars Road, was constructed between 1861 and 1864, at a cost of nearly £600,000, it was provided, along its entire length, with a subway for the gas and sewer mains; and the same was done for that other new street of slightly later date, Queen Victoria Street.

It was at this time, too—in 1856—that the parts of the Fleet Ditch still open were covered in. This was in connection with the new street—Victoria Street (now part of Farringdon Road) —which was built to connect Holborn Bridge with the Clerkenwell Sessions House. The remaining portion of the Fleet Ditch, extending from Peter Street to Castle Street, which had been an open sewer for centuries, was arched over—a sewer now in name as well as in fact.

We have already noted the close—and often dangerous— connection between sewage and water-supply. It was at about this time that the reservoirs situated within the boundaries of London proper began to receive long-overdue attention from the authorities.

In 1842, when the workmen were cleaning out the large reservoir in Claremont Square, removing the sediment of only eleven years, they found that the mud, in some places, was eleven feet thick—a foot of deposit for every year since its last cleaning.

Ten years later, the Act was passed which compelled all the water companies to roof-in or otherwise cover all reservoirs within five miles of St Paul's. The Act also required all water used for domestic purposes to be filtered.

7. The Lost Rivers of London

In August, 1875, a gang of navvies, opening up the surface of Oxford Street, just where it passes Stratford Place, came across the remains of an extensive stone structure—thick walls, pointed arches, decorative carvings, all in a fair state of preservation. In digging a sewer, they had come across the surviving parts of the great reservoir constructed by the Mayor and Corporation of London in 1216, to supply the Conduit in Cheapside with pure drinking water.

The reservoir collected the water which flowed into the Tyebourne or Tyburn brook from the nine springs which oozed out of the gravel subsoil of St Mary-le-bone (*i.e.* St Mary's lez Bourne, or 'St Mary's-by-the-Brook').

It was King John, that much-maligned victim of bureaucracy, who persuaded Gilbert de Sandford, the then owner of the land on which the springs were situate, to deed his property to the Mayor and Corporation; and after the reservoir had been constructed and a six-inch lead pipe made, at the expense of the merchants of Ghent, Antwerp and Bruges trading in London, to carry the water from Stratford Place to Charing Cross, along the Strand, over Fleet Bridge, and up Ludgate Hill to the west end of Cheapside, the Mayor and Corporation used to pay an annual state visit to the reservoir. For centuries there was a building here, known as 'The Lord Mayor's Banqueting House', where, after having hunted a hare or a fox in the neighbouring fields and woods, the company sat down to dinner.

For having used his good offices to get the water under the control of the City of London, the King was granted, by the grateful Corporation, the right to lay a lead pipe, 'of the size of a goose-quill', from the main pipe (as it passed Charing

106   LONDON BENEATH THE PAVEMENT

Cross) to the Royal Stables, on the site of which the National Gallery now stands.

In order to force the water through the pipe which ran up Ludgate Hill, the head of water in the reservoirs at Stratford Place was some thirty feet above the level of the Cheapside conduit's mouth; so that the level of Oxford Street must have risen considerably for the workmen to have found the remains of the reservoirs below street-level.

The considerable sewer-laying and rebuilding which were taking place in and around Oxford Street at this date were responsible for an even more important find in connection with the Tyburn—though archaeologists are still unable to explain the origin of the second find of mediaeval constructions.

A little farther to the west, at the corner of North Audley Street, digging the foundations of some new buildings revealed, close to the pavement, two well-worn flaps, obviously forming the door to a cellar. The navvies' curiosity being aroused, they lifted the flaps with the points of their picks, and saw beneath them a chamber, to which a flight of sixteen brick steps led.

'On descending', says a contemporary account, 'they entered a room of considerable size, measuring about 11 feet long by 9 feet wide, and nearly 9 feet high. The roof, which is arched, is of stone and, with a few exceptions, is in good repair. The walls to the height of about five feet are built of small red brick, such as were used by the Romans, in which are eight chamfered Gothic arches, with stone panels, as though originally used as windows for obtaining light. The upper part of the wall is of more recent date. In the four corners of the chamber, there is a recess with an arched roof, extending with a bend as far as the arm can reach. In the middle of the chamber is a sort of pool or bath, built of stone, measuring about five feet by seven feet. It is about six feet deep, and was about half filled with water, tolerably clear and fresh. A spring of water could be seen bubbling up, and provision was made for an overflow in the sides of the bath. From all appearances the place was originally a baptistery.'

The late Victorians (like the early Victorians) had as little interest in preserving the relics of old London as have their neo-Elizabethan descendants; but the Victorians had more excuse for their destruction. For one thing, there were still, even as late as 1875, dozens—perhaps hundreds—of such remains, where today there are but a few; and, for another thing, the Victorian economists were not persuaded that they 'needed dollars', and so had no interest in having something to attract tourists.

It is a pity that this subterranean 'baptistery' had to be swept away; looking it over might have been a welcome addition to the pleasures of shopping in Oxford Street. Besides, we have now a much greater knowledge of the 'underground' non-Roman and even non-Christian religious activities of the Middle Ages than was possessed by archaeologists in 1875. (We owe much of that knowledge to the bombing of our ancient country churches during the last war: but that is a story which does not fall into this book.) However, 'baptistery' or not, Christian or Adamite, this pool was fed by the waters of the Tyburn, or by a spring which fed that small river.

The Tyburn, like the Westbourne, rises in Hampstead; and the Tyburn's source, 'Conduit Fields', was a famous London water-supply until as late as the middle of the last century, when water-sellers still collected their water from the springs on Hampstead Heath, and retailed it throughout the local district at a penny or twopence the bucket, depending on how far the householder buying the water lived from the source.

The original course of the Tyburn ran from the Heath, along the line of what is now Fitzjohn's Avenue, along the west side of Regent's Park, crossing Mary-le-bone Lane and Oxford Street at Stratford Place, and so, by the west side of New Bond Street, across Brook Street (hence the name) and so, across Piccadilly, through Green Park, to the front of Buckingham Palace. Here the river went underground and split into two branches: the eastern branch supplying the lake in St James's Park, the western joining the Thames and forming, in its

winding course, the little island ('Thorney') on which Westminster Abbey now stands.

Some such phrase as 'at the gallows by Tyburn Brook',
was, at least three centuries ago, shortened to simple 'Tyburn',
and the meaning of the word transferred, from the place at
which the gallows were erected, to the gallows themselves, so
that—as I shall examine later—it seems certain that the word
'Tyburn' came to be applied to any place of execution in
London, just as the name 'Borstal', still that of a village outside Chatham, in Kent, is now applied to all reform-schools.

The place of execution which is immortalized as 'Tyburn'
stood just beyond the point at which Edgware Road joins the
'roundabout' at Marble Arch. There was a bridge here, carrying the main London–Oxford road across the Tyburn, and if
the bricks found in the underground 'baptistery' excavated in
Oxford Street in 1875 were really Roman, then the choice of
this spot as a place of execution may have been made at a very
early date indeed. The *limes* of Roman London did not extend
as far west as the Edgware Road; but it is more than probable
that the Romans would have built a way-station by a bridge
serving so important a route as the way to Oxford.

When, some years ago, in passing by Marble Arch, I saw
a party of devout Roman Catholics kneeling in the centre of
the roadway, I did not think that they were paying reverence
to the buried Tyburn. They were holding a ceremony com-
memorative of the men and women who had been hanged at
this spot in times past for having offended, through religious
conviction, against the existing Law. But, in a very real way,
these devout persons were acknowledging the fact of the
Tyburn—keeping alive, not only the memory of the men and
women of their faith who had perished here, but of the buried
river which had given its name to the system under which so
many men and women had been put to death.

To anticipate a later chapter: a quarter-century after the
workmen digging at Stratford Place and North Audley Street
came across traces of the Tyburn, the river was encountered

again—this time as the workmen were boring the tunnel to carry the Central London Railway ('The Tuppenny Tube').

Between Woolwich and Hammersmith, the Thames makes a winding course which is no less than twenty miles long, and many are the rivers and rivulets which still pour into the Thames along this extensive stretch. On the north side—beginning from the west—they are Stamford Brook, Counter's Creek, Westbourne (called Ranelagh at certain points in its length), Tyburn (or King's Scholars Pond), the Fleet (including the Oldbourne), Walbrook, Shoreditch, Hackney Brook, Black Ditch and Lea. On the south side of the Thames we find— still moving in from the west—Beverley Brook, Wandle, Graveney, Falcon Brook, Effra, Ravensbourne (itself with a number of smaller tributaries, including the Pool), Quaggy Brook and Kid Brook.

Most of London's 'lost rivers' have given their names to streets above; but these are not the more remembered—*as rivers*—for that reason. Westbourne Grove is a populous and popular district of west London, containing, as it does, several well-known shops, including Whiteleys, the big department-store. But how many who use the name 'Westbourne Grove' even daily recall the buried river which gave the street (and district) its name?

Yet tens of thousands of Londoners not only pass under the Westbourne each day, but actually see it. It passes, in a large cast-iron pipe, above the uncovered platforms of Sloane Square Station; and the extraordinary fact about the piping is this: though the Westbourne was 'piped' here almost a century ago, when the (Metropolitan District) 'underground' station was built, the cast-iron pipe is that originally placed here. In November, 1940, an aerial bombing attack upon London demolished most of the old station, above, around and below the pipe carrying the Westbourne over the rails and platforms. But though the station buildings and the permanent way were very badly damaged by the bombing, not the smallest leak was sprung in the old iron pipe, and above the shattered station the

Westbourne flowed on, as it has flowed since before Chellean Man came to Chelsea.

An aside here: When I wandered through London, on my return from a war-wandering which had taken me into four of the five continents, and saw what had been shattered by the TNT or burnt by the thermite, I noticed that—apart from human beings—the three things which exhibited, in the highest degree, survival-value were trees, seventeenth- and eighteenth-century brick buildings and Victorian cast-iron. But even so, it takes some remarkably good cast-iron to survive the tremendous impact of a bomb's shock-wave.

Talking of London's many (now buried) water-ways, Sir George Humphreys rightly says: 'The story of the covering-in of these streams is, in fact, the history of London during the last four centuries.'

He should have added the adjective 'gradual' to the phrase 'covering-in', for the process of burying London's rivers and streams has been, like the building of London itself, a piece-meal and, at best, haphazard job. At the beginning of the last century, the 'upper reaches' of the Westbourne were a favourite resort of the Sunday fisherman, and it was not until the end of the first quarter of the last century that even in Sloane Square (where now the Westbourne travels through a pipe) the river was covered in.

When Edgar Allan Poe was at school in Sloane Street in 1817, he could see, from the windows of No. 146, a desolate expanse of marshy land, known as 'the Five Fields', in the lush swamps of which cattle grazed, and on the outskirts of which footpads lurked, to waylay the travellers from Chelsea to Hyde Park Corner.

What is now Cliveden Place was, until the building of Belgravia by Thomas Cubitt, on the site of The Five Fields, a bridge fording the Westbourne. The traditional presence of robbers and cut-throats in the desolate parts adjacent to this river-crossing doubtless gave it its name of 'Bloody Bridge', as it is called in Cary's map of 1810.

When the Earl of Westminster obtained an Act of Parliament, in 1826, authorizing him to drain the Five Fields, and Cubitt began to build the streets and mansions and houses of Belgravia in 1827 (from designs by George Basevi, Disraeli's uncle), the Westbourne had to go underground.

There were other things which, traditionally, had gone underground at a spot not far from here. The spot is now marked by the junction of Hobart Place and Grosvenor Place, a few yards from the stables of Buckingham Palace. What were buried were the corpses of suicides, whom ancient custom ordered to be interred at cross-roads.

The maniac murderer, Williams, whose crimes have been so vividly recounted by Thomas de Quincey, was buried here; his corpse, uncovered, being borne on a two-wheeled cart, and attended by a solemn procession which included a company of Guards. This grisly ceremonial was carried out whenever a suicide necessitated an interment at the Hobart Place cross-roads, and survived until the summer of 1823, when a young man, who had committed suicide after having murdered his father, was buried here.

However, this link with our demon-haunted past was to be broken: King George IV was setting out for a drive in the Park and, his carriage being held up by this macabre buffoonery, the King caused an Act to be rushed through, abolishing the ancient custom of cross-roads-burial for suicides. The Act was passed on 8th July, 1823. Competitive water and gas companies were busy tearing up the roads of London; it seemed, to the modernist King, intolerable that the unseemly ritual of suicide-interment should add to the traffic-obstructions.

I once spoke to an Irish labourer who was standing neck-deep in a trench upon this unhallowed spot.

'Have you found any bones?' I asked.

'That's funny you should have asked that,' Mick replied. 'I'm just after finding a handful. I'm thinking someone buried a dog here.'

De Quincey would have relished the deeper implications of that remark.

Between the two barrack-like houses—called, when first

erected, 'Gibraltar and Malta'—which flank Albert Gate, the Westbourne runs out of Hyde Park, in a culvert which passes under Knightsbridge. Albert Gate is, in fact, an arched bridge over the Westbourne; and the river can, at times, make its presence here uncomfortably obvious.

In January 1809, a month in which the Fleet River burst through its tunnel, the Westbourne overflowed to such an extent that not only were the lower stories of the neighbouring houses submerged, but travellers between Westminster and Chelsea had to be ferried over the 'lake' by Thames watermen.

The Westbourne, however, is still visible: the Serpentine River—in connection with which the late George Lansbury, a Labour 'statesman', acquired a dubious fame by constructing a 'Lido' on its grimy banks—is the still-visible part of the Westbourne.

The Serpentine River was constructed by Queen Caroline, wife of George II, in 1730, by enlarging the bed of the Westbourne and by including several small ponds adjacent. The cost—estimated at £6,000, but turning out to be over £20,000 —was defrayed by Sir Robert 'Every-Man-Has-His-Price' Walpole, without the King's knowledge.

The overflow from the Serpentine passes through an underground channel after having cascaded over a cliff of rocks which was constructed in 1817.

Until 1844, when 'Gibraltar and Malta' were built, the waterfall flowed into a lake of grubby water, facing Albert Gate. But, in connection with the building of the two houses—one of which has for years served the French for their embassy— this sheet of water was covered in, and the Westbourne put underground. Until the middle of the last century the Serpentine, in common with all London rivers, was nothing more than a sewer.

As late as 1855, two branches of the Ranelagh sewer, coming from Hampstead and Kensal New Town, joined to a stream a little to the north of the Harrow Road, passed through a sewer from Gloucester Terrace, and entered the head of the Serpentine by Bayswater Road.

In 1855, the sewage was diverted from the Serpentine into a main sewer, and the waters of the river became clean once more until, with the establishment of the 'Lido', the bathers re-commenced the dismal work of pollution.

Ranelagh Terrace, leading from the Pimlico Road to the (recently demolished) Guards' Barracks in Chelsea Bridge Road, marks the last lap of the Westbourne before it enters the Thames.

The Fleet River has been mentioned in this book: it has the distinction of being the last of London's great tributary rivers to remain uncovered throughout most of its length.

While Stow, writing in the early seventeenth century, could say of the Walbrook (to which we shall return shortly): 'This watercourse, having divers bridges, was afterwards vaulted over with brick, and paved level with the streets and lanes wherethrough it passed; and since that, also houses have been built thereon, so that the course of Walbrooke is now hidden underground, and thereby hardly known', the Fleet was still, in parts, an open river, even as late as 1863.

What is more, the Fleet, though it ceased to be a river navigable to river-transport in 1734, when the City Corporation arched over the Fleet from Holborn Bridge to Fleet Street, it is evident that the river was once navigable to a point very far from the Thames. Two anchors, at least, have been found at some distance from the river: one, discovered in the Fleet in the latter part of the last century, was found at Black Mary's Hole, near the end of Baker Street (now Baker's Row, Clerkenwell Road). But that the Fleet was navigable far higher is proved by the discovery of an anchor on the site of the now-demolished 'Elephant & Castle' tavern at Pancras Wash, where the road branches off to Kentish Town.

The Fleet, on its way from its sources in Hampstead, passes through Kentish Town, and then travels *under* the Regent's Canal, to St Pancras, where the river was arched over in 1766, and bore the name, Pancras Wash. From St Pancras—where it was piped, in 1860, in connection with the building of the Metropolitan Railway—the Fleet passes on to Battle Bridge, and thence into Clerkenwell, and so, beneath the valley between Turnmill Street and Saffron Hill, along (though below) Farringdon Street, Ludgate Circus and New Bridge Street, to empty itself into the Thames to the west of Blackfriars Bridge.

The Fleet, in Clerkenwell, was still turning flour, flatting and other mills in the early part of the last century; but the open existence of this famous river, though threatened so often before, was doomed when, as one of the metropolitan main sewers then vested in the Commissioners of Sewers, the Fleet was handed over to the newly-established Metropolitan Board of Works.

Beyond Holborn Bridge, at which point the Fleet was fed by the Turnmill Brook (or 'River of Wells'), the still open river passed through a maze of narrow streets, such as Chick Lane and Field Lane, Vine Street, Peter Street, and many others, all of them of more than dubious reputation.

To those who know the district around Holborn Viaduct, it will seem strange to read that a hundred-spindle cotton-spinning mill was erected there, to be powered by the waters of Turnmill Brook: but though the unsuccessful cotton-spinning venture passed away in 1740, the doubtful taverns of the district—'The White Hart' in Turnmill Street, 'The Horseshoe and Magpie' in Saffron Hill, 'The Red Lion Tavern' in West Street, and many another resort of thieves and murderers —survived until the sweeping away between 1844 (when Field Lane was pulled down) and 1863 (when the last of the Clerkenwell rookeries of the more infamous character were demolished).

This almost contemporary description of the great work involving the integration of the Fleet into the metropolitan main-drainage system will be quoted here, not only because it sums up the scheme, but because, with only the slightest changes, it is valid as a description of the system as it exists today.

The gigantic main-drainage system began with the great subterranean roads, the high, the low and the mid-level, which, intercepting all lesser sewers, carry their united floods

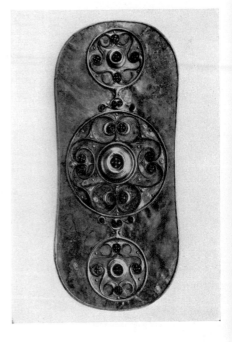

ABOVE Bronze portrait head of Hadrian A.D. 117–138.

RIGHT Bronze and enamel shield found at Battersea, first century B.C. or early first century A.D.

BELOW Bronze Celtic helmet found at Waterloo Bridge, probably first century B.C.

(Photos *British Museum*)

I

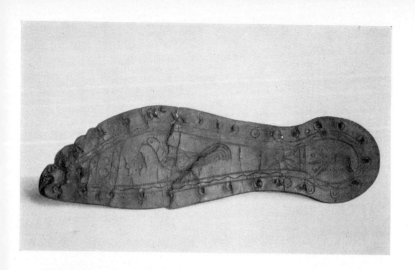

ROMAN FINDS FROM THE SITE OF THE BANK OF ENGLAND

Inner sole of woman's sandal.

"Mass-produced" Samian ware, exported from the Continent.

Locally produced domestic pottery—two pitchers, cooking pot (centre), triple vase and dish.

(Photos *Governor and Company of the Bank of England*)

The Pipe Borer, from Evelyn's *Sylva*, 1670, after De Caus, 1615.

(British Museum)

Waterwheel of Chelsea Water Works, from Switzer's *Hydrostatics and Hydraulics*, 1729.

(Science Museum, London)

The Tower subway, opened in 1870, the world's first iron-lined tube and also the first tube railway; a small cable-hauled car carried twelve passengers at a time from the Tower to Bermondsey. (*London Transport*)

The Tower Subway today, housing water mains.

(*Metropolitan Water Board*)

Flushing the sewers 100 years ago (from Mayhew's
London Labour and the London Poor).

Cleaning the sewers (many of them the same ones) today.

ABOVE How Bazalgette handled underground services. On left, Metropolitan Railway. At top right, water and gas mains. Beneath them, the sewer.

(*London Transport*)

LEFT Repairing a modern sewer.

(*London County Council*)

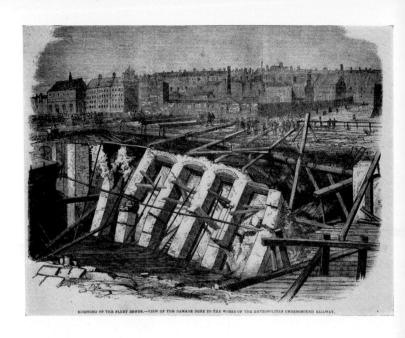

BURSTING OF THE FLEET SEWER.—VIEW OF THE DAMAGE DONE TO THE WORKS OF THE METROPOLITAN UNDERGROUND RAILWAY.

ABOVE The bursting of the Fleet Sewer in 1860 during the construction of the Metropolitan Railway near Farringdon Street Station.

(*London Transport*)

RIGHT Examining the culverts of the Fleet Sewer when the water level is low.

(*Keystone Press Agency*)

[Three Divisions of the Shield of the Thames Tunnel.]

ABOVE The three-tiered shield used by Brunel for excavating the first Thames tunnel, between Wapping and Rotherhithe, opened in 1843.

RIGHT Rear view of a Greathead shield, first used for boring most of London's original tube railway tunnels.

BELOW Diagram showing the principle of the Greathead shield.

(Photos *London Transport*)

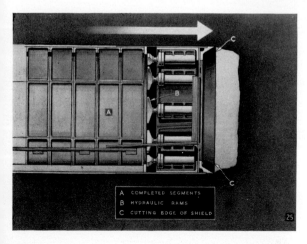

A COMPLETED SEGMENTS
B HYDRAULIC RAMS
C CUTTING EDGE OF SHIELD

The Metropolitan. The world's first underground railway, opened
March, 1863.

(London Transport)

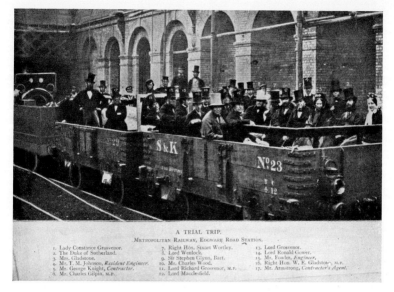

A TRIAL TRIP.
METROPOLITAN RAILWAY, EDGWARE ROAD STATION.

1. Lady Constance Grosvenor.
2. The Duke of Sutherland.
3. Mrs. Gladstone.
4. Mr. T. M. Johnson, *Resident Engineer.*
5. Mr. George Knight, *Contractor.*
6. Mr. Charles Gilpin, M.P.

7. Right Hon. Stuart Wortley.
8. Lord Wenlock.
9. Sir Stephen Glynn, Bart.
10. Mr. Charles Wood.
11. Lord Richard Grosvenor, M.P.
12. Lord Macclesfield.

13. Lord Grosvenor.
14. Lord Ronald Gower.
15. Mr. Fowler, *Engineer.*
16. Right Hon. W. E. Gladstone, M.P.
17. Mr. Armstrong, *Contractor's Agent.*

Mr Gladstone (nearest the camera) is a passenger on this trial trip on the Metropolitan Railway in January, 1863, shortly before it was opened. Passengers on the regular service did not travel in trucks!

One of the G.W.R. trains which provided the service on the Metropolitan Railway for the first eight months.

(Photos *London Transport*)

First despatch of mail-bags through the pneumatic tube from Eversholt Street to Euston Station, 1863.

A modern pneumatic tube terminal—Central Telegraph Office.

(Photos *by courtesy of the Postmaster General*)

The Carmelite Crypt which lies under the offices of the
News of the World. (*News of the World*)

The Vicar, the Rev Cyril M. Armitage (right), and the
archaeologist, Dr H. Leaver, inspect the Wren vault
under St Bride's which, when discovered, was full
of coffins, skulls and bones. (*Fox Photos*)

The Court of Arches, under St Mary-le-Bow, Cheapside, where the Supreme Court of Appeal for the Southern Province of the Church of England has been held for eight centuries.

Excavations in progress at the site of the Roman fort in the Falcon Square area of Cripplegate. *(Fox Photos)*

ABOVE The Egyptian god of the harvest, Serapis.

RIGHT Mercury, messenger of the gods, seated on a ram.

BELOW Marble head representing the goddess Minerva.

(*Fox Photos*)

Some of the many thousands of Londoners whose imaginations were fired by the Mithras finds and who visited the site of the temple. (*Fox Photos*)

16′ 0″ diameter hand shield used for Northern City Line diversion at Highbury.

(*London Transport Executive*)

Roman barge discovered in excavating the site of County Hall in 1910.

The Adelphi arches at Lower Robert Street.

to Barking Creek and Crossness Point. The high level runs from Hampstead to Bow; the mid-level from Kensal Green to Bow; the low level, from Cremorne to Abbey Mills, on the marshes near Stratford.

Talking about the district, north of Holborn Bridge, which was affected by the scheme, the writer says:

From Goswell Street to Wilderness Row it [*i.e.* the Fleet Sewer] was an open cutting, with the exception of a short tunnel under the Charterhouse grounds. The distance from Old Ford, Bow, to Kensal Green is 9 miles 2,850 feet, exclusive of 2½ miles of junctions. The sewer through Clerkenwell is 8 feet 9 inches in diameter. There were generally 400 or 500 men at work, with eleven steam-engines to pump water and draw earth.

Pinks has this to add:

The Fleet Sewer, the 'Cloaca Maxima' of our metropolis, receives the drainage of parts of Hampstead and Highgate, all Kentish Town, Camden Town and Somers' Town, parts of Islington, Clerkenwell and St Sepulchre, and nearly all that part of the Holborn division of sewers south of the New Road, the total surface draining into it in the Holborn and Finsbury Division being about 4,220 acres. In 1746, about 400 acres of this district were covered with houses. At present, there are nearly 2,000 acres built upon, of necessity requiring a sewer of large capacity to carry off the refuse waters. The dimensions of the Fleet vary according to the locality: at its northern portion it is 6 feet 6 inches high, and 6 feet 6 inches wide; at other parts it varies from 12 feet high and 12 in width, to 9 feet high by 10 feet wide; then 8 feet 6 inches wide by 8 feet 3 inches high; and before reaching the Thames the dimensions of this huge sewer are 14 feet wide by 10 feet 6 inches high, and at its mouth 18 feet by 12. The ordinary movement of the current from Bagnigge Wells is three miles an hour, but after heavy showers, when sometimes the water rises almost instantly five feet or more, the speed is greatly accelerated. The amount per day of sewage discharged by this monster sewer is on the average 1,741,775 cubic feet.

We have seen how turbulent the Fleet has always been within its confines, even of so large a sewer as that through which it runs.

In 1846, the Fleet did more than merely 'overflow'—it blew up.

The rush from the drain at the second arch at Blackfriars Bridge drove a steamer against one of the piers, and damaged it. The overflow of the Fleet penetrated into the cellars on the west side of Farringdon Street, so that one draper alone had £3,000 of goods destroyed or damaged. In the lower part of Clerkenwell, where the sewer ran open, the effects of the flood were most severe, especially in the valley below Brook Hill and Vine Street. In Bull's Head Court, Peter Street, the water rose five feet, and swept away cattle and furniture. Three poor-houses in Round Court, Brook Hill, were partly carried away. From Acton Place, Bagnigge Wells Road, to King's Cross, the roads were impassable, and the kitchens were inundated. One baker alone lost thirty-six sacks of flour. A few days after, another storm produced a renewed flood, and two more houses fell in Round Court, Brook Hill. The introduction of the cholera into Clerkenwell Prison, in 1832, was attributed to the river Fleet, then opened.

For the convenience of criminals and others on the run from the Law, the houses of this district—particularly the brothels and taverns—were amply provided with hiding-places, secret doors and passages, and—to cross the Fleet from one thieves' kitchen to another—up-and-away-in-an-instant drawbridges.

'The Red Lion' tavern, No. 3 West Street, was pre-eminent among the rat-holes of the Turnmill Lane district, not only for its raffish clientèle but, too, for its wealth of criminal conveniences.

Sometimes called 'the Old House in West Street', or sometimes 'Jonathan Wild's house', No. 3, 'from its remarkable
adaptation as a hiding-place, with its various means of escape,
was a curious habitation. Its dark closets, trap-doors, sliding
panels and secret recesses, rendered it one of the most secure
places of robbery and murder'.

It was here that a chimney-sweep named Jones, who had
escaped from Newgate, was holed up for six weeks, even
though the police searched for him, at 'The Red Lion', every
day. He might never have been found at all had not a fellow-
inmate given the escaped prisoner away.

Sometimes, as when a sailor was robbed and his naked body
thrown into the Fleet, the criminals responsible were convicted
of their crime—in this case, two men and a woman were
transported—but mostly the crimes were rarely detected, the
criminals almost never.

When the time came for this noxious tavern to be pulled
down—and (to 'date' this story) the details of the finds were
sent out by electric-telegraph and published in newspapers
printed on a steam-press—the cellars were full of human bones.

'Numerous parties daily visited the premises, among whom
were many of the police and county magistrates. It was said
to have been the rendez-vous, and often the hiding-place,
of Jack Sheppard and Jerry Abercorn; and the place looked
as if many a foul deed had been there planned and decided
upon, the sewer or ditch receiving and floating away anything thrown into it. On one occasion the police had surrounded the house to take a thief, whom they knew to be
there, but he made his escape in their actual presence.'

The Fleet yielded up many a strange piece of flotsam. We
have seen how a pig, fallen in, added a guinea and a half to his
value in its murky waters. A drunken barber, who fell in
in 1765, was not so fortunate. He had come up to London for
the day, from Bromley, in Kent. He was found, drunk no
more, but standing upright in the Ditch, frozen to death.

But it was not only fattened pigs and frozen barbers that the

Fleet gave up. After the digging and widening of the Fleet
Ditch in 1676 had yielded up those relics of Roman and
mediaeval London described earlier, any work in or about the
Ditch drew the amateur archaeologists in quest of 'curiosities'.

We have mentioned the anchor found in the Ditch, near
Baker Street; another was found, in 1843, nearby.

But the large-scale operations connected with the main-
drainage scheme gave the archaeologists, for the first time, a
really big chance to examine nearly the whole bed of the Fleet.

Between 1838 and 1863, many objects, of no great intrinsic,
but of great antiquarian, value were found: among them, a
'beautiful seventeenth-century hunting knife' (1838); a 'jug of
hard-baked pottery (the upper part covered with a mottled
green glaze), of the sixteenth century' (1854); a 'globular iron
padlock, so constructed that the whole shackle could be drawn
out when the bolt was thrown back' (1856); 'two target bosses,
of latten, of the time of Henry VIII' (1862). Other finds included a Roman sharpening steel. The remains of ships'
timbers were too numerous to be noted, as were the remains
of human beings.

But by far the most interesting finds made when clearing the
valley of the Fleet, between Coppice Row and Farringdon
Street, in 1855, are described in an article in *The Builder* of the
time:

In making the excavation for the great sewer which now
conveys from view the Fleet Ditch, at a depth of about thirteen feet below the surface in Ray Street, near the corner of
Little Saffron Hill, the workmen came across the pavement
of an old street, consisting of very large blocks of ragstone
of irregular shape. An examination of the paving-stones
shewed that the street had been well used. They are worn
quite smooth by the footsteps and traffic of a past generation. Below the old street was found another phase of Old
London. Thickly covered with slime were piles of oak, hard
and black, which had seemingly been portions of a mill-dam.
A few feet below were very old wooden water-pipes, nothing

but the rough trunks of trees. The course of time, and the weight of matter above the old pavement, had pressed the gravel, clay, granite, portions of tiles, &c., into a hard and almost solid mass, and it was curious to observe that near the old surface were great numbers of pins.

With the irresistible fascination that death—or at least danger —has for so many people, many persons used to venture into the foul night of the sewers, armed, they tell us, with thick sticks, to ward off the rats.

As the old sewers came nearer to destruction by the Metropolitan Board of Works, the number of these hardy visitors seems to have increased. Sentimentality mixed with horror was responsible for this passage:

... of the thousands who pass along [*i.e.* above ground], not one is even conscious of the proximity of the wretched wanderer creeping in noisome darkness and peril beneath his feet. A source of momentary destruction ever lurking in these gloomy regions exists in the gases, which generate in their confined and putrefying atmosphere, and sometimes explode with a force sufficient to dislodge the very masonry; or which, taking light from the contact of the lantern, might envelope the miserable intruder in sudden flame. Many venturers have been struck down in such a dismal pilgrimage, to be heard of no more; many have fallen suddenly choked, sunk bodily in the treacherous slime, become a prey to swarms of voracious rats, or have been overwhelmed by a sudden increase of the polluted stream.

I have remarked somewhere else that 'Dickens seems all cellars'; but this is a remark which could apply, with considerable truth, to the majority of nineteenth-century novelists of the period up to the completion of the Metropolitan Main Drainage System. If we think of our beneath-ground London too little, they thought of it too much. But, where they had a reason for this all-engaging preoccupation with the Darkness Beneath, we have no more reason for casting our eyes upwards rather than below.

No matter what the newspapers say (and the Government propagandists which feed them their information), Man's immediate concern should not be with the stratosphere, the troposphere and, beyond them both, with Inner and Outer Space. It may be romantically exciting to read of dogs and apes 'hurtling through space' at so many miles a second, when the train-service from Chatham, say, is slower than it was in 1850: but the Common Man should be, at this moment, most deeply concerned with What Lies Below.

Like a sort of Megalomaniac Moles, the world's Rulers and their hatchet-men are taxing out for themselves miracles of rare device far, far below the surface of city and plain.

By common, even if unspoken, consent, the Lithium Hydride and Cobalt Bombs will not be used until the Rulers will have the right depth or the right strength—or both—for these sub-terrene shelters of theirs. As soon as a really bomb-proof shelter may be constructed for the Rulers, the Common Man will enjoy the testing experience of full-scale atomic bombing. Certainly, the bombs won't fall until all the 'Key Men' are safely tucked away, with their dam-fool forms in triplicate and their tinselled yes-men, far underground. But they won't fall a minute later.

One may safely predict that, for a few anxious hours, the Common Man will find himself even more preoccupied with what lies beneath than even such a nineteenth-century novelist as Eugène Sue.

It is a sobering thought, indeed, that this book of mine may not only be the last that I shall ever write but, perhaps, the last which will ever be written—at least, of a 'non-classified' nature.

For the Hidden Ones, the Top-Dog Troglodytes, will still be tapping out reports on their electric typewriters as the last amp comes from the last emergency battery, and the nerve-gas seeps through the cracks in the gas-proof doors. . . . Will that be the end? Of course not.

Cro-Magnon had a far greater cranial capacity than have we. If we are *Homines Sapientes*, Cro-Magnon was something more. What, we cannot say. He represented a super-jump. At one moment, progress had got no farther than to produce the apeish Neanderthal. Then Cro-Magnon appears—without ancestors. What caused the tremendous mutation which gave *him* birth? A vast sun-spot activity? A super-nova, blazing out within the Galactic Limits?

The old tales are full of hints: the insistence on the deep connection between a Star and some basic Regeneration; some tremendous Stride Forward and Upward.... And what cosmic truth lies behind that all-too-obscure reference in Genesis to the coming-down of the Sons of God to visit the Daughters of Men?

Nothing ends. Cro-Magnon vanished as abruptly and as totally as he had arrived. But, in some sort, we *Homines Sapientes* took his place. If we go—if we have to go—we shall be going only to make room for others.

If I say, 'the Walbrook rises in cornfields between Islington and Hoxton', am I speaking of the 'past' or of the 'future'? Before the buildings came, there were cornfields where the Walbrook still rises. When the buildings go, the cornfields will return again.

The linking fact is the perpetual flow, the perpetual presence, of the river, once bearing the hide kayaks of Acheulean Man, later bearing the corn-barges of Syrian traders, and now neatly encased in cast-iron pipe or brick-tunnel, which runs from Islington to Dowgate.

As late as 1810, the water of the Walbrook was turning a lead-mill hard by the City Road Turnpike. The Islington of those days was still pleasantly rural, and it was by the waters of a stream that Charles Lamb lived in self-sacrificing celibacy with his sister, Mary.

We have seen how Stow, writing in the early seventeenth century, remarked that the Walbrook, within the City limits, had been covered over; but, from beyond about where the Honourable Artillery Company now have their headquarters in City Road, the Walbrook remained open, for most of the

length to its source, to well within the memory of our grand-
fathers.

Even in Stow's day, the covering-over within the City was
a recent happening: that the Walbrook remained uncovered
until the end of the sixteenth century is apparent from the story
that Stow tells of a tragedy which occurred on 4th September,
1574, when, following heavy rains, an eighteen-year-old
apprentice, 'minding to have leapt over the channel, was taken
by the feet, and borne down with the violence of the narrow
stream, and carried towards the Thames with such a violent
swiftness, as no man could rescue or stay him, till he came
against a cart-wheel that stood in the water-gate, before which
time he was drowned and stark dead.'

That the Walbrook was navigable at least as far as the
beginning of the City Road is evident from the discovery of a
boat's keel under Moorgate Street; and, in 1871, during the
building of Queen Victoria Street, a barge, still containing its
cargo of corn, was found buried within the mud.

From the cornfields between Islington and Hoxton, the
Walbrook ran—and still does run—along the course of the
City Road, entering the City proper between Moorgate and
Bishopsgate, proceeding then, as Stow says, 'to St Margaret's
Church in Lothberrie; from thence beneath the lower part of
the Grocers' hall, under St Mildred's Church [sold by the
Ecclesiastical Commissioners to the Gresham Insurance Com-
pany in 1872; the site is now occupied by the head office of the
Midland Bank Ltd—M.H.], through Bueckles berry, by one
great house built of stone and timber called the Old Barge.'

The house was thus called, Stow adds, because barges were
rowed up from the Thames as far as Walbrook Street, a remark
which is confirmed by the discovery of the corn-laden barge at
this point in 1871, though it should be noted that reputable
archaeologists have dismissed as false the report that Walbrook
was ever navigable at all after the tracing of the *limines* about
Roman Londinium.

Before dismissing, in turn, the contention of these archaeologists that Roman Walbrook was an un-navigable (and mostly

covered-in) river, let us examine the facts upon which they base their theory.

It is a fact that the Walbrook was the only considerable river or stream to have run through proto-London (the Fleet and the Shore Ditch were not only outside the City but, indeed, marked its western and eastern boundaries).

It is a fact, too, that when the City came to be completely walled, in the second century (by extending outwards from the Cripplegate fort, as was noticed on page 25), the wall was built over the Walbrook. It is certain, too, that the Romans built culverts in London Wall to permit the entry of the Walbrook into the City.

More than a century ago, inescapable proof of such culverts was found in Moorgate when, according to a contemporary account, 'opposite Finsbury Chambers, at a depth of nineteen feet, what appeared to have been a subterranean aqueduct was laid open. It was found to run towards Finsbury, under the houses of the Circus for about twenty feet, and at the termination were iron bars fastened into the masonry to prevent the sedge and weeds from choking the passage.'

The contention that the Walbrook did not merely enter the City wall through a culvert, but was channelled underground for the length of its course through the City, to discharge— still channelled—into the Thames at about where Cannon Street Station stands today, is supported, in the view of those who hold the theory of a Roman covered-in Walbrook, by the finding of relics of the London Mithraeum on both sides of the street now called 'Walbrook', and commonly held to be merely the cover of the river bearing the same name. Two pieces of classical sculpture were found in Bond Court, Walbrook, in 1889, and a further piece, still on the east side of the street, in 1954, just before the uncovering of the Mithraeum itself on the west side of the street.

Assuming that all these figures not only belonged to the same religious foundation, *but were found in their original positions*, the finds would appear to argue that, either the Walbrook river was covered over before the Mithraic temple was built upon the street (as it is now) covering the river, or the river itself ran either to east or west of the temple, and thus over a course not traced by the modern street which bears its name.

One important point which seems to have escaped the attention even of those archaeologists most intimately concerned with the discovery of the Mithraic temple is that the ritual of Mithraism insisted upon an *underground* siting for the Mithraeum. At Housesteads, Rome, Carrawburgh, Rudchester, York, Chester, Colchester, Caerleon and Heddernheim, the Mithraea are all underground: why, then, should the Walbrook Mithraeum have been an exception? Why not the Mithraic building complex in two parts, each established in a subterranean chamber on the west and east bank of London's principal river?

The evidence that the Walbrook was navigable *continuously* from pre-Roman times until the end of the sixteenth century seems irresistible. We have the boats found in Moorgate and Queen Victoria Street; and though it is possible that the Romans covered the Walbrook in, and later generations either allowed the cover to decay, or deliberately uncovered the river, it is, on the face of it, unlikely.

The Walbrook itself was used, during the Middle Ages, to drain the Great Fen or Moor upon which, in the winter, the City apprentices and other young men used to skate.

'This Fen or Moor Field,' says Stow, 'stretching from the wall of the City betwixt Bishopsgate and the postern called Cripplegate, to Finsbury, and to Holywell, continued a waste and unprofitable ground a long time, so that the same was all letten for four marks the year in the reign of Edward II; but in the year 1415, the 3rd of Henry V, Thomas Falconer, Mayor, caused the wall of the City to be broken down toward the said moor, and built the postern called Moorgate, for the ease of the citizens to walk that way upon causeys [causeways] towards Isledon [Islington] and Hoxton.'

The attempts to effect a complete drainage of the Great Fen came a century later, when, after an abortive attempt in 1512, success was achieved in 1527. The Great Fen was drained by 'conveying the water over the City moat into the channel of the Walbrook, and thence to the Thames, so that by degrees the Fen was drained and made into hard ground.'

In May, 1869, a fine tessellated pavement was discovered in the course of excavating for the new Queen Victoria Street: the pavement, with 'traces of a building of importance on the western bank [of the Walbrook], attracted, it is said, 30,000 sight-seers before it.was removed to the crypt in which the Guildhall Museum was housed until 1955.

This tessellated pavement, found at a depth of some fourteen feet below the level of modern London, could well have been the original floor of that series of buildings which culminated in Stow's 'great house of stone and timber called the Old Barge'.

J. R. Green did not doubt that 'on the [Walbrook's] navigable channel the trade of the foreigner was brought up from the Thames to the very heart of the "chepe" or market at the port or hythe [commemorated in Barge Yard], fixed by tradition in the modern Bucklersbury', and, according to A. S. Foord, the mouth of the Walbrook must have been close upon three hundred feet in width, the channel narrowing to some one hundred and twenty feet as it passed under the City wall into Moorfields.

I think we may reject the idea that the Walbrook was ever covered, save by the bridges that Stow mentions, before the Royal Act of 1462 began the task of covering by commanding that 'such as had ground on either side of the Walbrooke should vault and pave it over as far as his ground extended'.

When the new Bank of England came to be built within the still standing outer walls of Sir John Soane's Bank, not only the Walbrook, but six other smaller, tributary rivers had to be piped before the workmen could dig the foundations of the present structure. The relics of Roman London which were found during the excavations will be noticed in a later chapter.

This mention of the Walbrook's tributary streams recalls the fact that the site of the first Londinium (that is, the nucleus of the Roman or present Londinium) was not merely along the banks of a single river, but on a delta formed by the fanning out of many a rivulet and stream. All became, in the course of time, as unsavoury as could be, before they were covered in and forgotten. The name of Sherborne Lane recalls one of these forgotten tributaries of the Walbrook. Once, says Stow, the lane ran 'by a long bourne of sweet water', but, by 1300, that bourne had grown so corrupt that Sherborne Lane had become known as 'Shiteburn-lane'. It is reassuring to observe that the original name has returned to general usage.

Sometimes these little rivers, though long covered-up and 'forgotten', are remembered and re-employed for modern uses. Such re-employment came to the Cran, a small stream which once fed the so-called 'Queen Elizabeth's Bath' at Charing Cross—a square pool with steps surrounding, where the bathers sat, under a brick vault. (It was closed in 1831.)

When, at the end of the last century, the present Hippodrome Theatre, at the corner of Cranbourn Street and Charing Cross Road, was being planned as a circus (the quadriga surmounting its dome still commemorates its original purpose), the buried Cran was remembered, and its waters were tapped to fill a large pool built within the arena of the Hippodrome. But, fifty years ago, the circus shows having failed to appeal to London audiences, the Hippodrome was converted into a 'straight' theatre, and stalls placed over what had once been the arena. The Cran was returned to its obscure existence: commemorated now only in the name of Cranbourn Street.

There is another small river which is fed by one of London's once most famous wells: the Holy Well in St Clement Danes, from which Holywell Street (on the site of which Australia House now stands) took its name. The well is still marked on the Ordnance maps as standing within the little plot to the west of Clement's Inn. This well still supplies, with crystal clear water, the reputed Roman Bath in Strand Lane, in which David Copperfield often took a plunge. Once a place of resort for pilgrims, the Holy Well gave its name to the nearby street which ran parallel to the Strand until the 'Aldwych improvements' demolished its old houses.

Towards the end of its long life, Holywell Street (in which was to be found the Globe Theatre) enjoyed a dubious reputation—it was called 'Booksellers' Row'—by reason of the literature and other things which were on open display there. An old gentleman, to whom I was talking the other day, chuckled when I mentioned 'Booksellers' Row'. 'We used to call it "French Letter Row",' he said.

Shoreditch, that the earlier school of etymologists derived from Jane Shore, is, quite simply, 'sewer ditch'. (The Effra, in south-east London, is called 'the Shore' on Rocque's map.)

The Shoreditch, a foul sewer even from the earliest times, was the common ditch of the city, in which all kinds of rubbish, including corpses, might be thrown. Here on its banks, in mediaeval times, stood a great Benedictine nunnery, that of St John Baptist; and after the Dissolution, the first theatres in England sprang up in this part, Richard Burbage, the tragedian friend of Shakespeare having lived and died here. It was accounted an unsavoury neighbourhood in old days; and even the covering-in of the Shore Ditch has not greatly raised it in the popular esteem.

Yet a discovery made in 1841 would seem to show that the Romans had not only developed a small settlement in the neighbourhood of Hoxton and Shoreditch (that is to say, well beyond the eastern boundary of the wall of Londinium), but had done so because of their regard for the medicinal qualities of a well which, all through the Middle Ages, gave this district its importance.

Before the Reformation, much of the Shoreditch and Hoxton area was covered by the great abbey of the Poor Clare nuns—Whitechapel High Street marks the northern boundary of the farm (later known as Goodman's Fields) belonging to the abbey.

The abbey, in all probability, grew up about the well which had been 'developed' by the Romans, and which transmitted its reputation, transformed into 'holiness', through the Dark Ages, and into mediaeval times.

Fashion, though, began to drift eastwards even before the Reformation; and baths, on the site of the Roman baths, were erected here in the early sixteenth century. Both Queen Elizabeth and Charles I lived in Shoreditch, and a house which had once belonged to Oliver Cromwell stood here until 1844.

In 1841, some repairs were being made to the Hoxton public swimming-baths of St Agnes-le-Clair, lineal descendants, not only of the fashionable baths of Henry VII's time, but of the baths built at this place by the Romans.

At about fourteen feet below the ground level, a spring was discovered, which no longer fed the baths but which, obviously, had done so in times past. The stream issuing from this spring passed through an aqueduct of Roman tiles, well cemented, the tunnel being still in excellent condition. That it had served its purpose until Tudor times was proved by a date marked upon it during an earlier repair: 1502.

The old Hoxton baths were situated in Tabernacle Street, Finsbury; and were destroyed by fire in 1845, four years after the discovery of the Roman origins had been made. The spring which fed them was one of the smaller tributaries of the river from which the 'Sewer Ditch' had developed.

A little farther to the east is another forgotten river, the oddly-named Neckenger, which was that grimy tributary of the Thames whose windings formed that 'Jacob's Island' in which Bill Sykes met his death.

In such a neighbourhood [says Dickens], beyond Dockland in the Borough of Southwark, stands Jacob's Island, surrounded by a muddy ditch, six or eight feet deep and fifteen or twenty wide when the tide is in, once called Mill Pond, but known in these days as Folly Ditch. It is a creek or inlet from the Thames, and can always be filled at high water by opening the sluices at the Lead Mills from which it took its old name. . . . Every repulsive lineament of poverty, every loathsome indication of filth, rot and garbage; all these ornament the banks of Folly Ditch.

After having passed around—and so made—Jacob's Island, the Neckenger (or 'Folly Ditch', as Dickens calls it) was widened at its mouth to form St Saviour's Dock. The Neckenger emerged into the River between Mill Street and Shad Thames, and F. L. Stevens suggests that the name 'Neckenger' may be a shortened version of some such phrase as 'the stream near the Devil's Neckenger'—the latter being the riverside place of execution for the ancient Manor of Bermondsey, whose (originally ecclesiastical) prison has given a generic name to all the prisons of the Anglo-Saxon world: The Clink.

St Saviour's Dock is still with us, and so, therefore, is the Neckenger, whose mouth the Dock is: but the rest of the Neckenger, like most of the rivers of London, lies underground.

8. Tunnels under the Thames

WE have seen that, when the great Main Drainage question was exercising the minds of the Victorian scientific amateurs, one gentleman put forward 'the bold proposal to defile the Thames Tunnel, and wake up this wonder of joint-stock credulity', again to quote Hollingshead, 'from its long sleep of idleness'.

When Hollingshead wrote thus contemptuously, its first period of service—as a subway for foot-passengers—was drawing to a close: five years later, the Tunnel was to be closed down, the growing neglect of the public having made its upkeep no longer economically possible. The coming of the railways had ended the Tunnel's usefulness as a footway, though, paradoxically enough, it was to the coming of the railways that the Tunnel was to owe that extension of its existence which has kept it with us until today.

Before the railways had come to London, the Tunnel between Wapping and Rotherhithe had shortened the cross-Thames journey for foot-passengers by no less than four miles, since, before its building, the only crossing of the River, save by boat, was by London Bridge. But when the railways came, there were easier ways of crossing the Thames; and the usefulness of the Tunnel declined.

Yet Hollingshead's sneers were not deserved: the Tunnel had not only served its purpose at the beginning of its existence; it was rendered superfluous by a newer means of transport that the Tunnel's builders and backers could hardly have foreseen. And even though Hollingshead's typically Victorian contempt for failure was keyed to a financial assessment, the Tunnel, in fact, was eventually to recover its cost—though not as a foot-passengers' subway.

It was not the first tunnel ever to have been constructed under a river, but it was the first under-river tunnel of modern times; and, so far as scale went, it had no predecessor.

Even today, compared with some other great cities, London is singularly lacking in bridges; but it is richer than any other city, greater or smaller, in the number of the tunnels which link its two river-banks.

The last years of the eighteenth century and the first years of the nineteenth saw the sudden rise of a widespread interest in tunnels—with ambitious proposals for tunnelling, both in this country and in France. When I say that I cannot recall anyone having sought to explain this sudden and general interest in the tunnel at that time, I may mean that I feel that it has never occurred to anyone to account for it. I shall venture an explanation that I trust the reader will not think too fanciful: but I suggest that the equally sudden appearance of aerial warfare may well have turned men's minds, even if only unconsciously, to the cool safety of the submarine (or subfluvial) depths. But to me it is impossible not to connect the establishment, by decree of the French Republic, of the *Corps des Aérostatiers*, in 1792 (which makes the French Air Force the oldest in the world), with the sudden and spontaneous interest in tunnels.

When Mathieu submitted his plans for a Channel Tunnel to Napoleon I, in 1802—during the short Peace of Amiens—it was already three years since work on the excavation of an under-Thames tunnel from Gravesend to Tilbury had begun; and though that was abandoned before the end of the century, another tunnel, about a mile down-river from the present tunnel at Wapping, was not only begun in 1804, but was successfully driven to within a mere hundred and fifty feet of the Middlesex side.

But it was left to a French émigré, Marc Isambard Brunel, to give London its first under-river tunnel; and though the story of how he solved the problem of boring the necessary tunnel has often been told, we may briefly recount it here.

(If it has a type-resemblance to the story of Bruce and the Spider, it may be none the less true for all that.)

Brunel was called in to do some work in one of the great dockyards; and while there he heard of the ravages caused to the wooden ships by the *teredo* or timber-worm. Marvelling that so small a creature could wreak such damage, Brunel studied it, to be wonderfully impressed with 'the pair of strong shell-valves wherewith the creature bored its way into the hardest oak, working under the protection of its own shell'.

Inspired by the practical example of nature, Brunel designed a 'shield', to do, for burrowing men, what teredo's shell did for teredo—and, having demonstrated to a group of capitalists that he had the means, they found the money to give the clever French engineer his opportunity.

Had Isambard Brunel adopted compressed air, as Greathead was later to do, the first Thames Tunnel would not have taken nineteen years to construct, nor would the Thames have broken through nearly a dozen times between 2nd March, 1825, when the first brick was laid amidst the ringing of bells, and 25th March, 1843, when Brunel led the first members of the public through the completed Tunnel.

Its building had taken nineteen years, and had cost lives as well as money. It was a triumph of resolution over adversity; and that it is sound and dry today is a testimony to the quality of Brunel's work, done without the modern guards against such troubles as he was constantly encountering.

Fifty thousand people paid a penny to pass through the Tunnel within twenty-four hours of its opening; within fifteen weeks, more than a million people had used it. All the guide-books of the day list it among 'The Sights of London'; and there was even a 'Tunnel Waltz' specially written to celebrate it. But in 1866, it was closed down; and to many people it must have seemed that the Thames Tunnel belonged now only to the past. How, three years later, it was saved from being swept away, and given a renewed lease of life which has endured to this day, belongs to another chapter of this book.

We have mentioned Greathead, in connection with the

compressed-air tunnelling-shield, now called, after him, the Greathead Shield. James Henry Greathead and his partner, Peter William Barlow, F.R.S., began to build the second tunnel under the Thames in 1869, the year in which the original Thames Tunnel, which had been bought by the East London Railway Company in 1866, was incorporated into London's underground traffic system.

Reasoning that the Thames Tunnel had failed because it was too far, at either Wapping or Rotherhithe, from the central parts of London to attract visitors, Greathead and Barlow proposed to build a subway through the bed of the Thames between Tower Hill and Tooley Street, to relieve the congestion of the traffic crossing London Bridge. It was originally Barlow's scheme—Greathead being called in to look after the technical details, with Barlow's son as his assistant.

In a number of aspects, the Barlow-Greathead scheme was not only unprecedented—it was revolutionary. For one thing, Barlow offered to construct the tunnel at a cost within £16,000 —Brunel's tunnel had cost close on a half a million of money. For another, he guaranteed to complete the job within one year —Brunel having, as we have seen, taken nineteen years.

Barlow, by the way, had Brunel well in mind—both in his success and in his failure. Remembering that, in some places, the Brunel tunnel came to within four feet of Thames water, Barlow planned to drive his tunnel through the solid river-bed, so that the top of his tunnel was never less than thirty feet below the water.

In February, 1870, the tunnel was completed, thanks to the use of the Greathead Shield, which 'every eight hours, night and day, Sundays and week-days... went forward eighteen inches, and eighteen inches length of iron was added to the tube, which so advanced at the rate of 5 feet 4 inches every twenty-four hours'.

For this was London's—and the world's—first true 'tube' railway.

'It has been built,' says a contemporary account, 'in 18-inch lengths of cast-iron tubing, perfectly circular, each 18-inch

circle being built up of three segments, with a key-piece at
the top, which, fitting in like a wedge, holds the rest with
the rigidity of a solid casting. The cast-iron shield used for
excavation was less than two and a half tons weight. In front
of the shield, which was slightly concave, was an aperture
about two feet square, closed with a sliding iron water-tight
door, and at the back of the shield were iron sockets, into
which screw-jacks fitted, and, when worked by hand, forced
the shield forward.'

'The first example of the tube method of tunnel construction, utilizing a shield to excavate a circular tunnel which is
afterwards lined with a segmental iron cylinder', the Tunnel
Subway—with its approaches, 1,340 feet long—provided the
pattern for all future Underground railways, even to its
laying the track in a 'dip', so that the vehicles would com-
mence their journey by moving down a fairly steep gradient,
and ending it coming 'uphill'.

Access to the underground—under-river, rather—railway
was gained by descending a newel-staircase with iron treads.

'On this railway formerly ran an omnibus capable of conveying twelve passengers. The omnibus was constructed of
iron; it was light, but very strong, and ran upon eight
wheels, and was connected with a rope of steel wire by means
of a gripe that could be at any time tightened or relaxed at
pleasure, and at each end of the tunnel this wire ran over a
drum worked by means of a stationary engine.

If the carriage was stopped in the centre of the tunnel, the
beat of the paddles of the steamers above could be heard, and
even the hammering on board ships. In time there will be
subways at Gravesend, Woolwich and Greenwich. The next
to be formed, however, is one from St George's Church, in
the Borough, to Cannon Street. The Tower subway is now
only used for foot-passengers, at a charge of one halfpenny.'

When the railway was still running, the fare was one
penny (or twopence, first-class, which meant that one could go

to the head of the queue). The journey by the windlassed train took one minute and a quarter.

On Tower Hill, close by the ancient church of Allhallows, Barking, where you may see the tessellated pavement of a Roman-London barber's shop, there is a sort of large pillar-box, painted brown. This is the Middlesex entrance. From Tower Hill, the subway runs under the River in a south-westerly direction, passing under Barclay's Brewery ('Wealth beyond the dreams of avarice!' said Dr Johnson), and joins a similar newel-staircase and brown pillar-box in Vine Street, near Pickle Herring Street, just by London Bridge Station.

London's rulers, though so contemptuously wasteful of the city's above-ground treasures, are jealously careful of the city's tunnels—especially those under the Thames.

The building of nearby Tower Bridge ended the Thames Subway's usefulness to foot-passengers—it had carried a million every year until the opening of the Bridge in 1894—but its life of general usefulness was not ended. Today it carries beneath the Thames the pressure-mains of the London Hydraulic Power Company, which bought the subway, as well as the water-mains of the Metropolitan Water Board, which leases space in the tunnel which was London's first 'tube'.

Today, if we count the soon-to-be completed Erith–Purfleet Tunnel—the pilot tunnel of which was driven through the Thames bed in 1939—the River runs over no fewer than seven tunnels, not counting, of course, the tunnels constructed for carrying the Underground trains, nor those made to convey hot-water from the power-stations to flats and other buildings on the opposite bank of the River. But the list of seven does include the Thames Tunnel, which has been a railway tunnel since 1869; though it was not built as such.

Walter Thornbury, whose remarks on the Thames Subway were quoted above, was very nearly accurate in his prophecies of future tunnelling.

As he predicted, subways were built beneath the River both at Woolwich and Greenwich, the latter, linking a secluded garden in the Isle of Dogs (from which is a wonderful prospect of Inigo Jones's Queen's House at Greenwich) with a promenade over which the hull and masts of a cement-embedded Cutty Sark tower.

There is no subway yet from Gravesend to Tilbury, though the Erith–Purfleet Tunnel is only a few miles up-river from Gravesend; and though no subway for foot-passengers was ever built from St George's ('Little Dorrit's) Church, Borough, to Cannon Street, an underground railway does run from that church to Fish Street Hill.

The people of Woolwich have the best of it, with a subway *and* a ferry, the twin black funnels of whose steamers recall the Mississippi, though the murky Woolwich waters and murkier Woolwich skies somehow do not.

Blackwall Tunnel, which took eight years—1889 to 1897—to construct, is London's oldest road-traffic under-river subway. Even today, its dimensions are impressive; and in more than design it was the predecessor of the Hudson Tunnel: the engineers—led by the first Lord Cowdray—who built the Blackwall, building the Hudson, too.

Curiously near the water—at places it is within five feet of the Thames—the proximity of the tunnel to the river-bed called for some laborious and slow work: at one period of several weeks, the workmen were excavating the earth in small handfuls, taking them out through the shield through manholes measuring only three inches by seven inches.

It is a long tunnel—as long as the distance from Charing Cross to St Paul's Cathedral. The bricks used totalled seven million; and one million white glazed tiles—now a characteristic smoked-meerschaum colour—were used to face the tunnel walls.

A twin tunnel has now been built, to relieve the traffic-pressure on the original tunnel. Nothing very spectacular has been done in the way of building a monumental approach, such as was done for the Mersey Tunnel; and though the East End has grown very respectable in these days—a sort of dingy respectability, proper to the blocks of 'council flats' in which the once highly-individualistic East Ender has been barracked

—there are still traces of the Old East: Lee Fat Tun's chop-suey joint, and one or two Alf's or Joe's Caffs, not yet all hissing Gaggia espresso-machines and tarnished chromium-plate.

Crumbling places of unorthodox worship, that Lovecraft would have seen filled with devotees of Cthulhu or Nyarlathotep, but which are, in fact, the last strongholds of sweated labour—mostly in the Rag Trade—alternate with fine Georgian houses and seamen's hostels and one-story shops selling anything from radios to jellied eels. Some of the one-storied shops have their plate-glass windows painted over, and these bear the names of doctors and dentists which, outlandish though they are, yet grow more familiar every day.

Rotherhithe is the other road-traffic tunnel: it is rather grand, and—for all it is only five years younger than Blackwall's original tunnel—seemingly much more modern. Opened in 1908, and built at a cost of something over a million and a half pounds of still-gold-backed money, this pompous tunnel is a tribute to the window-dressing ability of the Greater London Council, and of its chief engineer, Sir Maurice Fitz-Maurice, who must surely enjoy an unique distinction, not only as an *Irish* engineer, but as one bearing a Norman name.

Time's whirligig does indeed work his changes! The building of Tower Bridge ended the Thames Subway's usefulness as a subterranean thoroughfare—but now, because Tower Bridge is unable to cope with a volume of traffic quite unforeseen by its builders, a new tunnel is to be built to 'help out' Tower Bridge. The bridge, say the experts, cannot continue to carry heavy traffic after about 1980.

The planners of County Hall have approved, in principle, a new river-crossing east of Tower Bridge, as part of a new route linking Gardner's Corner, Whitechapel, with Dockhead, Southwark. The consulting engineers appointed by the City Corporation in 1969 were instructed to look at three possible solutions of the problem involved: a high-level bridge, a bored tunnel or a 'cut-and-cover' tunnel—a tunnel, constructed and laid in sections, assembled within a drained trench. The engineers' recommendation will almost certainly be a tunnel— so bridge replaces tunnel, and tunnel replaces bridge.

9. The Trains go Underground

TRAFFIC congestion is no new problem in London; nor are plans for relieving it. But to find the boldest and most successful scheme ever devised to bring order out of street-chaos, we have to go back more than a century, to a time when the Metropolitan authorities had a far more serious traffic-problem to face than has ever confronted their successors. The problem came to a head within a matter of only a few years. It says much for our ancestors that the answer was found, and the remedy supplied, within a period only a little longer.

The immediate cause of the trouble was the invention of steam locomotion. The railways suddenly multiplied the number of visitors to London ten-thousand-fold, and London's narrow old streets—even narrower than they are today—simply could not handle the vast increase.

The newly-established Metropolitan Police force was both untrained in traffic-control, and generally mistrusted as a uniformed, para-military 'instrument of repression'. The Police could enforce no real authority in the matter of keeping the traffic moving.

It was left to one man to supply the solution to the problem: but before his solution was adopted, with results which have affected urban development throughout the world, many other solutions were tried; for the Victorians were not lacking in either ingenuity or the experimental itch. Traffic-control by semaphore and light signals, by whistles and hand-bells, by one-way streets and passenger footbridges over the busier streets; by broad new thoroughfares, like Queen Victoria Street and the Embankments—with these, and a dozen other palliatives, Authority tried to ease the burden of too many people using too little street-area. In the end, Charles Pearson's bold plan was adopted ... and London could breathe again.

Charles Pearson, member of the Common Council of the City of London, and afterwards City Solicitor, was a genius of the type that the Victorian age had the secret of producing: the gifted, tireless amateur, dedicated to the single idea. His contemporary, Samuel Plimsoll, the brewers' manager, knew nothing of ships ... and became the immortal champion of a square-deal for sailors. Pearson knew nothing of civil engineering, nothing of tunnelling and nothing of railways ... and became the inventor of London's (and so, of the world's) underground railway system, which celebrated the centenary of its commencement in 1959.

Pearson was all the more extraordinary in that he began campaigning *in anticipation* of the traffic-congestion that the coming of the railways would, in his opinion, inevitably cause. As early as 1833, we find him lecturing before the Lord Mayor and the Common Council; speaking to societies and clubs; pamphleteering and writing to the newspapers.

Pearson eventually persuaded the Government to appoint a Royal Commission to inquire into the possibility of dealing with the traffic which, by then, had grown to the proportions that Pearson had foreseen. The Commission began its sittings in 1845, and one of the first things that it did was to reject a proposal to build a central railway station in London, to unite all the lines coming into the Metropolis. 'The confusion and congestion that would exist inside and outside a central station would be intolerable.'

The Royal Commission finished its sittings, and presented its report, without having found a solution. This was Pearson's moment: he came forward with his improved plan for a railway connecting the various main-line termini with a station 'at Farringdon, so that traffic might reach that spot, using the City roads'.

But Pearson's genius showed best in his bold suggestion that the railway should be subterranean. 'The line,' he said, 'for the greater part of the distance will run beneath the surface of the roadway through a spacious archway. It will be thoroughly lighted and ventilated.'

The opposition was as loud as it was widespread; but the North Metropolitan Railway was incorporated by Act of Parliament in 1853, and, in the following year, re-incorporated as the Metropolitan Railway Company, with an enlarged capital of £1,000,000, and powers to borrow up to a further £333,000.

As the money was being raised and the plans drawn up, the original Pearson scheme was modified. Pearson had suggested an 'arcade' railway, with 'blowholes' at intervals, cut in the street. The new plan provided for no 'blowholes', but 'smokeless' locomotives instead.

Various ideas were tried out, the most ingenious (as also, in trial, the least efficient) being the 'hot water' and 'hot brick' engines, which had no fire, and therefore could emit no smoke. The 'hot brick' engine was the invention of John Fowler, the Metropolitan's engineer. To avoid smoke, his engines were to start their run with hot water in the boilers and hot bricks in the fire-box. Only one trip did the 'hot brick' engine—'Fowler's Ghost', as it was called—make: from Bishop's Road, Paddington, in November 1861.

Finally, Mr (afterwards Sir) Daniel Gooch, locomotive superintendent and later chairman of the Great Western Railway came up with the suggestion for a steam locomotive 'emitting neither vapour nor smoke', and as the G.W.R. was to work the line, the Gooch loco was adopted. The Gooch locomotives were standard steam locomotives fitted with a condensing apparatus which, as A. J. F. Wrottesley describes—*Famous Underground Railways of the World*—consisted of long pipes, through which the exhaust steam passed into a tank, and not into the atmosphere, until the more open sections of the line were reached.

Due to the powerful influence of the Great Western in the organizing of the original Metropolitan system, the line was laid with a 'mixed' gauge, having outer rails 7 ft. apart, for 'broad gauge' traffic such as ran on the then Great Western, and an inner rail for 'standard' (4 ft. 8½ in.) gauge.

Some trial runs were made, with the passengers sitting in open goods-trucks; and Mr Gladstone, then Chancellor of the Exchequer, and Mrs Gladstone, were present on one of these trial runs.

The work on the 'cut and cover' tunnels began at the end of 1859, and the difficulties of construction—pick, shovel and wheelbarrow being the main equipment used—were enormous. As has been mentioned already, the Fleet River overflowed the cuttings in June 1862, to a depth of 10 feet, as it was to do again in 1915.

But the greedy litigants were even more ferocious menaces to the success of the scheme than London's hidden streams and rivers. Every time that a crack appeared in a house, the Metropolitan's directors were served with a writ for damages, so that William Arthur Wilkinson, the chairman of directors, was to dwell bitterly on 'papering with banknotes the allegedly cracked walls of a chapel'.

The claims for compensation were terrific—and unending. Nevertheless, the first section of the line was opened in January 1863, just three years after work began. The rush of passengers was so great that the doors had to be closed, and it was apparent that the £200,000 lent by the Common Council—as well as the money advanced by the Great Western and the Great Northern—would not be lost. (In fact, the City of London sold its shares later, at a fine profit.)

Then the really crippling blow fell. A quarrel broke out between the Metropolitan directors and those of the G.W.R. which threatened to close London's Underground almost in the moment of completion.

The line had been opened from Bishop's Road, Paddington (where a junction was made with the G.W.R. main line) to Farringdon Street: a distance of three and a half miles. Using only 'broad gauge' trains, a half-hourly service was provided from the beginning; 30,000 passengers being carried on the first day.

The quarrel was based upon a decision of the Metropolitan's directors to extend their system without 'cutting in' the

G.W.R.; and the G.W.R. directors retaliated by serving notice, on July 18th, 1863, that they would discontinue working the Metropolitan line on December 1st. The Metropolitan retorted by announcing that they would work the line themselves after October 1st; upon which, the G.W.R. gave notice that all G.W.R. rolling-stock would be withdrawn from service on the Metropolitan on August 10th—just one week ahead.

This was little short of blackmail; and Myles Fenton, the Metropolitan's general manager, was not the man to submit to such unfair pressure. Fortunately for Fenton, the habitual high-handed attitude of the G.W.R. directors had made them plenty of enemies elsewhere; and both the Great Northern (which had subscribed money for the Metropolitan) and the London and North Western came forward with carriages. [I am much indebted for information at this point to Messrs C. A. Johns, of Coulsdon, Surrey; K. Benest, of Claygate, Surrey; and Stanley R. Miller, F.R.I.B.A., of Harrow, Middlesex.]

In expectation of the opening-up of the G.N.R. service to Farringdon Street, the Great Northern had a number of tank-engines already converted to 'consume their own smoke', as required by the Act. The engines had been fitted with condensing apparatus by Archibald Sturrock, the G.N.R.'s locomotive engineer who, ironically enough, had spent some years in the service of the Great Western at their Swindon yards. These already-fitted engines were hastily augmented by the conversion of about a dozen tender engines, modified so that the exhaust steam was piped into the tender, and condensed in the water-tank. The flexible pipes leading into the tenders worked reasonably well, although some trouble arose, due to leaks at the joints. One other small modification consisted in the shortening of the chimneys.

'The spirit of "getting a move on",' Mr C. A. Johns comments, in a letter to me, 'exemplified in this incident, was typical of the Great Northern authorities of those days, and makes refreshing reading in these days of so much planned economy.' It does indeed. And the policy of 'getting a move on' paid off—handsomely.

For all that the G.W.R.'s ultimatum had given the Metropolitan only seven days in which to find new rolling-stock, there was no break in the Met's half-hourly service. So resiliently did the Metropolitan rally under the hammer-blow of the G.W.R.'s ultimatum that not only was the Underground service not interrupted: by the beginning of October, the Metropolitan was placing its own carriages in service. By the following year—1864—the Metropolitan was running its trains with its own locomotives as well as its own carriages.

Friendly relations were soon re-established with the G.W.R., whose 'broad gauge' carriages reappeared on the Metropolitan line, on through trains from Windsor and Ealing to Farringdon Street, in January 1864. But the broad-gauge locomotives ran to Moorgate Street for the last time on March 15th, 1869; after which, there were no more broad-gauge trains. The 'Battle of the Gauges' had been won—the narrow gauge being the winner.

Before we go on to see how, with very little interruption, the pattern of underground transport, initiated (and, as it turned out, established) by those first three and a half miles of the Metropolitan Railway, developed into the vast subterranean traffic network of today, let us consider how those earliest of Underground travellers were conveyed. To particularize: in what degree of comfort they were carried.

A photograph of a trial run made by Distinguished Guests (all whiskered, top-hatted and self-consciously Conscious of Event) shows the passengers sitting rather uncomfortably in open goods-trucks; and this photograph has given rise to the false opinion that the first Underground trains, like the first overground trains of forty years earlier, used open trucks for the passengers. This was not so. In all respects, the Metropolitan was as modern as could be. Unlike the first overground railways, which used converted stage-coaches and trucks taken over from the railway system of pre-locomotive days, the

Metropolitan began with 'the very latest' in stations and travel-ling-accommodation for its passengers.

The carriages—eight-wheeled—had accommodation for first-, second- and third-class passengers: socio-financial trichotomy which was practised on all contemporary railway systems in Great Britain (the 'undemocratic' Foreigner even had a fourth class), and extended to embrace, not only restaurants, bars and waiting-rooms, but lavatories and 'conveniences' as well. The idea that engine-drivers and plate-layers, their clothing thick with the grime of their trade, could use the same restaurants and bars as the more cleanly-clad passengers (to say nothing of their expecting and receiving priority of service from the matey counter-hands) would have been as distasteful to the Victorian engine-driver as to the Victorian passenger. *Tempora mutantur, nos et mutamur in illis!*

All the carriages were completely roofed, and the first-class compartments were fully enclosed; the second and third having only the 'half-back' partitions which were still to be seen on the trains of the London & North Eastern line from Fenchurch Street to Tilbury at least as late as 1930 (for I remember them well).

To make a comparison: the lighting on the first Metropolitan trains was, in 1863, far in advance of that to be seen in the L.N.E.R. antiquities that I have just mentioned, where the dim blue fish-tail gas-flame was enclosed in a circular tin box, pierced with small holes. When setting out on a journey from Fenchurch Street to the docks at Tilbury, the guard used to lock the carriage-doors, and then put his head in the open window, with a curt, 'Beware of card-sharps on this train!' One feels that the card-sharps cannot ever have practised their craft after daylight hours!

But, as far as the passengers of the early Metropolitan trains were concerned, they had gas-lighting, at a time when even the crack overground expresses still used oil-lamps. In his book, *The Metropolitan Railway*, published in 1951, Mr C. Baker says that lighting was by 'incandescent gas' from india-rubber bags placed on the roof of the carriage; but the Science Museum

Handbook, *Land Transport*, says that the District Railway—
to which we shall come shortly—introduced a patented system
of compressed oil-gas in 1876.

There appears to be a little confusion here. Karl Auer von
Welsbach did not exhibit his first incandescent gas-mantles
until the Jubilee Year of 1887; and though Drummond had
discovered limelight in 1828, 'incandescence' had to wait,
so far as gas-illumination was concerned, for Welsbach's
invention.

The first Metropolitan trains were illuminated by gas, stored,
under compression, in containers placed on the roof of the
carriages, and the gas-jet, enclosed in wire-netted glass shades,
was of the ordinary fish-tail variety that many of my readers
will remember in old-fashioned theatrical dressing-rooms (there
enclosed in wire, not glass) and—particularly—in the dingier
London alleys, notably those threading their way through and
around the Adelphi Arches.

The stations were airy, well supplied with waiting-rooms and
bars; and a link with the earliest days of the Metropolitan—
nicknamed 'the Underground' by Londoners even before the
trains began to run—is preserved in the fact that all but one
of the cosy little bars on the Metropolitan and District railways
(now called by the generic name of 'District') are still managed
by the firm which received the original contract of management: Spiers & Ponds—of whom more hereafter.

After some teething-troubles of a financial character, the
Metropolitan soon established itself as a profitable concern;
and its success was reflected in its extension of its services.

Still using mixed-gauge rails, the Metropolitan pushed the
line Citywards, reaching Moorgate in 1865, the farthest point
to be reached in an eastward direction before the abolition of
the broad gauge.

A further extension eastwards—to Bishopsgate (now called
Liverpool Street) was not made until ten years had passed;
but, in the meanwhile, extensions were being made in the
opposite direction. A line was constructed from Edgware

Road to 'Praed Street' (a station behind Paddington main-line terminus—to which it was later joined by the existing subway), and then, through Bayswater, to High Street, Kensington, which was reached in 1866.

Connections were also made with various overhead railways —the G.W.R., the Hammersmith & City, the London, Chatham & Dover and the L.N.E.R.; but, as the joint services ran in open-to-the-sky viaducts, they do not concern us here, any more than does the open-air line running from Baker Street to Swiss Cottage and beyond.

What this linking-up with the overground railways meant was that 'main line' traffic used parts of the Metropolitan track, so that the nuisance from the smoke of these trains must often have been excessive. But nothing stayed progress; nothing kept passengers away: by 1872, less than ten years after the opening of the Metropolitan Railway, the system was carrying 44,000,000 passengers a year.

Pearson's original idea had been to link all the main-line termini by a 'circular' underground railway—the present so-called 'Inner Circle' (because there were once a 'Middle Circle' and an 'Outer Circle'); but the completion of this 'Inner Circle' was achieved by a rival concern: the Metropolitan and District Railway, or 'District', as it has been more commonly known.

This railway—constructed mostly on the same 'cut-and-cover' principle adopted in building the Metropolitan—was incorporated in 1864 (the year after the Metropolitan opened), and began as a continuation of the rival Metropolitan's line, from the (Metropolitan) station of High Street, Kensington, to Gloucester Road, a district then being developed with the profit made by the Great Exhibition of 1851. (This still-wealthy, still-solvent concern is to be found in the London Telephone Directory. The dingily unsuccessful 'Festival' of 1951 is already forgotten—and better so.) Gloucester Road station was opened in 1866, the original buildings, to which Sherlock Holmes and Watson went in connection with that nationally important case, *The Second Stain*, being still in existence, not much altered after a century of use.

Further extensions to South Kensington and Sloane Square followed; Westminster being reached in December 1868, the howl which went up at the 'threat' to Westminster Abbey and the Houses of Parliament (the Cassandras of the day prophesying that both would fall into the cut-and-cover pit in Parliament Square) being comparable nowadays only with the sort of howl which goes up if a Little Doggie falls into a well. Mansion House station—which, in a typical London fashion, lies a good quarter of a mile from the Lord Mayor's residence —was reached in 1871.

Though not so 'advanced' as the Metropolitan in the matter of passengers' comfort—the 'District' carriages were four-wheelers—and though, for the first five years of the 'District's' life, the service was actually run by its rival, the Metropolitan, the construction of the line was decidedly more so, and showed how the pattern of Underground traffic would be developed. For not only 'cut-and-cover' construction was used in building the District, but true tunnelling, both in Kensington, where the already built-over area made it necessary to tunnel under the houses, and under the newly-constructed Embankment, from Westminster to Temple and Blackfriars stations.

After the Metropolitan had extended its line eastwards to Bishopsgate (Liverpool Street) in 1875, its development towards the completion of the 'Inner Circle' was undertaken jointly with the District. By 1878, only the gap between Aldgate and Cannon Street was needed to complete the 'Circle' that we use today. A further joint line, with junctions to enable trains to run direct to and from both the Metropolitan and District, at the present Aldgate East station, was opened to Whitechapel, to connect with the East London line. (Information taken from A. J. F. Wrottesley: *Famous Underground Railways of the World*.) This connection was made in 1884.

The 'Inner Circle' was completed too, in 1884: Pearson's dream of forty years earlier had been realized. What is more, all the final work had been effected by tunnelling: the lines ran completely underground, with openings to the surface only at the stations.

The time had come for the next important step in the development of London's underground traffic-system: the change from the shallow 'cut-and-cover'-and-open-cutting system of construction to the modern 'tube' system.

That, from 1869, the East London Railway had been running its trains through the Thames Tunnel had not really effected the essential change from covered-in cuttings to the modern 'tube' system; for though the East London's trains ran, under the Thames, through Brunel's famous Tunnel, the rest of the five and a half miles of the line, from Bishopsgate, through Whitechapel, to Wapping, ran in the open, save for the small stretch which ran under the London Docks themselves. The construction of the part under the docks was, as Mr Wrottesley says, a 'formidable undertaking', as 'docks, quays and warehouses had to be underpinned with concrete, and coffer-dams were actually built below the docks in some cases'.

The first part of the East London, utilizing the Thames Tunnel, was opened in 1869; the next part in 1876; while the extension, made to connect the railway with both the Metropolitan and District systems, was opened in 1884. It was in that year, too, that the East London was leased to a committee of railway companies, all of which ran trains over the East London tracks at some time or another.

Though we are solely concerned in this book with the development of London beneath the surface, it is necessary to mention here the early linking up of the Underground railway system with the overhead lines; as the extension of the purely central Underground systems into the suburbs—Hammersmith, Twickenham, Richmond, and so on—by means of these linkings-up with the main-line systems brought an immense volume of passenger-traffic into the central regions, and so forced extensive development of the Underground system in the central—and strictly underground—regions that we have under notice. For the linkages meant not only that the Underground system extended its services far out into the suburbs and, through the main-line services, to the remotest parts of the Kingdom; it meant, too, that the main-line trains used the Underground tracks—and forced upon London the need to extend its Underground traffic-ways very greatly indeed.

As so often in human affairs, the means to satisfy a need were developed simultaneously with the development of the need itself.

The 'cut-and-cover' tunnels ('archways', their designers called them) of the Metropolitan and District railways had, in serving sparsely-populated districts, filled them with streets and houses. Such now densely populated parts of London as Earl's Court and Baron's Court and Brompton—Earl's Court and Baron's Court were hardly more than vast market-gardens —were literally populated only through the coming of the Underground railways.

It was now impossible to contemplate extensions of the Underground system by the original method of 'cut-and-cover': only tunnelling, taking the 'tube' clear beneath the foundations of the new districts, could be considered.

We have mentioned the Greathead Shield in an earlier chapter: it was the availability of this highly efficient tunnelling device which made a large-scale extension of London's Underground possible.

But before we proceed to the description of how London got its 'tubes', there is another universal convenience whose adequate functioning and general availability were necessary before the 'tube' could be developed: the 'lift' or, as both Charles Dickens and the Americans prefer to call it, the 'elevator'.

Stairways were adequate to serve the platforms of the first just-below-street-level Underground railways; but the deep-level 'tubes' called for mechanical and quick-acting means of raising and lowering the millions of Underground passengers. Already, by 1894, the total passenger-traffic was to top 88,000,000 in one year.

Above ground, the need for the efficient 'lift' had already made itself obvious. The iron (later steel) frame system of building construction had made the tall building possible. But it was not enough to know how to build high; the means had to be found to 'supply' to the same height. Water had to be brought up to the top floors, not only for drinking, washing and general culinary purposes: it had to be squirted up as high, if need be, in order to fight fire. It was the inability to develop the high-pressure mobile pump which caused the panic passing of the London (Height of Buildings) Act in 1894.

But what the builders of the tall buildings needed, if they were ever to hope to get tenants for the upper floors, were lifts —quickly-acting, eminently safe.

The steam-lift was developed in the 1860s, but a number of accidents, some of them fatal, caused Government to prohibit the steam-powered lift. The hydraulic lift, used by the Romans at their warehouses in Ostia and elsewhere, was 're-invented' by Murdoch, 'inventor' of illumination by coal-gas.

The hydraulic lift was reasonably efficient, but it called for the expensive installation of subterranean high-pressure mains, and so could only be supplied, as a service, where the demand would justify the laying of the necessary high-pressure mains.

The answer to the problem of finding a quick, efficient means of 'lifting' people was found in the development of electric power for commercial purposes: the great industrial-scientific advance which is the most notable achievement of the decade 1877–1887. The electric motor made electric traction— and so 'tube' transport—possible; and the electric motor made possible the safe lift, without which the 'tubes' could not have been run.

From the beginning of 'tube' construction, the electric lift was part of the system, and even today, though the 'escalator' or 'moving stairway' has demonstrated its superiority over the lift as a means of handling passenger-traffic to and from the platforms, there are ninety-nine lifts still in operation at thirty-six London Underground stations.

The first escalator to be seen in London was that installed, as a 'novelty', at the Earl's Court Exhibition, in 1911, where it excited much interest. The advantage of the escalator over the lift is that the elevator or lift offers a discontinuous service, with a restriction imposed by its size; whereas the escalator is continuous in flow, and will not 'jam' before a much higher 'saturation-point' is reached than is the case with the lift.

The majority of lifts are controlled by attendants stationed either in the lift or on the landings, where they can control a group of lifts.

At some stations, operation at street-level is by the booking-clerk, but arrangements vary according to station-layout and traffic conditions. Fully automatic lifts needing no operator are now installed at five stations—Earl's Court, Strand, Goodge Street, Oxford Circus and Hampstead—and, naturally, this is a modern development which was unknown to earlier users of the electric-powered underground railways.

At Earl's Court and Strand, the automatic control gear was added to existing manually-operated lifts. At Goodge Street and Oxford Circus the lifts are new, high-speed types, capable of moving at speeds of up to 600 feet a minute. The newest lifts at Hampstead are even faster: they are, in fact, the fastest lifts in Great Britain, having a speed of 800 feet a minute, and taking only twenty-one seconds to pass up or down a lift-shaft 181 feet in length.

The development of the various safety-devices on lifts has been a matter of many years' experiment, but even the earliest lifts were adequately protected against human error or mechanical breakdown, and the first tube-passengers were free of an annoyance which is fairly common today—the stoppage of lifts owing to the capricious moods of the operators, most of them suffering from the neurosis originating in nostalgia for the life of *dolce far niente* in a Jamaican mangrove-swamp. (The fact that white operators, who have been no farther west than Bournemouth, also suffer from this neurosis, I leave to the psychiatrists to explain.)

Lifts today have safety devices which ensure that no lift may leave a landing until all doors are locked and closed. Another device, a 'governor', ensures that the lift will be brought to a

halt should it develop a speed in excess of normal when travelling in a downwards direction. An automatic 'warning voice'
—'Mind the doors, please!'—is fitted to many lifts.

On the physical side of safety, all lifts are supported by at
least four ropes, the combined breaking-strength of which is
more than six times the weight of the lift when carrying the
maximum number of passengers. Breakage of only one rope
(a stranded-steel rope, of course) would immediately bring
into operation the safety-gear which would bring the lift to
an abrupt halt.

A further safety-measure, unsuspected, it is safe to say, by
the majority of those millions who use London's Underground
lifts, is the door—concealed behind posters—which opens out
of the lift-cage itself. Lifts are constructed in pairs; so that, in
the event of the stoppage of one, the second lift can be brought
down level with the stopped lift, and the passengers transferred
to the still-working lift through the door in each lift-cage.

The history of invention is littered with the dead bones of
ideas which were 'before their time', or which 'didn't quite
come off', or which failed because materials or accessories were
not up to the task of carrying out the main idea. Such a failure
in the history of the development of Underground transport
was the Pneumatic Despatch, constructed by T. W. Ramell,
and opened for the carriage of mails between the North-west
District Post Office in Seymour Street to Euston Station.

The line was opened in February 1863, a month after the
Metropolitan Railways began to carry passengers. The line
was extended from Euston to the General Post Office at
St Martin's-le-Grand, in November 1865, and a description of
the line and of the opening of the extension appeared in the
November 18th, 1865, edition of *The Illustrated London News*.

Though not designed to carry passengers, the usual Victorian
Distinguished Company, always available to give its blessing
to any commercial enterprise, turned out for an uncomfortable
ride. *The Illustrated London News* had to describe it at second-

hand: apparently its reporter was not considered grand enough
to join the Distinguished Company:

> 'The sensation at starting, and still more so upon arriving
> (say some of the passengers) was not agreeable ... but once
> fairly within the tube, these sensations were got rid of, or
> left behind.'

After constant patching-up, the tube was abandoned by the
Post Office in 1880, some parts of it being now used to carry
telephone-cables. The trouble with this idea rested in the inability to perfect proper sealing of the tube. The trucks were
pushed forward by compressed air—they were, to put the
matter almost too simply, 'blown along' the tube; and the
difficulty of sealing meant that much of the pressure was
wasted.

Many misconceptions have arisen concerning this experimental and (as it turned out) dead-end idea; I myself having
entertained some in the past. However, research among the
recollections of men contemporary with this pneumatic tube
has revealed that the Post Office Pneumatic Despatch was not
the only one of its kind. In the memoirs of Alfred Rosling
Bennett, a distinguished civil engineer who was a founder
Member of the Institution of Electrical Engineers and some-
time Vice-President of the Institution of Locomotive Engineers
and a Member of the Newcomen Society, I came across this
interesting passage, which clearly demonstrates that the G.P.O.
pneumatic tube had at least one rival in the 1860s:

Writing of 1865, Bennett says:

> Early this year I saw at the Crystal Palace a tunnel 10 feet
> by 9 feet in diameter and 60 yards long, with some very
> sharp gradients, through which a large railway carriage con-
> taining sightseers (if they who travelled in darkness could
> be so called) at sixpence each, was blown by compressed air
> in one direction, and sucked back by vacuum to the other.
> This was an illustration of the principle of transport then
> being exploited by the Pneumatic Despatch, which had
> already laid down an underground iron tube 33 inches by

30 inches in diameter for the conveyance of mails and parcels between Euston Station and the North West District Post Office, and were busily constructing a tube 4 ft. 6 in. high and 4 ft. wide, from the same terminus to St Martin's-le-Grand.

This was eventually completed, but never seemed to work satisfactorily, great difficulty being experienced in keeping the joints air-tight.

According to Bennett, it was closed down after only eight years' service.

The mystery over which all these contemporary commentators pass is this: were those 'not agreeable sensations' of which the passengers complained nothing but 'the bends'? They can hardly have been otherwise. It is just as well that the tube did not succeed: over-compression of the nitrogen in the blood would have caused more fatalities than any crashes.

Bennett himself contributed an idea, in 1891, which was not to be realized practically until December 1927: *An Electrical Parcels Exchange* (this being the title of a paper that he read at the British Association's meeting at Cardiff in that year).

'It was well received,' Bennett records, 'by all but Post Office officials, one of whom was a member of the Engineering Committee which had accepted the paper; and another present when it was discussed.

'But,' Bennett continues, 'shortly before the [1914] war, the Post Office asked Parliament for leave to construct electric tubes between the chief metropolitan railway and postal centres,' borrowing the ideas from Bennett's Cardiff paper, 'but in an unnecessarily expensive manner, using two tubes where one would suffice.'

Bennett expresses an excusable annoyance at the high-handed way in which the *chinovnik* selected by the Postmaster-General to present the case for the 'electric tube' before the Select Committee tried to hog the credit for originality—'Both the Pneumatic tube of the Sixties and my own Cardiff proposals forgotten!'—and swore on oath that nothing of the sort had ever before been suggested.

The necessary Parliamentary sanction having been given, work on the construction of the electric underground parcels and mails railway for the General Post Office began in the year in which the first World War broke out, and much of the tunnelling had, in fact, been completed when what we learned to know as 'the exigencies of war' brought work to a standstill.

The already-constructed tunnel was used as a bomb-proof store for national treasures; and work was not resumed until 1923, being practically completed in 1927, the full system being completed in 1930.

Six and a half miles long, the Post Office tube—carrying no passengers—runs from the Eastern District Post Office in Whitechapel to the General Post Office at Mount Pleasant, touching, on the way, at the main post offices at Liverpool Street and Newgate Street. Then, from Mount Pleasant, to the West Central post office, to the Western Parcels Office at the back of Selfridges, and so to Paddington.

Though constructed on the same principles as those employed in building the tubes of passenger-transport, the Post Office tube is much smaller in diameter: only 9 feet, which gives space for two 2 ft.-gauge tracks.

The only defect that a philosopher (as distinct from a mathematician) will find with Newton's Third Law of Motion is that its classical definition is much too narrow, too restricted. It is possible to re-state the Law in other terms, but only two of these possible re-statements need concern us here: For every weapon there is a defence; for every need there is an available means of supplying that need.

The many needs which may be summed up in the statement that some such traffic-system as the Tube Railway was necessary were satisfied—at least temporarily—by the existence of a whole body of devices which, in working association, could construct a Tube Railway.

The principal of these devices were the Greathead Shield, which made speedy, *deep* tunnelling possible; the electric motor, the only possible power-unit for use in deep-level traction; and the incandescent electric-lamp, the only possible source of illumination in trains running through the deep, tight tunnels constructed with the Greathead. Shield. The electric motor also powered another necessary device: the 'train' running in a vertical rather than a horizontal direction— the 'lift' or 'elevator'. With all these devices available, the development of the tube-system of underground railways could begin.

Electric traction had been tried out, with a fair degree of success, in New York, in 1836; but it was not until the latter half of the 1870s that electrical engineering made a dramatic stride forward, and introduced the Electrical Age. In 1877, the exterior of the Gaiety Theatre, in London, was illuminated by electricity; and electric lamps were installed at the cross-roads centering upon the Royal Exchange in 1880. In 1879, the first telephone exchange was opened in King William Street, City; and in that same year, Joseph Swan perfected the incandescent lamp that he had first demonstrated, in crude form, in 1861— the year in which Reis, in Frankfort-on-Main, had first demonstrated the electro-magnetic telephone that Edison and Graham Bell were to perfect.

The year 1880 is, indeed, an *annus mirabilis* in the history of commercial electric technology; for it was in that year that the first International Electrical Exhibition was held in Paris, the 'sensation' of the Exhibition being the new Bürgin generators. This Exhibition marked the fact that a complete—even if still uncertain—technology had been developed within the space of little more than a decade; and the following decade was to see the development of that decade brought to the stage immediately before that of today. In America, Fessenden was to achieve wireless telephony before the century was out; but the great achievements in electrical technology of the 1880s were the electric motor (made effective, of course, by a corollary development of generators and accumulators), the incandescent lamp and the telephone.

Electric power was first applied to commercial traction in

the tramways, on which large-scale electrification took place
even in the early part of the decade.

The first electric motors, principally of the Daft and Vander-
poel type, were hardly satisfactory: not particularly reliable,
and excessively expensive.

Then, in 1887, the English electrical-engineer, Sprague,
'began the first serious scientific exploitation of electric traction
apparatus', with the result that the now historic Richmond,
Virginia, line was equipped with Sprague apparatus. Defects
which became apparent in the use of the 7½ h.p. Sprague
motors were remedied by another Englishman, Dr H. F.
Parshall, who thus describes his work:

This first [Sprague] motor was superseded by a double
reduction 15-H.P. motor, for which the writer was responsible. Several hundreds of these were built, but the experience
gained during the first year was generally to the effect that
something better had to be discovered, otherwise the future
of electric traction would be limited. As a result of studies,
the modern four-pole single-reduction motor with projection
armature was evolved, and a machine that was fairly commercial produced.

Two—or, rather, three—other great names now came into
the picture of rapid, 'inspired' progress.

After the consolidation of the Edison and Thomson-Houston
Companies, the designs of the two companies were merged
into the motor very widely known as the G.E.Co.800, which
motor [Parshall is writing in 1916] is still in operation in
some places, and which has, in many respects, a strong simi-
larity to the most advanced designs of today.

It was now possible to begin construction of an electrically-
powered, electrically-lighted, electric-lift serviced underground
'tube' railway.

The first underground electric railway in the world was
opened to the public in December 1890, with impressive ceremony; the Prince of Wales (afterwards King Edward VII)

being among the Distinguished Company which made the first trip over the three-mile stretch from King William Street, City, to Stockwell, then a pleasant suburb of respectable middle-class character, and not, as now, a slum Negro quarter.

The digging of any underground railway—or even underground water-conduit—had always produced the usual howl; but this time, though the expected howl came, it was of a novel character. The howlers did not protest against 'undermining' London's streets and houses, but London's *faith*. For the world's first electric tube railway must be the only railway in the world which built a station in the crypt of a church— in this case, the Hawksmoor church of St Mary Woolnoth. The directors of the railway paid the then Bishop of London the still very considerable sum of £250,000 for the permission to build a station in the crypt of St Mary's, and the staircase from Lombard Street and King William Street to the station led past an old wall decorated with the carved stone heads of George I angels. But this did not happen until ten years after the railway's opening.

Originally called the City of London and Southwark Subway Company, London's first tube—re-named the City and South London Railway—was not at first intended to be electrified. It was proposed to draw the trains along the three-mile length by cable-traction, the cable-drums at each end to be worked by steam-engines. However, when Charles Grey Mott, a director of the Great Western Railway, was elected Chairman of the City and South London, he recommended electric traction, and his recommendation was adopted.

Even so, the fact that electric traction was not originally contemplated accounts, doubtless, for the fact that all stations were equipped with hydraulic, and not electric, passenger-lifts.

The two tracks ran in separate tubes, the tubes sometimes running side-by-side and sometimes top-and-bottom. Power was supplied, at 500 volts, from a power-station at Stockwell, and because at first the carriages had no windows, the passengers referred to them as 'padded cells'. The conductor had to

stand at the doors and call out the names of the stations. There
was a five-minute service, and the fare was a uniform twopence.

Ten years later, as the City terminus was on an awkward
curve, the directors constructed a new tube under the river,
from London Bridge to the Monument and Moorgate.
The old tube under the river was abandoned, and given over
to gas and water mains. During both wars it was also used for
the storage of valuables. In 1901, the City and South London
was extended south to Clapham Common, and north to the
Angel, Islington.

The next electric underground railway to be built in London
was the Waterloo and City line, running from Waterloo
Station to a sub-surface station near the Bank. The line was
opened in 1898 and, alone among London's tubes, has remained
independent through the 'centralizing' of London's transport
systems and the 'nationalizing' of Britain's railways.

Known to the many City workers who use it as 'The Drain',
the Waterloo and City was, at the beginning, controlled by
the London & South Western Railway (owners of the major
part of Waterloo Station), and absorbed into the L. & S.W.R.
in 1908. It was the only tube railway in London not taken over
by the London Passenger Transport Board when the L.P.T.B.
was established in 1933; and even today the 'Drain' is not
controlled by the London Transport Executive. Not until 1940
were the original carriages replaced by sliding-door coaches of
modern design, and American visitors to this country should
spare a moment from seeing Westminster Abbey and St Paul's
to travel in this curious little tube, which has defied the political
shibboleths of Tory and Socialist alike. For this is a completely
American railway: constructed in the United States, shipped
over in parts, put together in the Eastleigh works of the
L. & S.W.R., and taken down to the tube in a lift—still the
only method of bringing up worn-out parts and taking new
ones down. In one respect it is now the most modern of
London's underground railways: a 'travelator', or moving

pavement having been installed at the Bank terminus in October 1960.

We shall see shortly how strong was American influence in shaping the pattern of London's underground railways—even the lifts were supplied by a firm originally American: Otis— and it was in the construction of the Waterloo and City Railway that this American influence was first introduced in an important way.

But the world's first electric tube of the completely modern type was the Central London, opened in 1900—as a brass-plate in a subway at Bank Station still commemorates—by Albert Edward, Prince of Wales, K.G., in the last year before he succeeded to the throne. This was the famous 'Tuppenny Tube', so called from the uniform fare which was charged for any distance up to the total of its five-miles run from the Bank to Shepherd's Bush.

The improvements which have since been effected in the Central London line have all been of a relatively superficial nature; the most important of them being the substitution, at the majority of the metropolitan stations, of the escalator for the elevator.

Other improvements have involved the provision of 'self-opening' doors (the doors being operated by pneumatic pumps, and controlled by the conductors), sprung upholstery and more brilliant electric-lighting. But all these improvements, even in totality, do not add up to change: the Central Line today is still, in essentials, what it was when it opened in 1900. It is longer, some of its stations are bigger—notably at Notting Hill Gate—but, on the reverse side of the medal, it is far dirtier (since socialism seems to be inseparable from mysophilia), and —since the staff need have no slightest interest in the passengers —far less efficiently run.

'Mechanization' has taken much of the responsibility from the human element in the railways' running: it seems certain that, in order to recover something of the original 'Tuppenny Tube's' sparkle and vim, we must first 'mechanize' the system entirely. The hortative or minatory cries at the stops—'Mind the doors!' or 'Let 'em off, *please!*'—could be 'canned' in the familiar adenoidal whine of Bexleyheath or the dark bass of Barbados.

Indeed, apart from a dubious decorative value, it is hard to see why the London Transport Commission's employees are ever to be seen below. They have no purpose which could not be more adequately served by a mechanism; and a fully automatic system would not get in the way of the passengers.

If the reader feels that my prejudice is impairing my appreciation of the facts, permit me to remind him that the most efficient underground railway in London is *completely* automatic—the Post Office tube.

But to return to the opening of the Central London Railway —London's first underground railway in the modern style, fully electrified, with electric traction, electrically-lit trains, stations and lifts (which were electrically operated as well), the Tuppenny Tube was not only a success from the very start; it established, by its immediate and incontrovertible success, the certain pattern upon which all future underground railways were to be constructed. Within three years of its opening, it was not only carrying some 140,000 passengers a day: it had presented an unavoidable ultimatum to the forty-year-old Metropolitan-District system.

Even before the first motor-bus appeared on the London streets in 1904, Londoners were abandoning the Inner Circle in order to travel by Central, using the horse-buses of the London General, Atlas and other omnibus companies, to cover those distances that the Central Line did not serve.

Receipts from passenger traffic dropped alarmingly on the District and Metropolitan lines—for who would travel in the sulphurous murk of a District tunnel trying to read the *Pink 'Un* by bottled gaslight, when one could travel in the still-close but smokeless air of the Central, and read one's paper by an Ediswan electric-lamp?

Faced with bankruptcy—it was no less a threat—the directors both of the District and the Metropolitan met to work out a scheme whereby London's oldest and still most extensive underground railway system could be saved.

Enter, to save the situation, some Hungarian-German engineers and an American financier. The effect of the Hungarians' intervention in the older underground railways' affairs was to be momentary; that of the American financier, permanent.

Let us take the Hungarian engineers first. The Budapest firm of Ganz approached the directors of the District and Metropolitan lines—who had sent out tenders—with a proposal to electrify the system, using overhead wire transmission, and 3,000 volt A.C. experiments with the Ganz method on an experimental stretch of line between Kensington High Street and Gloucester Road seemed to prove that the Ganz apparatus, easy to install, was cheap to run and to maintain. The directors of the Metropolitan signified their approval; there was no reason to suppose that the directors of the District would not do likewise.

But here enters Mr Charles Tyson Yerkes, the American financier, the man to whom—crude political propaganda apart —we can credit the foundation of London Transport. It was capitalist Mr Yerkes, followed by capitalist Bert Stanley, first and last Lord Ashfield (another American), and not socialist Mr Herb Morrison, who welded the underground railways of London into one transport complex.

Yerkes first gained financial control of the District—remember that its full name was 'Metropolitan District'—and banned the Ganz system in favour of the low-voltage D.C. system of electrification. To carry out the electrification and general modernizing of the (Metropolitan) District, he formed the Metropolitan District Traction Company Ltd, and, by 1905, had not only completed the electrification of the District, but, by linking up with other overhead railways, had laid the foundations of a vast network of suburban electric railways.

When it had become obvious that the Greathead shield had made deep tunnelling beneath London possible, at speed and at relatively small cost (as these things go), several groups of promoters had applied for, and received, permission to construct underground railways. Authorized railways, planned during the previous decade, but not yet begun, now received Mr Yerkes's attention.

Turning from the District, now, with electrification, once more solvent, Mr Yerkes gave his attention to the construction of the Charing Cross, Euston and Hampstead line, authorized in 1893. This line, stretching from a station on the Embankment, near to Charing Cross Station, ran under Charing Cross Road and Tottenham Court Road to Camden Town, where it split into two: one half continuing to Hampstead and Golders Green, the other to Highgate (now called 'Archway' station). The total length was eight miles, and the line was opened in June 1907.

Among the other underground lines authorized during the 1890s were the Great Northern and Strand (1899), the Brompton and Piccadilly Circus (1897), and the Baker Street and Waterloo (1893).

The first-named was backed by the Great Northern Railway Company, and was planned to run under the G.W.R. tracks from Wood Green to King's Cross, and so continue to Holborn and the Strand (at the corner of Surrey Street).

The extent of the other two lines can be inferred from their titles.

Yerkes did not build these lines: he took them over, and linked them up with his own systems. The District was linked with the Brompton and Piccadilly line by a tunnel at South Kensington. Then the Brompton and Piccadilly was joined to the Great Northern and Strand, the combined railway being known after that as the Great Northern, Piccadilly and Brompton. The whole line, nearly nine miles in length, extended from Finsbury Park to Hammersmith; it was completed in December 1906. The Strand branch—the 'spur line' from Holborn to a station in the Strand adjacent to the recently-built Aldwych and Kingsway—was opened in 1907.

The Baker Street and Waterloo ('Bakerloo') was opened in

March 1906, running between Edgware Road and Elephant and Castle, where it linked with the City and South London.

The older lines—the District and the Metropolitan—had set out to serve the already built-up City; the newer lines set out to serve not only the already built-up West End, but also the as-yet-undeveloped inner and outer suburbs. When Yerkes died in 1905, he had already established the pattern, not only of the future development of London's underground railways, but of London itself—for it was the railways which created the suburbs, and not the other way about.

In 1910, the already-begun amalgamation was carried a stage farther, when the three lines, the Brompton, the Piccadilly and the Hampstead were merged as the London Electric Railway.

The company that Yerkes had founded to carry out the eventual merging of all London's transport into a single system —the Underground Electric Company—not only acquired control of the London Electric Company, but of London United Tramways and the London General Omnibus Company (originally a French concern, opening in London in 1856).

Two brilliant men succeeded Yerkes in the management of this vast financial and managerial project: George Gibb, formerly general manager of the North-Eastern Railway, and, on Gibb's retirement, Albert Stanley, created Baron Ashfield in the peerage of Lloyd George.

Bert Stanley was an Englishman who had emigrated to the United States as a boy, and had acquired an insatiable taste for company-amalgamation in the tough monopolist school of that American finance which had thrown up the Rockefellers, the Astors, the Morgans, the Carnegies and the Flaglers. Under Stanley's direction, the Underground Electric Company acquired control of both the City and East London and the Central lines, the two companies' shareholders being guaranteed fixed dividends on their holdings in 1912.

All the companies in the Underground Group retained their legal identities, with their own boards of directors, until the formation of the London Passenger Transport Board in 1933 brought them, in name, as they had long been in fact, into one concern.

The Metropolitan and the Great Northern and City were the two systems which had not been absorbed by the Underground octopus; but, with the formation of the London Passenger Transport Board in 1933, these two independents were roped in—forcibly.

After that, the developments planned by Yerkes, Gibb and Stanley were pursued; though, now, anything in the nature of an extension to or improvement on the existing system was held to be creditable to State-Socialist 'enterprise'.

One small credit must be conceded to Stanley's Underground: it commissioned Johnstone, the typographer, to design a type-face for general use on Underground signs and posters. This type, now sometimes confused with 'Gill Sans' (poor Johnstone!), did much, by its austerity, to influence the disappearance of marzipan in directions other than typography.

The tubes of London, though they begin underground, finish their journeys in what were once green fields; but their work in covering the countryside with dismal little jerry-built houses and 'parades' of chain-stores does not (thank God!) concern us here. Let us stay in the dark matrix of the earth, where all walls are grey.

These extensions into the open air have brought many more stations to the reticulate maps against which the slothly 'attendants' lean, but, in its hundred years of existence, the London Underground system has lost many a station.

I am indebted to Mr C. A. Lyon, of London Transport, for the list of London's Lost Underground Stations. Mr Lyon, in writing to me, remarked that much work had gone into the list's compilation: I am happy to take this opportunity of thanking Mr Lyon and his admirable staff not only for this piece of assistance, but for all the other work that they have so willingly and efficiently done on my behalf.

There was a successful play, before the last war: *Passing Brompton Road*. The title would be meaningless today. There is no more Brompton Road station—the building, yes, its façade brave with faience of a porphyry colour—but the trains all pass Brompton Road, as they pass Dover Street (a name inexplicably missing from Mr Lyon's list).

Some of these vanished stations lasted only a short while: Tower (of London), on the Metropolitan line, was open only from 25th September, 1882 to 13th December, 1884; Hounslow Town, on the District, only from 1st May, 1883 to 31st March, 1886. It was reopened on 28th February, 1903, but closed again —for good—six years later.

Some, on the other hand, enjoyed a long life: among them, Uxbridge Road (Metropolitan) which, opened on 1st July, 1864, was not closed down until 21st October, 1940. Lord's and Marlborough Road—also Metropolitan—were opened on 13th April, 1868, and lasted until 19th November, 1939.

The full list is: Tower (of London), Hounslow Town, King William Street, City Road, South Kentish Town, Dover Street, Down Street, York Road, Brompton Road, Brill, Waddesdon Road, Westcott, Wood Siding and Wotton (these four are interesting in that they were stations on the Metropolitan [Brill] branch, which opened as a private 'tramway' in 1871; passing into passenger service in 1872: they remained open until 30th November, 1935), Verney Junction, Winslow Road, Granborough Road, Quainton Road, Waddesdon, St Mary's, Lord's, Marlborough Road, Swiss Cottage, Uxbridge Road, South Acton and White City—this last opened on 1st May, 1908, for the great Exhibition of that year.

In addition, there are seven stations which, though closed down, have been replaced by others on a nearby site. The seven are: Hounslow Town, Park Royal, British Museum, Osterley & Spring Grove, Aldgate East, Chancery Lane, Uxbridge and Wood Lane. The replacement for British Museum has been named Holborn; Osterley & Spring Grove is now known as plain Osterley.

Other stations, still open, have had their names changed: Post Office is now St Paul's; Mark Lane is now Tower. One should remember never to call a changed-name station by the old name—it betrays one's age.

But, since I've already done that, let me recall a memory of the Central London (I don't, I admit, remember it as the Tuppenny Tube). Sometimes, after the first 'rush' had died down, I used to travel to the City. I often saw, sitting quietly over his opened paper, a neatly-dressed man, noticeable only by the fact of his neatly-trimmed beard. He looked rather like a self-assured Hall Caine. He was Mr Montagu Norman, Governor of the Bank of England, in the days before the Bank was not a mere department of the Treasury. Few men can have wielded more power than did Norman in his apogee: he spent sixpence a day on fares.

Travel by Underground today is a dull business, though the advertisers obviously believe that glazed photographs and drawings of women's breasts in every style, a hand's-breadth from the glazed eye of the traveller as he is carried aloft by the escalator, add something to his fragment of life.

It was a livelier business for a period of about thirteen years, commencing in 1881, when the Dynamiters, who had begun their campaign of terror by blowing up the wall of Clerkenwell Prison in 1867, to release a comrade, exploded a charge of nitro-glycerine in the tunnel of the District Railway between Charing Cross and Westminster Stations.

In the fourteen years which had passed since the bombing of Clerkenwell Prison, many dynamite attacks had been made upon public buildings, including the Mansion House, but it was not until the second explosion in the Underground—this time at Praed Street Station—that the Dynamiters achieved what, presumably, was to them a resounding success. It was on the evening of the same day—October 30th, 1881—when the nitro-glycerine had been exploded between Westminster and Charing Cross that, at 8.13, a third-class carriage exploded, injuring sixty-two passengers, most of whom would have been far better off dead.

'False alarms,' as I have said elsewhere, 'explosive packets found before they had a chance to ignite, kept such Londoners as could manage it out of the Underground, and inaugurated a Burglars' Golden Age, as all available police were put to work combating the Dynamiters.

'Victoria Station—the Underground, not the main-line station—was the next to suffer damage from a bomb. At three minutes past one o'clock, in the early morning of 27th February, 1884, the cloakroom suddenly went up—and two men went with it. The damage to property was described, at the time, as "serious", the building being wrecked.

'Another charge of high-explosive was found in the south-west end of London Bridge on 30th December; the police were getting vigilant indeed; but on 2nd January, following, the Dynamiters scored a success when they exploded a "bomb-shell" at 9 p.m. on the Metropolitan Railway (Underground) near Gower Street.'

The last attempt on the Underground did not happen until 30th April, 1897, when the Dynamiters avenged Rollo Richards (who had been sentenced to seven years' penal servitude for having sent the explosive parcel which blew up the New Cross Central Post Office in August 1894) by exploding a bomb at Aldersgate Station, on the Metropolitan line, which killed a man. As I have commented in another book: No wonder that Sherlock Holmes preferred to take a hansom!

To some older people, sheltering from the German bombers on the platforms of Underground stations, that earlier bombing —sporadic, small-scale and largely ineffective—must have seemed as nothing to the throbbing death high overhead, still heard above the guns below. Propelled by the blind justice of Anangke as well as by human malice, the bombs often seemed to seek out the shelterers deep within the tunnels. One such bomb broke through the pavement, at the feet of the Duke of Wellington's statue, outside the Royal Exchange, passed across the wide booking-hall, and shot along the course of the escalator, to explode only when it reached the sort of victim for which it had been designed.

We owe God a death, and he that dies today is quit of it the next. We know that—or we should. But to many who died in the Underground of London during the last war, it must have seemed that Death had pulled out his Jest Book to make his accounts.

Among those many must have been the people who were, we may say, drowned by a German bomb under Clapham Common. The bomb did not touch the shelterers: it simply fractured a water-main, and the escaping waters took a heavier toll of human life than, perhaps, the bomb's explosion would have done.

There were many such grisly happenings in the intestinal tract of our City; but as the attitude of mind which made such happenings inevitable seems still to be with us—directing our suicidal destiny—it might be more charitable not to remind our rulers of these unhappy inevitabilities.

An entirely new tube line, linking Victoria station with a rebuilt Oxford Circus Underground station, and taking in the existing Green Park and Warren Street stations on its way to Euston and the north-east, was opened by H.M. Queen Elizabeth II in 1969. At the completion of this Victoria Line, as it is called, Walthamstow will be linked directly with the south-west suburbs across the Thames, joining Brixton with Victoria and other stations in London's West End shopping districts.

Taking London's major traffic below ground has called also for two other important extensions to the present Underground system.

The first will prolong the existing Piccadilly Line, by joining Hounslow West to Heathrow (London) Airport, making it possible to reach the metropolis's principal air-terminus, by tube, from any part of London and its suburbs. The cost is estimated to be in the neighbourhood of £15,000,000.

The second—'enabling London Transport to withdraw up to 100 buses during the rush-hours'—will connect Stanmore with the principal south-east suburbs at Lewisham, via the Strand, where the existing Aldwych Underground station has been something of a 'white elephant' since it was built in 1908. It will be called the Fleet Line.

10. Buried Light and Heat

IMMEDIATELY after the last war, an estate-agent was showing me over a house in Chelsea which, at that period, was enjoying a brief respite from slummery. Chelsea of the great houses had degenerated into a slum; but the efforts of the trustees of the Sloane-Stanley and Cadogan estates, to say nothing of the personal efforts of Mr William Willett, inventor and apostle of the Daylight-Saving idea, had given Chelsea a chance to become, if not 'grand' again, then at least respectable. Chelsea missed this chance; and it is once more a slum. Perhaps it was destined, even from before the days when the Bishops of Winchester had their palace at the point where the Albert Bridge links Chelsea with Battersea ('Officers in command of troops should instruct their men to break step [Irked by the Hyperborean gloom, a wag had crossed out 'step', and substituted 'wind'.] when crossing the bridge'—a notice cautions), to become a slum.

But, just after the war, Chelsea was still enjoying its brief interregnum between the two periods of decay, and the modestly spacious house, in a quiet street, took my fancy. The rent was cheap, even for those days; and, apart from the fact that the back garden had been given over to an immense concrete bunker, built, I was told, by no less than an Engineer-Admiral, the house seemed, in every way, desirable.

We went—the estate-agent and I—rapidly through the house; he pointing out that the floor-boards were solid, the walls, satin-stripe-papered, were free from blemish; and that all 'services' were present and correct. ('Very particular, the Admiral was. Had to have everything just *so*.') I had remarked that the rent seemed very low, when my body began to shudder, every part of it. I could not move otherwise; I seemed to be rooted to the carpetless floor-boards, while some irresistible force began to shake me to pieces. I was reminded, in no reassuring fashion, of the night on which I had been lying in my bed and an earthquake had shaken both the bed and me in a similar fashion. The whole house was shaking, too; but, after a few seconds, the alarming vibration ceased, to be succeeded by a hollow rumbling.

Reproachfully, the estate-agent muttered something about the Underground. What he added was: 'You soon get used to it.' What he had in mind to add was: 'Had you been a bit more brisk in looking around, I could have got you out before you heard the noise of the trains winging their way through the darkness to South Ken.'

Yet, to be just to the builders of Underground London, it is rarely indeed that the presence of that other—that subterraneous—London forces itself on our collective consciousness. At certain points above the shallow-level underground tracks, the houses are shaken; and, of course, we cannot walk abroad on any day in London without seeing, in some street or other, the evidence that pipes are laid below the level of the streets. But, once laid, the pipes are hidden well out of sight; and London—in its subterraneous aspect—is as out of mind as out of sight.

We grumble—perhaps, not without reason—at the constant uprooting of London's streets, with the consequent slowing-down of the traffic; but elsewhere in this book I have pointed out that there was a time when matters were worse; when, with several water- and gas-companies competing for business, the streets can hardly ever have been 'down'. Indeed, we might, with justice, treat of the *concealing* of London's bowels as something ancillary to, but quite independent of, the construction of London's bowels; and concede to each aspect of the London Beneath Us the credit proper to a notable technical achievement. To keep so vast a complex of service-pipes in order and concealed, without more uprooting of the streets and disruption of the traffic, is a feat of which the responsible authorities may well be proud.

We take the presence of the services—gas, water, the telephone, electricity—so much for granted, at least in the cities and towns, that we rarely give a thought to the complexity and immensity of the hidden piping which carries heat, light and sound to our houses, flats and offices.

Even at the very beginning of the Gas Era, the figures were impressive—indeed, astonishing. Within two years of the establishment of the Gas Light and Coke Company by Royal Charter, in 1812, subterranean gas-mains totalling 122 miles in length had already been laid; this mileage not counting the smaller pipes used to bring the gas from the mains to the domestic lighting-points.

We are now used to the idea, put forward by the apologists of War, that the stepped-up energy-release called for by 'war conditions' sharpens the inventive capacity of man, and accelerates the speed of industrial development. What is not so commonly accepted is the fact that this applied to earlier wars.

The Napoleonic wars produced, 'before their time', iron-construction building, steam-locomotion, the 'tinning' of foodstuffs, electrically-operated mines, water-purification and coal-gas as an illuminant.

That the distillation of coal could yield an illuminating gas which could be collected and stored for later use was known as early as 1688, as appears from a letter written to the Royal Society by the Reverend John Clayton, D.D., Rector of Crofton, near Wakefield.

Mr Clayton, unaware that he was the herald of a revolution in no way less glorious than that of which the recently-landed William of Orange was the harbinger and executant, wrote of what he had done

> with some sulphurous Spirits which I have drawn from Coals, that I could no way condense, yet were inflammable, nay would burn after they had passed through water, and that seemingly fiercer if they were not overpowered therewith. I have kept this Spirit a considerable time in bladders, and tho' it appear'd as if they were only with Air, yet if I let it forth and lit it with a Match or Candle it would continue burning till all was spent.

Analytical chemistry of a primitive sort had been at work in investigating the physical properties of 'firedamp' (CH_4) and 'chokedamp' (CO_2), throughout the latter part of the seventeenth century and the first three-quarters of the succeeding century when, in 1779, George Dixon, of Durham (1731–1785), established the first works for extracting tar from coal. Dixon had begun his experiment with coal-distillation at Cockfield in 1760, using an ordinary domestic kettle, filled with coal, and placed over a fire! Fortunately for Dixon, the explosion that such risky methods made inevitable did not occur until after he had established the feasibility of lighting his house and works with gas; and though, after the explosion, Dixon abandoned the use of gas as impractical for domestic lighting, others followed where Dixon had shown the way.

Dixon, indeed, seems to have been anticipated by Carlisle Spedding, agent of the Whitehead Collieries, who, in 1765, collected mine gas for lighting his offices, and suggested that the town should be illuminated in the same way. Not until 188 years later was Spedding's idea realized on a large scale, when the National Coal Board—at Whitehead—embarked on its great scheme of mine-drainage, using the methane recovered to light the town.

Lord Dundonald, in 1782, illuminated some rooms in Culross Abbey by gas; and in 1785, Professor Minkelers, of Louvain University, who had experimented with coal-distillation in search of a lighter-than-air gas for lifting balloons, lectured to his students in a class-room illuminated with coal-gas. The Gas Industry, as we know it, was about to be born.

With this birth, four Great Names—two British, one French and one German—will always be associated. The four are: William Murdoch (1754–1839); Samuel Clegg (1781–1861); Philippe Le Bon (1767–1804); and Friedrich Albrecht Winsor (1763–1830).

Murdoch, son of a mill-wright, joined the well-known engineering firm of Boulton & Watt as what we should now call a 'mechanic', and, two years later, was promoted to be the firm's Resident Engineer in Cornwall, where his chief duties consisted in the erection and maintenance of the pumping-machinery supplied by Boulton & Watt to the mines of that district. Here Murdoch remained until 1798. He was a brilliant mechanical engineer, inventing a steam-driven road-carriage, a hydraulic lift and a number of specialized machine-tools, as well as his plant for gas-distillation and illumination by gas. In 1808, the award of the Rumford Gold Medal of the Royal Society to Murdoch marked the fact that illumination by gas had passed the experimental stage and was now a practical commercial undertaking.

Philippe Le Bon, son of an official of Louis XV's court, survived the troubles of the Revolution through being a student at the time of the terror: he had been entered as a pupil of the École des Ponts et Chaussées in 1787. Like Murdoch, he was primarily an engineer, and Le Bon's own contribution to the development of the steam-engine came in his inventing the tube-boiler and the superheater. From 1792 onwards, he worked methodically on the problems of extracting gas from coal, and using the gas as an illuminant. After having patented his ideas, he summarized the results of his achievements to date in a paper that he read to the Institut National. He had made even further progress when he was murdered in 1804.

Friedrich Albrecht Winsor—he changed the spelling 'Winzer' after he had come to England—was more of a showman than a scientist; but we should recall, to the credit of such showmen, that they acted as necessary 'publicity agents' for the scientific marvels of the past; the interest that the showmen inspired in the public inspiring, in due course, an interest in the capitalists able to back the inventors.

Winzer had been impressed, while in Paris, with Le Bon's work; and Winzer, with plans for distributing gas under streets to individual houses, came to England in 1803, during the short peace which followed the Treaty of Amiens.

'Winsor,' says Sir Compton Mackenzie, 'may have been a charlatan as an inventor; but he was a wonderful impresario, and he knew how to catch the public ear.'

That he was a showman, we cannot doubt; and that he

arrived from Paris with a claim to have invented gas-lighting shows him to have been something of a charlatan also. But it is hard to withhold from Winzer his claim to have been an inventor as well; for, while Le Bon had used gas extracted from wood, Winzer always maintained that the future of gas-lighting would depend upon distillation from coal. He was a quick worker, too. He had a house in Pall Mall, in which he had installed two carbonizing furnaces. From his house to the wall which divided the Mall, in St James's Park, from the gardens of Carlton House, Winzer ran a 1½ in.-diameter pipe of tinned iron.

On the King's birthday, 4th June, 1805—four months before the Battle of Trafalgar—London saw its first gas-illuminations.

The inflammable gas [commented a writer in the *Monthly Magazine*], which is quite transparent or invisible, began to flow into the pipes soon after eight o'clock, and a lamplighter or a person with a small wax taper (the evening being quite serene) appeared and lighted the gas issuing from each burner in succession. The light produced by these gas lamps was clear, bright and colourless, and from the success of this considerable experiment hopes may now be entertained that this long-talked-of mode of lighting our streets may at length be realised. The Mall continued crowded with spectators until nearly twelve o'clock, and they seemed much amused and delighted by this novel exhibition.

By 1807, from his offices in Pall Mall, about where the Carlton Club now stands, Winzer was lighting the street with gas, so that Pall Mall enjoys the distinction of being the first street in the world to be so lit.

Winzer lectured and demonstrated incessantly, and all the Top People were against him: scientists and others. The scientists included Dr Thomas Chalmers, Sir Humphry Davy and William Wollaston. The non-scientists included Sir Walter Scott and Napoleon—'*une grande folie*', said the latter, of Winzer's proposal to light London by gas.

By the test laid down for greatness by a thinker greater than any that the nineteenth century produced, Winzer was a very great man indeed. He may not have been a scientist; he may well have been showman, charlatan, and even fake; but, by the classic test of greatness, he was great indeed.

Here is how Machiavelli talks of that greatness:

There is nothing more difficult to take in hand, more perilous to conduct, or more uncertain in its success, than to take the lead in the introduction of a new order of things.

So spake Niccolò Machiavelli, in the book called *The Prince*. Winzer could—and did—take the lead in the 'introduction of a new order of things' that we may call the Gas Age.

He was a big—a bouncy—thinker. He asked for a capital of One Million Pounds for his New Patriotic Imperial and National Light and Heat Company (the title betrays the man: the sort of title that Monty Tigg might have chosen for one of *his* companies). He didn't get his million—and so his offer to pay £570 interest on every £5 invested was never put to the test.

Lord Brougham, opposing the application to register the company, watered down the idea, and got it rejected. However, with more modest claims, the Winzer project went through, and the Gas Light and Coke Company was granted its Charter of Incorporation, on 30th April, 1812. It had an authorized capital of £200,000; its stated purpose: 'for lighting the Cities of London and Westminster and the Borough of Southwark'.

It will astonish no one that Chalmers, Davy, Wollaston and Walter Scott were as enthusiastic about gas as they had been contemptuous of it a little while earlier; Scott even went into the gas business (literally: no punning reference to his books!).

They got rid of Winzer, of course—something that Machiavelli was no doubt referring to when he talked of the 'perilousness' of taking the lead in the introduction of a new order of things. In the year after the incorporation of the Gas Light and Coke Company, Winzer was voted, by his fellow Directors, an annuity of £600, in recognition of his work in establishing the British Gas Industry. Two years later—it was the year of

Waterloo—the annuity was withdrawn. Winzer, to avoid his creditors, fled to France; promoted a French gas-company; failed, and died in poverty in 1830.

Not until the year of Queen Victoria's accession was Paris lighted with gas: by 1837, however, the gas-industry in England and Scotland—but more particularly in London—had made gigantic strides forward. This progress was due to the work of one man: Samuel Clegg.

The gas-industry had needed the perhaps catch-penny methods of a Winzer to get it started; it was fortunate that a man such as Winzer was available at the right moment. But to get it *established*, it needed—and got—the constructive services of a mind at once intensely imaginative and highly practical. Clegg supplied the need. Samuel Clegg was also a Boulton & Watt man, though he was some thirty years younger than Murdoch, the other Boulton & Watt man whose career Clegg's own so closely parallels. Unlike Murdoch, however, Clegg rather belonged to the modern type of engineer: the man who has received a good grounding in theory before moving on to the practical work. Murdoch, like so many even of his successors, 'learnt as he went'. Clegg, though, was not a 'working apprentice'; he entered the engineering industry as a theoretically-qualified 'trainee engineer'. He had studied physics under one of the most celebrated scientists and mathematicians of all time: John Dalton, the first to give practical expression (and thus practical application) to the Aristotelian Atomic Theory.

In 1802, when Clegg was just twenty-one, Boulton & Watt put him to work on the development of Murdoch's experimental work on gas, which had been begun in Murdoch's house at Redruth, but which had been transferred to the Boulton & Watt main works at Soho (Birmingham, not London).

As early as 1804, Clegg felt sufficiently sure of himself to leave the service of Boulton & Watt and set up for himself in the then almost unprecedented profession of 'gas engineer'. He built and installed a number of gas-plants in factories and large institutions, including Stonyhurst College, the famous Roman Catholic public school. At Stonyhurst, he used his perfected lime gas-purifying machine, which remained the standard type for well over a century.

Clegg was an inventor of prolific output; and produced a number of new devices and improvements on existing ones which are still widely employed in the gas industry. He invented, which is even more important, all those devices which enabled gas to be properly 'marketed'; to be distributed in such a way that the user could be fairly charged. He suggested the gas-meter (the pre-payment, 'penny-in-the-slot' meter was not developed, by Thorp and Marsh, until 1889), the first self-acting governor, and the adaptation of the Argand oil-burning lamp to gas.

Moving to London, Clegg's first customer was the famous print firm of Ackermann, then in the Strand. Clegg's apparatus, installed in a room at the back of Ackermanns' print-shop, not only supplied heat for warming the copper-plates used in the firm's engraving, but light, too; and after the apparatus had been going for some three years, Ackermanns estimated that the Clegg installation had saved the firm close on £350 a year.

In 1813, Clegg became Chief Engineer to the Gas Light and Coke Company; left the Chartered Company in 1817, to install a gas-plant of advanced design for the Royal Mint; left the token-manufacturers to establish the gas-industries of Bristol, Birmingham and Chester; accepted a call from the Portuguese Government; returned to England, to end a long life, in 1863, as surveying officer for the Government, his duties being to supervise the applications for permission to start new gas-companies.

There was, at first, considerable public opposition to gas—it is interesting here to note that a series of cartoons, not designed to allay the public fear of gas, was issued by Ackermanns, *after* that firm had had its gas-plant installed.

But 'progress' would not be stayed. In 1815, the Guildhall was lighted with gas; and a report made by Sir William Congreve to a Select Committee of the House of Commons in 1814 made it clear that the dangers from gas were few—and small. (The report was not issued to the public until 1823, which gave the fears that much longer to mature.)

Clegg and his employers pushed on, undeterred as much by praise as by condemnation. Like Colonel Crompton and his associates, when they came to install electric light in the buildings of London, Clegg had to improvise the smallest, most taken-for-granted appliances: gas-pipes, stop-cocks, mains, burners had to be thought out by Clegg, just as switches, lamp-holders, fuse-boxes and other things had to be 'thought up out of nothing' by Crompton.

But Clegg designed the large, as well as the small, devices needed by the growing gas-industry. His 'horizontal rotary retort', a masterpiece of practical design, was first used at the Royal Mint's gas-works. Clegg was responsible for introducing the hydraulic main and the hydraulic valve, and purification of gas by 'cream of lime'. He also evolved the idea of the gas-meter, though it was to another brilliant Gas Light and Coke Company engineer, John Malam, draughtsman at the Great Peter Street works of the Company, that should go 'the merit of rendering the gas-meter a practical instrument, and of effecting great improvements in retort-settings, in gas-holders and in the purification of wet-lime purifiers'. [Chandler & Lacey: *The Rise of the Gas Industry in Britain*.]

Just inside the Decimus Burton arch at Hyde Park Corner are some gas-lamps whose bases bear the cypher of William IV. They are elegant yet practical in design, and they are still working, after one hundred and thirty years. One may, indeed, imagine the gas-supply and distribution system of London as perfected, in all but some minor details, by the accession of William IV.

As far as the consumer was concerned, all the improvements which had brought the development of the actual illuminant up-to-date had been completed by 1816, the successive steps in that development having been carried out over a period of less than a decade.

Nothing ever quite disappears in the development of the complex from the primitive: there are trees and fish and animals (even if we accept the non-existence of the Loch Ness Monster) which are survivals from a distant past; and even today, in London, you may see gas-burners of the original— the *very* original—type: the Rat-tail, burning away, for all the world as though a century and a half of development has not passed. Such a 'rat-tail' burner can be found on the counter of Ye Olde Segar Shop, at the corner of Wine Office Court, in Fleet Street—and many another old-established tobacconist has his rat-tail burner still alight on the counter.

This primitive form of burner was the only one in use, until it was succeeded by the 'cockspur', in 1808. The 'cockspur' was a burner consisting of three 'rat-tails'. A cubed 'cockspur', giving nine rat-tail jets, succeeded the simple 'cockspur'—this was called the 'cockscomb'. Clegg's ingenious adaptation of the circular-wick Argand oil-lamp to gas-burning followed in 1809, and this, in turn, was superseded by the 'batswing' flame—the name describes the shape—itself superseded by the double-batswing, or 'fish-tail', the type which was to remain the standard (and only) shape in general use until the invention of the incandescent 'mantle' by Karl von Welsbach in 1887 gave gas an intensity of illumination rivalling that of the recently-introduced electric light.

Though this is above-ground material, a word here on the invention of the 'incandescent' gas-light need not be out of place. The production of the incandescent mantle burner was made possible only by the threat from the electric light. Earlier seekers after increased intensity of illumination in gas-light had not enjoyed the emotional pressure that the threat of electricity gave.

Experiments to find the secret of making the gas-burner 'incandescent' had been carried out by Frankenstein, in Paris, in 1849, and English, French, American and Swedish inventors —among them Hogg, Edison, Wenham, Lewis, Clamond and Fahnehjelm—had all tried, unsuccessfully, to find the secret of incandescent gas-light, when the introduction of the electric

lamp (both arc and incandescent) virtually forced the invention
of the long-sought modern gas-lamp.

The earlier experimenters had used either platinum baskets
or 'rare earth' rods made of zirconium. Welsbach, in using a
'mantle' of cloth mesh, impregnated with a mixture of thorium
and cerium, achieved success.

The first Welsbach 'mantle'—very dear, by the way: a
Guinea (what the makers of Beecham's Pills claimed that a
box of their pills was worth!)—was upright. The 'inverted'
form was introduced in 1900, and further improvements followed, the most notable being the 'regenerative' high-pressure
burner, which, using gas supplied at a pressure of 3 lb. to the
square inch, could give intensities of illumination from between
3,000 and 4,500 candle-power, and thus bring the gas-lit street
lamp into competition with the most powerful electric arc.

But mention of these high-pressures takes us back to the
gas-mains—to the underground network of pipes which, as we
have already seen, had reached a length of 122 miles by 1814.

Pressure today is controlled by a mechanism no different in
principle from that with which the brilliant Samuel Clegg
solved the problem of pressure-control in the year of Waterloo:
the 'governor'.

'Basically,' says Mr E. G. Stewart, in *Town Gas; Its Manufacture and Distribution* [Ministry of Education: Science
Museum—published by Her Majesty's Stationery Office;
London, 1958], '[the governor] consists of a valve in the
main, suspended from a small gasholder bell. The interior of
the bell is in communication with the outlet side of the valve.
So if the outlet pressure tends to fall, the bell falls and opens
the valve to restore the pressure, and vice-versa. The actual
level of pressure desired is secured by adding or subtracting
weights to the falling bell.

'The original Clegg governor [Mr Stewart continues] was
elaborated by Hunt, Cowan, Parkinson and Braddock, to
secure more precise operation, by balancing of the valve,
water loading of the bell, and making the valve parabolic

in form to secure a straight-line relationship between valve-opening and flow. Governors have also been constructed with a flexible diaphragm in lieu of the floating bell.

'The control of pressure desired can be effected manually by changing weights or water-tank loading, or by gas pressure acting on a diaphragm. It can also be effected automatically by a clock-driven apparatus which loads the governor according to a predetermined plan.'

We have seen how the coming of gas—or, to be more specific, the coming of the gas-mains—rendered inevitable, and greatly accelerated, the change-over from the wooden and stone water-main to that constructed in cast-iron. The change was rendered inevitable because the gas, seeping through its own mains, disagreeably flavoured the water flowing in adjacent mains in pipes permeable by gas. This happened because, at the very beginning of the Gas Era, the methods then in use for water-distribution were adopted to the distribution of gas; and the gas-companies used pipes—even underground—of wood, stone and lead. Had the cast-iron pipe been adopted from the beginning, it is possible that the wood, stone and lead water-mains would have survived even beyond the 1850s.

Here was a sort of symbiotic union: gas and water adapting so that each could survive. The early cast-iron gas-mains were coupled up either with flange-joints or cast-lead-filled sockets, and though the first cast-iron mains to be laid beneath London's streets were of only 2 in. diameter, mains on the principal distribution circuits had already grown to a 16 in. diameter by 1820, a 36 in. diameter by 1850, and a 48 in. diameter by 1870.

Improvements in jointing, too—and thus in securing maximum strength of the piping-system—were early devised. It was found that the flanged joint made lengths of piping too rigid, and thus encouraged fracture of the mains. The turned and bored socket and spigot joint were developed in 1826, and with the cast-lead-filled socket, these remained standard practice for a century.

Not until 1919 did the spun-cast iron pipe replace the pipe cast in a pit-mould, which could be produced only in lengths of from 9 ft. to 12 ft., while pipes produced by the spun-cast method can be turned out in lengths of from 12 ft. to 18 ft.— the increased length reducing the number of necessary joints, and thus the capacity for leakage.

Lead-sealed and bored joints, of the earliest pattern, are still in widespread use; but a joint sealed by a compressed rubber-ring (introduced in 1921) and an even more modern (1928) type, using a tapered lead ring held in place by a screwed flange of the stuffing-box type, will—unless themselves displaced by something even better—gradually supersede the more primitive methods of jointing.

In one respect, there has been a deliberate return to a practice of the earliest days. The pioneer gas-distribution networks employed a practice used by the water-supply companies: that of employing control-valves at various points. The practice, however, was soon discontinued by the gas-companies, which found that, with the low pressures then obtaining, necessary interruption of the flow of gas, for repairs and so on, could be easily made by inserting inflated bladders or rubberized canvas bags into the mains. The use of valves was given up.

However, the war-time necessity of cutting off gas-supplies at a moment's notice, together with the high pressures now involved in the national grid-system, have rendered a return to the early practice of valve-control desirable.

Were you to have stood, for the past sixty years, among those idlers who can always be found clustered about the workmen laying a gas-main, you would have seen that the pipes under London reflect the technological advances made, not only in the manufacture of pipes but in the development of materials, notably the 'synthetics'.

London air may be unkind to our lungs, our linen and our buildings, but London soil treats our buried pipes kindly. Cast-iron stands up well in London soil—we have seen that much of London's water, gas and sewage is still being carried in pipes made and laid down more than a century ago—and Chameroy's invention of the sheet-iron asphalt-coated pipe in 1830 found little adoption in England, mostly because anti-corrosive treatment of buried cast-iron is rarely called for in this country.

An important development in the production of metal pipes, beginning about 1840, was inspired, not so much to make pipes last longer in the soil, as to make them stronger, in situations where excessive strain was imposed upon them. To secure the desired tensile strength in pipes used for, say, crossing bridges, a pipe of flat-section was called for, and this was produced either in wrought iron or in steel. The steel pipe, however, did not come into general use until, in 1900, the Mannesmann process by which the seamless steel pipe could be produced in quantity (and therefore economically) put the steel pipe into general supply.

Steel pipes are called for both by the use of high pressures and by siting in ground where subsidence may happen. But steel, unlike iron, is highly susceptible to corrosion, and pipes made of steel call for anti-corrosive treatment. The former method of coating steel pipes with an 'envelope' of bitumen and hessian has now largely been superseded by coverings of glass-silk (first demonstrated at the Great Exhibition of 1851) and of a product of the most modern technology: poly-vinyl-chloride (P.V.C.).

When first introduced, steel pipes were jointed either by the rubber-ring method or by long-socket-joints packed with lead wool. But the relatively high flexibility of the steel pipe has made it possible for great lengths of steel piping to be welded—even steel pipes of the gas-grid of up to 36 in. diameter, and carrying gas at working pressures of up to 700 lb. per square inch.

One other important development in actual working practice, following on the proven possibility of welding—rather than jointing—great lengths of pipe, has taken the pipe-gang from the surface to beneath, when it comes to repairing a length of pipe.

An ingenious tool, recently imported from America—the

Porter 'Wheeler' pipe-cutter—cuts pipes cleanly by means of a chain, which is wrapped around the pipe, and then squeezed, either by a hand-operated grip or by a hydraulic pump. Iron, steel, cement-lined steel, glazed earthenware—every type of pipe, up to those of 36 inches diameter—can be cut, without any splintering of the pipe, with this ingenious tool. What is more, the pipe can be cut in position: this means that work on the pipe can, in future, take place below ground level.

To say that the systems of gas- and water-distribution have changed but little, in essentials, since the beginning of the last century is to ignore the fact that the 'refinements' may often involve the introduction of techniques, not only undeveloped, but even undreamed of when pipe-laying began to uproot our streets and built up that reticulate inner skin which 'lines' the outer surface of our City.

For instance, apart from the measures to guard against corrosion of the steel pipes already mentioned, there is the system of 'cathodic protection'. This consists in neutralizing ground electric currents, 'either by impressing an electric current of the correct polarity on the main, or by the attachment to it at intervals of alkaline metal anodes [magnesium], buried in the adjacent soil' [E. G. Stewart].

Asbestos, a material in common supply, owing to the opening-up of so many sources of supply both in the Old World and in the New, is available for the manufacture of pipes, and has been so used since 1933; but as asbestos cannot be used by itself for piping, but needs cast-iron bends, and special attachments to service the supply, it is used only as a 'relief' material—that is, when there is difficulty in obtaining pipes of other materials.

The gas-companies early made the practical distinction between 'mains' and 'service pipes'. At the beginning, lead was used generally for the service pipes—that is, the pipes which actually lead the gas from the mains to the consumers' premises.

Lead soon demonstrated its unsuitability as a material for service pipes: any slight deviation from level resulted in a blocking of the pipe by accumulated deposits of moisture. To hand, then, as a more satisfactory replacement of lead pipes, were the numerous iron gun-barrels which had become 'redundant' with the end of the Napoleonic Wars. (Above ground, they were used for the equivalent of the modern pavement-kerb.)

The guns were modified so as to be able to screw into each other; and even before the end of the war—in 1813—a London gun-maker, James Russell, adapted his craft to the making of 4-foot lengths of wrought iron, made to be screwed and socketed together. The Russell type of piping—improved by the 1825 Cornelius Whitehouse patent for butt-welding longer lengths, that Russell took over—was further improved in 1840 by the introduction of the lap-welding process. Even though wrought iron was completely superseded in 1940—steel taking its place—the memory of the origin of the wrought-iron pipe still persists in the name for the smaller sizes of tubing—'barrels'.

'House carcassing'—to use the term by which the gas-suppliers describe that complex of smaller pipes which conducts the gas from the inlet of the service pipe to the lighting and heating points in the house—hardly comes within our survey, though there are still some underground premises and tunnels lit by gas; and, if we take into account the *industrial* use of gas—especially in the cake- and biscuit-making trade—gas takes us well underground.

So it does in the matter of gas-fired central-heating, the boiler being usually situated below the ground level.

Go to a house occupied by a plumber or builder-and-decorator, and you will be struck by the fact that, for his water-supply piping, he has ordered nothing but copper—he has no vested interest in pipes which burst in *his* premises.

In the early days of the gas-industry, copper, too, was used for 'house carcassing' by the gas-companies. But the ammonia in the early gas—not then purified to the extent that is now common practice—mixed with the copper to form a compound which was often explosive. (I remember, as a child, the explosion from an old Ewart's geyser when this compound ignited.)

Lead piping was then used, and in old basements and

kitchens you may still see lengths of heavy lead piping, festooned across iron brackets, on which the rust is edging its way through the dusty whitewash. Mice and damp brick and old whitewash and London mould and a hint of vanished cooking, all faintly overlaid with the unmistakable presence of London gas ... cellars mean many things to as many people; but to me they will always bring back these associations, with gas the most potent memory-evoker of all.

In 1860, just a century ago, a partner in a Sunderland firm of commercial photographers, Joseph Swan, exhibited his electric lamp at a Newcastle-on-Tyne exhibition. It was an incandescent electric lamp, the first of its type ever to have been produced, and though the carbon-and-silver-bromide filament became 'incandescent' only to the point of a cherry-red glow (I am aware of the apparent contradiction in terms), the Swan lamp demonstrated beyond argument that the principle of 'incandescence' had been established, and that it needed now only further research to make the lamp a marketable appliance.

The extra work needed to perfect the lamp took, in fact, another nineteen years; and when, in 1879, Swan announced his perfected incandescent electric light, the simultaneous perfecting of the lamp—by Edison—was announced from America. Later, Mr (afterwards Sir) Joseph Swan joined with his rival, and the well-known 'Ediswan' lamp was the result of a happy collaboration between the two gifted inventors.

The (old) Gaiety Theatre, in the Strand, had been illuminated with 'the Electric Light'—arc-lamp—in 1877; and, as I have noted, arc-lamps were used to light the cross-roads at the Mansion House in 1880. Arc-lamps of portable size were also fairly widely used for the popular magic-lantern at this time; but there were many reasons why there was a demand for a light which gave off no fumes and which consumed no oxygen —or very little. For one thing, such a lamp would have been ideal for the lighting of tunnels and for the trains which ran in tunnels. A demand which was *felt* rather than openly evident impelled the inventors to set about the task of providing such a lamp. In 1879, the incandescent electric lamp, consuming hardly any oxygen, and 'fire proof', was on the market. An industry then had to be created to supply the demand that another industry had to be created to create.

A great fillip to public interest in the development of the electrical industry had been given by the Exhibition in Paris in 1881; and the interest was sustained by the Exhibition, in the following year, at the Crystal Palace. Indeed, progress in the industry was so far advanced by 1882 that the Government, always a generation behind industry in its recognition of economic change, promptly clapped a restrictive measure upon the electrical industry, in the shape of the disastrous Electric Lighting Act. Not until six years—by which time Members of Parliament had got their money invested in electric lighting —were the remedial Electric Lighting Acts passed.

As in the case of gas, the first practical applications of electric light were to be seen in private houses; among the first to commission installations of electric lighting was the well-known novelist, (Sir) Henry Rider Haggard.

As early as 1881, an 'electric light station' was founded at Brighton, as an outcome of the Public Health Exhibition held in the town. The founding of this station was carried out by Mr Arthur Wright, who converted the old engine-shed in North Road into a primitive generating station.

Eastbourne came next, but London soon had its first electric-light generating station, a real underground affair, beneath the arches of Cannon Street Station. Unlike the other power-stations which, as a power-source, used a locomotive-type boiler combined with a steam-engine and dynamo, the Cannon Street power-station was equipped in the most modern fashion. A Ferranti alternator was belt-driven from a new compound engine with boiler combined, the latter being supplied by John Fowler & Co., of Leeds.

In spite of the restrictive intentions of the Electric Lighting Act of 1882, the promoters of the new industry pushed on with their work; and among the first companies to be registered to give the public the benefit of electric lighting was the House-

to-House Electric Supply Company, in whose power-station a
water-tube boiler was installed—a choice which was to serve
as the pattern for the future, since the water-tube boiler is far
more powerful than the Lancashire-type boilers which were to
be installed by so many other companies.

Colonel Crompton, that Grand Old Man of the Electrical
Industry, has left a record of the improvisation which was
called for in establishing, not only the industry, but the
appliances upon which that industry could take its stand.
Crompton—he was a retired Colonel of Royal Engineers—installed electric lighting in Berechurch Hall, a large country
mansion, and followed up this pioneering feat by lighting with
electricity the newly completed Royal Courts of Justice in the
Strand. The latter installation was completed in time for the
opening of the Law Courts in 1882. At about the same time the
London Swan Company was formed, joining up soon afterwards with the Edison Company; and Crompton accepted the
post of engineer to the combined Swan-Edison companies.

'Referring to the ordinary familiar forms of electrical
apparatus' (wrote Crompton, nearly forty years later, as a
very old man), 'that is, switchboards, fuse boards, ceiling
roses, pendants, portable fittings, with which we are all now
so familiar—you can hardly believe how many of these were
thought out and developed by Harold Thomson and Lund-
berg, and how much of the theory of the magnetic field and
of the armature and magnetic winding of modern dynamos
was developed by the Crompton staff of the early days.'

Something of the excitement of those days lingers on in the
Colonel's clipped accounts of the establishment and development of the electric-lighting and -power industry of the 1880s.

'The success of the large generating station at Vienna led us
to start the Kensington Court Company in London on
similar lines—*i.e.* direct currents generated in parallel with
accumulators as a reserve, the current being generated by
dynamos coupled to Willans engines. About the same time,
Ferranti started the Grosvenor Gallery Station to distribute

electrical energy for lighting by high-pressure alternating currents transmitted through overhead wires, and transformed on the consumer's premises to a pressure usable on the Swan lamps by Goulard and Gibbs' development of induction coils which began to be called transformers.'

The reference to 'overhead wires' is a reminder that, in burying our electrical cables and the main through which they are carried, our modern electrical engineers have reverted to the practice of the first days of electricity's commercial application: to the transmission of messages by the electric telegraph, which was already in common use long before 1840.

In those early days, subterranean wires were largely used, the wires being insulated with windings of silk, then further insulated with a coating of gutta-percha, and still further protected by being enveloped in a lead tube, the practice being to bury the wires at a depth of about 20 inches.

The Magnetic Company—an early telegraphic concern—used gutta-percha-covered wires laid in troughs of creosoted wood covered with a galvanized iron lid—a striking anticipation of modern practice. This company usually laid six wires in each trough, but for its London-to-Manchester line—all underground—the trough carried ten wires.

This underground wire-laying was expensive: laying a six-wire trough cost from £180 to £200 a mile, while, for a ten-wire trough, the cost rose to £230 a mile.

Another telegraphic company—the Electric Telegraph Company—used best-quality glazed earthenware ('Doulton') pipes for their underground ducts, the cost of laying by this method being very much cheaper, at only £60 the mile.

However, the poor insulation of those days made burying the lines a practical impossibility; they had so frequently to be taken up for repair. In consequence, as most of the railway telegraphs were using pole lines, with porcelain insulators, by 1842, the telegraph lines came up from below ground and when, in 1879, London's first telephone-exchange was opened at 6, Lombard Street, with ten lines, the telephone-lines went overhead. The most noticeable difference between a street-scene, of say, 1897 and today, so far as London or any other big city is concerned, is the freedom of the modern sky-line from the criss-cross of telegraph and telephone cables and power-lines which (with the pigeons and starlings on them) darkened the murky sky of the late nineteenth and earthly twentieth century to an even grislier gloom—'within the lowest hell, a lower hell'.

Not until after the end of the first world war did the lines carrying light, power and sound begin to disappear from the London sky; the first underground telephone cables being those laid in connection with the long-distance Post Office telephone-system connecting London with the bigger provincial cities.

Today, we have returned to the earlier practice of putting our electric cables underground. Indeed, we have gone further, and adopted those 'subways' advocated by John Williams in 1823 and William Austin in 1853.

When, on 7th November, 1879, an official inspection was made of the telephone-exchange in Lombard Street, there were some fifty subscribers connected to the 'switch frame'. A line or two overhead, from Lombard Street, across the houses to the offices of the Exchange Telegraph Company in Cornhill, could not have mattered very much.

Today, when there are just on two hundred London exchanges, the necessary cables *must* go underground—as they have done. Vast cables they are, too; housed within subways or buried, though lavishly insulated, within the earth beneath the streets and pavements.

In the City and West End of London alone there are more than ten thousand miles of cable-carrying electrical energy in excess of one million horse-power—enough energy to light ten million lamps of the ordinary domestic kind. And the output of electric energy from London's unfortunately sited power-stations is increasing year by year, to meet a demand which never falls.

The tendency today is to carry as many cables as possible in subways: sometimes an old tunnel comes in handy for this, as when the Post Office used the parcels tube, built in 1863 by the Pneumatic Despatch Company (part of which runs under High Holborn), to carry no fewer than fifty main trunk cables.

As the old Pneumatic Tube carries, also, the modern pneumatic tube, a word must be said about this additional 'inhabitant' of the London Beneath Us.

I have noted that the original Pneumatic Despatch failed; this modern system of 'pneumatic' message-delivery works. It is by no means new: some of the narrow tubes in which messages in cylinders are blown along by compressed air are quite seventy years old, and the 2½-inch-diameter tubes vary in length from five hundred yards to over three miles.

Each cylinder sent through the pneumatic tube will carry from twenty to thirty telegraph messages, and the Central Telegraph Office in London is connected, by this system, with nearly seventy post-offices, which send the actual form on which the telegram or cable has been written, thus reducing the factor of error in the further transmission of the messages. So that, under our feet, at twenty miles an hour, the telegrams, with their messages of love, despair, hope and (to the City) greed, pass back and forth. As we stand waiting for a bus, a piece of paper may be shooting beneath us with news which may alter the destiny of the world.

Above-ground seems static, uncrowded, compared with the active, crowded space beneath us. In the City of London alone, there are no fewer than forty underground electricity substations, keeping the ticker-tapes, the telephones, the tape-recorders, the electric lights, the lifts, and all the other electrical 'necessities' in working order.

With over ten thousand miles of electric cable—all buried in the earth—to keep the lights of Greater London going; to make the telephones and the Telly work; and to fry kippers and set the electric sewing-machine going; there is not much room now in the underground space immediately beneath the pavement.

So, to find more space, those responsible for our public services are going deeper and deeper, as the buildings above are going higher and higher.

11. Buried London

THE story of how Sir Emsley Carr and, after him, Lord Riddell, built up the *News of the World* to the greatest newspaper that the world has ever known is *the* romance of journalism. Only sixty years ago, the *News of the World* was facing a certain (even if postponed) extinction; the weekly circulation had dropped to a mere 43,000; and there seemed no prospect of raising the figure. Today, the circulation touches the 7,000,000 mark and, for those who are interested in such things, the proprietors will ask you £10,000 ($30,000) for a full-page advertisement.

It is not the least romantic part of this romantic story that hard-headed businessmen find that advertisements in the *News of the World*, even at this high rate, are profitable. However, this romantic story has no place in this book, but the *News of the World* certainly has a place; and even more so has that great newspaperman, Lord Riddell who, in adjusting the present, and carving out a splendid future, did not forget the past.

Beneath the modern *News of the World* building, in Bouverie Street, Whitefriars, is a small mediaeval crypt, last visible relic of a vast monastic settlement which once sprawled across the river-bank south of Fleet Street. It is to the generosity of Lord Riddell that we Londoners owe the careful preservation of this remnant of a lost London; and I like to think that, no less than the modern building which towers above (and all that it represents), this small fourteenth-century cellar is a worthy memorial to the generous spirit of Riddell.

On a grey, drizzling day, I walked down Bouverie Street, and turned in through the wide doors of the *News of the World*'s large entrance-hall. 'Bouverie', like New York's

'Bowery', is the Dutch word *bouwerij*, a farmstead; but while
the Bowery is named after a homestead which once stood there
when New York was still New Amsterdam, Bouverie Street
is named after a Dutchman of that name ('van Bouwerij'), who
accompanied William III to England, and here founded a
noble family.

Well, I turned into the entrance-hall of the *News of the
World*, and there, in the right-hand corner, saw a square block
of stone set flush in the modern floor. This block of stone is the
top of what remains of an old wall, part of the great monastery
of the Order of Mount Carmel—the Carmelites; or, as they
were popularly called in England, the 'White Friars'.

From the year 1241, down to the Reformation, most of the
area south of Fleet Street and lying between the Temple and
Blackfriars had been covered by the buildings of the Order.
Save for a piece of wall buried under Ashentree Court, the
small length of wall of which the top can be seen in the *News
of the World*'s entrance-hall, the cellar of a nearby tavern, and
the wonderfully preserved crypt that we shall presently examine, nothing remains of the vast monastic settlement. Only
the name has been preserved in the name of the street which
runs parallel with Bouverie Street: Carmelite Street.

The crypt—its original purpose has yet to be ascertained—
lies under the site of what were formerly Nos. 2 and 4, Britton's
Court, a small *cul-de-sac* opening off Bouverie Street.

Until the rebuilding of the *News of the World* building,
which entailed taking in the houses of Britton's Court, Nos. 2
and 4 were occupied by Sunder Kabaudi's Oriental News
Agency—a sufficiently astonishing development to have happened within the precincts of a Carmelite monastery.

Fortunately, though only fragments of this monastery survive, we have a singularly detailed map, drawn up in the sixteenth century for the use of the Commissioners entrusted with
the dissolution of the monasteries, which shows us exactly how
the former monastery underlies the modern streets, alleys and
buildings which now cover this important area. What is more,
we have a drawing, no less singularly detailed, of the steeple

of the great Carmelite church which formed part of the monastery buildings. The distinctive conical steeple juts up above the Tudor houses in Van der Wyngarde's panoramic engraving of London as it was when the first Elizabeth was on the throne.

Little by little, the monastic buildings of the City, of which the monks and nuns had been forcibly dispossessed, decayed in both senses of the word. The extensive fabrics could no longer be maintained, so that they became ruins against which, and into which, newer, smaller houses were built; and the whole area suffered a severe moral decline into a lawless region, impenetrable under the name 'Alsatia'.

Little by little, the monastery disappeared above ground, until all trace of it had been lost. Then, in 1867, workmen, digging the foundations of new buildings in Bouverie Street, came across traces of the old Carmelite buildings. The crypt was uncovered under the paving of Britton's Court, and came in handy as a coal-cellar.

The Whitefriars area was excavated to a considerable depth in 1883—again for the purposes of rebuilding—when a length of the north wall of the nave of the Carmelite church was uncovered, Alas, though archaeologists presume that a great deal of the foundations of the Friary buildings was uncovered at this time, no record was made.

The first expert examination of the crypt was not made until 1895, when a Mr Henry Lumley, having had instructions to sell the property which included Britton's Court, investigated No. 4, then occupied by a family named Hurrell (who had been in possession for four generations), went down into the crypt, moved aside the coal and wood which filled the underground room, and recognized the quality (if not the purpose) of the room.

The crypt was fully described in a paper by the late Mr A. W. Clapham, F.S.A., printed in the journal of the British Archaeological Association, in 1910; and when, eighteen years later, the Association heard that excavations on the site of the Carmelite monastery were proposed, it appointed a Committee 'to take such steps as would ensure a record and the preservation of all . . . remains'.

This Committee found a responsive friendship in Lord Riddell who, independently of (though in association with) the Committee, asked his own architect, Mr A. Alban H. Scott, F.R.I.B.A., to take photographs of the site and of all remains, both before and after excavation.

'The vaulted cellar or crypt,' says the Committee's report, 'is a gem of its kind, and dates probably from the latter half of the 14th century. A straight joint between this building and the chamber on the west probably indicates the line of building. The whole [*i.e.*: of the crypt] is of dressed stonework. Deep ribs, springing from the angles and from the centre of each side, meet in a large boss carved with a rose and central ornament, now very obscure.

'The vault, which is of cornered pyramidal form, has been broken into on the south-east side. The preservation of this beautiful relic is much to be desired.'

The Committee did not desire in vain! By Lord Riddell's orders, a modification of the plans for the *News of the World* building ensured that the whole of the underground chamber was preserved, the architect providing a convenient access for the general public, for whom, as for 'those who are keenly interested in these historical studies', the crypt, in the words of the *News of the World*, is to be kept 'as a museum'.

Several other relics of the Carmelite monastery were discovered in excavating the area: notably, part of the winding stone staircase leading from the crypt to the Chapter House; portions of tracery from a post-Reformation building in Ashentree Court (the line of which follows that of the old Cloister walk), several tiles from the paving of that walk (they are 4½ inches square and half-an-inch thick, and are preserved in the crypt), the soles of two Roman sandals, a portion of a Roman lead water-pipe, and some relics of later times.

However, I myself being dissatisfied with even the British Archaeological Association's 'complete report' of the finds which had been made in the area of the Carmelite monastery, referred myself to a contemporary map; and here I was given a hint where to look for yet another survival of part of White-friars.

It is obvious from this map that a narrow lane ran along the wall bounding the east side of the monastery's garden, and that this narrow lane crossed Fleet Street, running north. This narrow lane, on the north side of Fleet Street, is now repre-sented by Wine Office Court, and it is clear that the tavern known as 'The Cheshire Cheese' not only stands on the site of the northern gate-house of the monastery (which extended over Fleet Street, and touched the boundaries of the lands of the Abbey of Peterborough, the Nunnery of Vale Royal, *Cheshire*, the Priory of Ankerwyke and the Abbey of Garen-don), but is actually built on a surviving portion of that gate-house. This old tavern, built in the reign of Charles II, immedi-ately after the Great Fire of 1666, and almost entirely deprived of its original interior when an electrical fault caused a fire during the last war, is well known to English journalists, who drink beer there, and American tourists, who eat their luncheons and dinners there.

Under the tavern lies the crypt; and the western part of this crypt is undoubtedly work of the fourteenth century. In recent times, the original stone-work—possibly, like the crypt under Britton's Court, of blocks of hard chalk—had been faced with brick; but the lancet arches and the whole 'lay-out' of the crypt clearly testify to the fact that we have here another surviving part of the great White Friars monastery (even though the modern name of the tavern links it rather with the Cheshire nunnery of Vale Royal.)

Cross Fleet Street and walk down the opposite side of the street until, having passed Salisbury Court, where Samuel Pepys was born, you come to a narrow alley called St Bride's Place. Turn up here, and enter the newly-reconstructed church of St Bride, Irish and holy before the Irish had ever heard of St Patrick.

I have earlier referred to this church, and to the wonderful achievement of its Rector, Mr Cyril Armitage, in raising the money for its complete rebuilding. Its ceiling gleaming with colours and gold, its walls as white as they must have been when Wren (working from his office in the house which is now 'The Bell' tavern) finished his task, the old church had a different charm for me when, with Mr Armitage, I walked through the still empty shell, and saw the stone-masons sawing and shaping and carving the new stonework on the very spot on which it was to be erected.

Advantage was taken of the bombing to explore the space beneath the crypt; and here, layer after layer, were the remains of successive churches which had been built here since the earliest days of the Roman occupation. But to the west of Fleet Street, just beyond the Griffin which marks the site of Temple Bar, there are two old lath-and-plaster houses which certainly stand upon Roman foundations.

One of these old houses, which dates back to 1629, is now occupied by the justly famous Wig & Pen Club, and it was the 'Wig's' creator, Mr Dick Brennan—the only London cuisinier to have crossed the Atlantic on the second *Mayflower*—who took me down to the basement of the club, around the kitchens, and there showed me what, without a doubt, is Roman construction.

It is not only in the quality of its cuisine and service, and in its 'atmosphere', that the Wig & Pen is unique among London's clubs; it is the only one I know which is housed in a building which has escaped both the Great Fire of 1666 and the Great Fire of 1940; which was erected in the year when Felton assassinated the Duke of Buckingham at Portsmouth, and which stands on foundations laid down probably eighteen centuries ago.

Over the road from the Wig & Pen, a little to the east, Chancery Lane runs north. Go up this street, at the corner of which, over a pawnbroker's shop, stands one of the most mysterious statues in London and, reaching Holborn, turn right again, until you come to Holborn Circus. On your left will be

Ely Place, still a part of the county of Cambridgeshire, as it was once part of the London palace of the Bishops of Ely.

Up to the beginning of the last war, the gates of this quiet *cul-de-sac* were closed at night, and the porter did the rounds, calling the hours, and adding: 'All's well!'

At the end of Ely Place is St Etheldreda's, named after the patron saint of this part of the Soke of Ely. St Etheldreda's is, today, the only Roman Catholic church in London dating from before the Reformation; but, as a visit to the crypt makes clear, it was possibly Roman even before it was Christian. The bricks are of the tile-like shape distinctively Roman; and even though we allow that the lower part of the present mediaeval church may have been reconstructed from Roman materials, the fact still remains that the Roman materials could hardly have been abundant on the site unless there had been a Roman building previously on the spot.

But it is farther to the east, at the part where Cornhill joins Leadenhall Street, that the greatest survival of Roman building has been recorded. Gracechurch Street joins the junction of Cornhill and Leadenhall Street at roughly a right angle; and the corner of Cornhill and Gracechurch Street, now filled by St Peter's Cornhill, represents, more or less, the north-eastern corner of the Basilica of Londinium, a vast structure which, with a length which has been estimated at 690 feet, was the second largest in the Imperium.

From the eighteenth century onwards, the remains of this basilica and of the buildings adjacent have been uncovered; many of the tessellated pavements having escaped the workmen's picks, and coming to rest in museums and public buildings.

When, a few years before the last war, an extension to Barclay's Bank was being made at the corner of Gracechurch Street and Lombard Street, a further large section of the basilica's foundations was uncovered; further, because, when the site was being cleared for Leadenhall Market at the end of the last century, extensive foundation walls of the basilica were discovered and, fortunately, mapped with care. However, though the remains under Leadenhall Market and Barclay's Bank (and, indeed, many other offices in the vicinity) were not preserved, a recent discovery of part of the basilica's foundations will ensure that a fragment, at least, of Londinium's principal edifice will be visible for years to come.

The City branch of Messrs T. R. Blurton & Co., Ltd., the well-known Strand haberdashers and tailors, is to be found at 90, Gracechurch Street, hard by the entrance to that Leadenhall Market under which so much of the basilica was found nearly a century ago. Recently, some alterations were made in the basement of the shop, and behind a Victorian wall was the characteristic masonry of the basilica's builders.

What is most interesting about this discovery—a careful examination of which I owe to the courtesy of Mr T. R. Blurton —is that the Roman remains lie so near to the present street-level. Only a short flight of stairs takes one down from the ground-floor shop to the room below; hardly more than a ten-foot descent.

Possibly the fact that Gracechurch Street is a hill—and, once, a much steeper one—accounts for the relatively small accumulation of that rubbish which causes street-levels to rise over the centuries.

Here we are in the very heart of Roman London—and whether or not one believes that the authorities of St Peter's Cornhill were justified, in 1874, in celebrating the 1700th anniversary of the foundation of this church by the British King Lucius, one must accept the fact that so serious a claim to a venerable antiquity could hardly have been put forward for a church in any other street than Gracechurch Street, where it meets Cornhill.

Sometimes, when I reflect how the fine church of St Benet Gracechurch was swept away in 1867, to make place for a dreary Victorian office-building (which, in turn, has given place to a drearier 1960 one), and how the 'Spread Eagle' inn, with its galleried courtyard, had been swept away, two years earlier, for a similar purpose; and how the church on the opposite side of Gracechurch Street, All Hallows, which was completed by Wren in 1694, was pulled down in 1938, to give more room to Barclay's Bank, I find an anger surging up in me at the power that savage money-grubbing has over nobler things. But a little further thought, and I realize that the strictly commercial quality of the modern street has more in common with Roman Gracechurch Street than with the Gracechurch Street of, say, a century ago, when the banks and the insurance companies and the usurers' dens had to share their 'valuable sites' with such useless things as churches and picturesque, ancient taverns.

For there was never, in all this world's drab history, a culture more firmly based upon conscienceless money-grubbing than that of Rome in the days of the Imperium. It was, indeed, to recover the money lent to the British princes by such 'philosophers' as Seneca that the Romans quickened up their plans to conquer this country.

Once a typical Londoner of the first century had recovered from the shock of seeing the new buildings, he would feel more at home in the Gracechurch Street of modern commercial practice than in the leisurely Grasschurch Street of the fourteenth or even the not-quite-so-leisurely Gracious Street of the seventeenth century.

Around the corner, if we turn into Fenchurch Street, and walk along to Mark Lane, we shall find one of the most marvellous relics of the past: but this is a mediaeval, and not a Roman, relic. Opposite the entrance to Fenchurch Street Station, in Mark Lane, stands a stone tower—all which now remains of the ancient church of All Hallows Staining—the nave of the church being demolished in the middle of the last century to allow for the extension of Clothworkers' Hall. This second Clothworkers' Hall was destroyed during the last war by bombing, and has now been rebuilt.

Now, when the then Clothworkers' Hall was destroyed by fire in 1666, the Clothworkers, whose master was Samuel Pepys, conducted their business in a Norman hermit's chapel —'William Lambe's Chapel'—which stood in Monkwell

Street, London Wall, a property of this Livery. In 1708, after having been without a Hall for forty years, the Clothworkers opened their new Hall in Mark Lane; this was demolished and a larger Hall built upon the site, in 1856—an ornate affair, in the style, a contemporary notes, of Louis XIV.

Then, in 1872, when rebuilding in London Wall threatened William Lambe's Chapel, the Clothworkers determined to save the twelfth-century Norman crypt, and conveyed it to a site adjoining their Hall in Mark Lane.

The bombing of the last war completely destroyed the 'Louis XIV' hall of the Clothworkers' Company, but it spared both the thirteenth-century tower of All Hallows Staining, and the Norman crypt which had been buried in the earth alongside of the tower.

A not unpleasant little red-brick parish hall has been built beside the forecourt of the tower, and a stone plaque records:

THE PARISH HALL OF ST OLAVE HART STREET

This Hall which stands on part of the site of the former church of Allhallows Staining was built in 1951 by the Clothworkers' Company for the benefit of the united Parish of St Olave Hart Street with All-hallows Staining and St Catherine Coleman

The tower of All Hallows is, another notice states, now open to the public as a quiet place for reading and study.

While St Olave's is still awaiting rebuilding, after the damage of the Blitz, the parish services are held in the crypt of William Lambe's Chapel. There has been no weathering of the white stone of this small crypt-chapel; the adze-tooled round-headed Norman arches are as the mason left them eight hundred years ago; and though, above, the tall, soulless buildings rise so incongruously above the castellated tower of All Hallows, here, beneath the hustle and the bustle of Fenchurch Street and Mark Lane, is an ancient peace as well as an inviolate silence.

I first went down the few steps into the crypt when only the tower of the church stood above the flattened area around Fen-

church Street Station. The bombs had—miraculously, said the
churchwarden who was my guide—spared the tower, as the
fires of 1666 had spared it. And the few feet of London earth
covering the chapel were ragged but beautiful with London
weed.

We went down into the chapel: and it was like going from
darkness into light. The silence thrilled like a thunder-clap.
There were flowers on the altar, and red hassocks on the
kneelers of the few chairs: something to pray on, and something to pray with.

In a way, though one could see that the churchwarden was
proud of this unique place of worship, one could see that he
was not as impressed as I confessed myself to be; for he conducts his important business—he is a wine-bottler—in a large
building which, three hundred years ago, was a warehouse of
the Honourable Company of Adventurers Trading with the
East Indies, and the coat-of-arms of 'John Company' still
adorns the front of his place of business.

What is more, one of the walls of this warehouse—one hundred and ten feet long—is part of the Wall of London; with its
sentry's walk along its top, and two arrow slits pierced in its
thickness.

Beneath it, in Cooper's Row—as in nearby Crutched Friars,
and Frenchman's Ordinary and America Square—lie remains
of more ancient days than even saw the building of Lambe's
Chapel. For this, again, is old London—Roman London; and
many things are in our museums which have been dug up here.

Re-tracing our footsteps a little, and going back to Fenchurch
Street, we find, between that street and the new Lloyds building, a small, paved space hemmed in by modern glass-walled
skyscrapers. There are trees in this paved space, and there is a
beauty here which is rather augmented than diminished by the
tall buildings which surround it. Under the trees, typists and
clerks were sitting—when I last passed through—on teak
benches, reading or talking or just enjoying the fugitive sun-
shine.

In the middle of this oasis in the desert of office-London is an early nineteenth-century mausoleum: a plain affair, on the sides of which are recorded the names of the people whose bodies once lay in the vault beneath.

> In this vault are deposited the remains of
> Ambrose Weston Esqr, of Fenchurch Street;
> who died the 28th. of January 1810, Aged 55.
> Also of Mary, wife of the above;
> who died the 30th. of November 1811, aged 50.
> Also William Stiles, son of the above Ambrose
> and Mary Weston;
> who died the 12th. of November 1807, aged 17.

We are not far, here, from the Tower of London which, if not 'built by Julius Caesar', as mediaeval and later historians believed, is at least built upon the site of a Roman river-fort. But we shall deal with the subterranean parts of the Tower later.

Here, since we are now close to Cornhill and Threadneedle Street let us see what has been found under the Bank of England.

Mr Woods received me when I visited the Bank's new building, begun, after designs by Sir Herbert Baker (architect of New Delhi), in 1925, within the still-standing walls of Sir John Soane's Bank.

After the founding of the Bank of England by William Paterson, the first directors' meetings were held, for some time, in the old hall of the Mercers' Company, in Cheapside; the first offices of the Bank being the private residence of the first Governor, Sir John Houblon, which stood, surrounded by its garden, alongside the church of St Christopher le Stocks (that is, 'St Christopher near the Stocks Market').

A new office was built by George Sampson in 1734, the first real 'Bank' that London knew; additions were made between 1766 and 1786 by Sir Robert Taylor, during which the church of St Christopher was pulled down, and its site built upon. Then, at the very end of the eighteenth century, Sir John

Soane built the Bank which was replaced by the present structure.

I mention these various buildings and rebuildings to show that much excavation has taken place upon this site, whose antiquity, as a place of human activity, is attested by the objects discovered in the earth beneath the various Banks. Many of these objects have found a place in the museums of London—notably the British, London and Guildhall Museums—but sufficient have been retained to provide the Bank itself with the material for a not unimpressive museum of its own, around which Mr Woods kindly conducted me.

Now, apart from the fact that three churches have been pulled down about this part to make way for additions to the Bank and the Royal Exchange, and to provide space for the Sun Insurance Office, this part is historically important as being one of the busiest of Roman London.

Princes Street, which runs along the west side of the Bank, and which contains the offices of a number of leading New York banking houses, covers a part of the Walbrook, whose waters have often penetrated into the Bank's basement.

On this site, then, must have stood, in Roman times, the wharves and offices of those firms trading upon a navigable Walbrook; and two of the tessellated pavements of those offices have not only been found under the Bank, but are still to be seen very much in the position in which they were found. Carefully repaired, the two pavements have been re-laid in a hall which is approached by a winding staircase; and the link between Londinium and London is the more striking by reason of the fact that, in character, these two Roman pavements are barely distinguishable from the mosaic pavements which floor the modern hall above.

In the Bank's own museum, displayed in glass-topped cases, are the 'finds' that the directors have decided to keep. And here, all neatly ticketed, is the epitome of history in her most casual mood.

Outside, at the bottom of a staircase, are the pavements of Roman Londinium; inside this museum are the sandals and shoes and hob-nailed boots of the men and women who surely trod those pavements. There is the sole of a woman's shoe— the smallest that I have ever seen—yet it is not a child's shoe, but a woman's. The inner sole has been carefully and skilfully engraved with the figure of a running cockerel (did the foot of an outraged wife thus symbolically tread the symbol of an errant husband?).

There is a man's sturdy working boot, the sole liberally protected with stout hobnails. There are soles and complete shoes; many with elaborate openwork sides which show the skill of the London shoemaker of anything up to eighteen centuries ago. But the strangest 'shoe' of all is a vast, iron-shod object called a 'hippo-sandal'. Hippo-sandals were, as their name implies, horse-shoes; but they were more like the shoes we wear in that they were fastened around the horse's foot instead of being nailed to the hoof.

I have said that this museum of the Bank's tenders an epitome of London's history; there are later things here than Roman—Saxon, early and late mediaeval, Tudor, Jacobean and even Georgian. There are Elizabethan 'bellarmine' jugs to go with Roman Samian ware; but I found the tally-sticks as interesting as the 'hippo-sandals'.

For this method of accountancy—notching lengths of wood —strikes us, surely, as something even more primitive than hippo-sandals.

Yet, accounting by tally was practised up to the beginning of the last century, and it was through burning the tallies of the Exchequer in a House of Commons stove in 1834 that a careless caretaker set fire to, and consequently burnt down, the old Palace of Westminster.

Mr Woods showed a tally, eight inches long, on which the notches recorded a Government receipt for a Bank loan of £18,812 13s. 11½d.

'Look,' said Mr Woods, 'the eighteen large notches *above*— each mark one thousand pounds. Then, *below*, eight notches of one hundred pounds value. Then twelve and a half one-pound notches; three notches of one shilling, eleven of one

penny—and, look here, one small notch, on the side, of one
halfpenny.'

This, by the way, is a trifling tally, compared with that—
the size of a lecturer's pointer!—which records, in notches,
the receipt of the payment of the original subsidy of £1,200,000,
made to the Government in accordance with the terms of the
Act by which the Bank was established.

As I write, there is a strike of 'tally clerks' at the London
docks. One feels that, if they had to include the notching of
tally-sticks (which gave them their present name) among their
duties, they might have something reasonably to strike against.

I have mentioned that the first company meetings of the
Bank took place in the hall of the Mercers' Company, in Cheapside. It was in the Mercers' Hall which had been rebuilt after
the destruction of the original Hall in the Great Fire of 1666
that the Bank held its meetings; but a word must be said about
this rebuilding, for it closely concerns one of the most dramatic
finds ever made in London earth.

In 1538, the King's Commissioners had decreed the dissolution of the great monastic foundation, the Hospital of St
Thomas Acon; and in 1541, the Mercers' Company, which had
been permitted, some years earlier, to remodel the chapel of
the Hospital as the Mercers' Chapel, were allowed to take possession of the 'dissolved' Hospital.

The Mercers were already in trouble with the die-hard wing
of the Reforming party for having ordered, for the chapel,
stained glass windows which represented Henry II doing
penance for the killing of Thomas à Becket. Though no record
survives of the fact, it is certain that the Reformers took direct
action, and ordered their inquisitors or 'inspectors' to see that
the windows were removed—by the drastic method of destroying them, themselves. We shall see why, later, we may take this
for granted.

The Mercers settled down in the former Hospital in 1541,
and remained in peaceful possession (even during the reconciliation with Rome effected under Mary Tudor) until 1666,

when the Hospital was destroyed by the Great Fire, the church
of St Thomas Acon not being rebuilt.

A new Mercers' Hall arose on the site after the Fire; and this
again went when, in 1884, a new Mercers' Hall was erected,
the façade of the Restoration Hall being taken down, and used
to face the town hall of Swanage, in Dorset (which town also
has the Brunel suspension bridge which crossed the Thames
from Charing Cross to Waterloo).

Now, in these several rebuildings, the mediaeval foundations,
including the crypt of the chapel of the Hospital of St Thomas
Acon survived; they survive, indeed, to this day. What is more,
though their presence was known—and, for that matter, they
were used—during the four centuries between the Dissolution
of the Monasteries and the coming of Hitler's bombers, there
was a treasure concealed beneath the successive Mercers' Halls
which had to depend upon the bombing of the Second World
War for its revealing. In this manner.

Nearly fifteen years after a German fire-bomb had destroyed
the third Mercers' Hall to stand on the Cheapside site, a work-
man, clearing away the rubble, uncovered a vault which had
not been used since early Tudor days: the middle vault of the
old Hospital. Against the east wall of this vault, at a depth
of only about five feet, he saw what appeared to be the life-
sized figure of a man. The sealing of the vault had protected
the figure; four centuries had hardly touched the stone with
dust.

It was a mutilated figure of Christ, represented as He lay,
still and stiff in death, in the moment after He had been taken
down from the Cross. The sculptor has thrown a cloth hastily
over the loins, and the rough bier, of three planks, is covered
with the 'royal robe' with which, in mockery, the soldiers
'adorned' Him.

Though the feet are missing, as well as a part of the arm,
and though the tip of the nose had been broken off by the
iconoclast's hammer, the beauty of the sculpture remains inviolate. Here is Death which, through the genius of the
unknown artist, seems to justify completely the sonorous in-

vocation of Raleigh, with which he finished his last writing, as he himself came face to face with the one last mystery.

The 'royal robe' bears several inscriptions: a summary, as it were, of the whole drama of the Crucifixion. The inscriptions are in Latin and Greek; and the presence of Greek tells us, even if the character of the carving did not, that we are here in the age of the New Learning, though still with the old Faith. In Latin and Greek is the mocking title: *Jesus the Nazarene, King of the Jews*; and in Latin alone: *He made Himself obedient to Death, even the Death of the Cross* (*Paul: Epistle to the Philippians*); on the left-hand side of the Figure is another Latin inscription which, though much mutilated, can still be read as: *In peace hath He made His sanctuary*—a saying to which the strange accident of this statue's preservation through the accidents of the past four centuries has surely given a more than human significance.

The statue had been, obviously, placed with extreme care in the vault in which it was found in 1954. Its position shows it to have been laid directly beneath the part in which the altar of the Hospital stood; and it is beyond doubt that, having been mutilated by the iconoclasts, the statue, to save it from further damage, was hastily, though carefully, removed from the chapel, and put in a place of safety beneath the chapel— where it remained for four hundred years.

The record goes on to mention the name of 'oon Walter Vandale of Andewarp (Antwerp), Karver', but whether or not the said Walter executed the Lost Christ of Cheapside cannot now be known. The Van Dael family of Antwerp were better known as painters of stained-glass and murals, but it is not impossible that they were sculptors, too; the Mercers' records clearly mention that Walter Vandale was a 'Karver'.

So, though it destroyed so much, the bombing gave us back a lost treasure: lost, not merely in the sense of its whereabouts having been forgotten with the passing of the centuries; but lost in the sense that men had come to be ignorant that it had ever existed.

Just across the road from the Mercers' Hall stood, until the middle of the century before last, the ancient Stocks Market: it was here, during the reign of that Protector Oliver Cromwell, whose pedigree Rabbi Manasseh and the Jews of Amsterdam faked, in gratitude, to include King David, that a lesser London treasure was concealed, to be brought forth again when, with imperial pomp, His Highness had been buried among the consecrated kings in Westminster Abbey. This was the bronze statue of Charles I, by Le Sueur, which stood—and stands again—at Charing Cross.

You know the story? Oliver Williams, *alias* Cromwell (as he is described in the register of marriages at St Giles Cripplegate) had entered into secret negotiations with Charles I, when the King was imprisoned in Carisbrooke Castle. Oliver, whose great-uncle had been the Putney solicitor, Thomas Cromwell, created Earl of Essex by Henry VIII (which title died with Thomas Cromwell on Tower Hill), offered to turn coat in favour of the King, in return for amnesty, money and the Earldom of Essex. The King, prisoner though he was, turned Oliver's offer down and, in revenge, Oliver voted the King's death.

There was, then, something strictly personal in 'Cromwell's' ordering the statue of the King to be taken down from its plinth, and broken up. The statue was taken away and, although 'peices' of it were sold to diehard Roundheads during the twenty years of the Interregnum, the statue itself was carefully hidden, against the inevitable Restoration.

In the early days of a more recent Revolution, Lunacharsky, then Soviet Russian Minister of Education, warned his countrymen not to be too sweeping in their reforms, 'lest,' said Lunacharsky, 'our children may one day reproach us with the fact that, in our zeal to sweep away all which was bad, we swept away so much which was good.'

The warning was rightly given; but, in all times, and in all revolutions, there are men who heed the warning, as it were, even before it is uttered—often, without its being uttered.

The 'absolute power', to which Lord Acton credits the power absolutely to corrupt, rarely, if ever, has existed. Dictators are never completely obeyed—especially in regard to those small, symbolic sentimentalities which may seem so important to some.

The treasures which were ordered to be—and were duly reported to have been—destroyed, turn up again.

The 'Balass Ruby' of the Black Prince, sold by the Cromwellian commissioners for four pounds sterling, when the Crown Jewels of England, Scotland, Armenia and Byzantium were being sold, turned up again; it is now in the Imperial Crown.

The swords of Mercy and of Grace were found, sadly rusted, buried in the garden of an old house in Mitcham; the former Imperial Crown—'broken up' by the commissioners—is still in the possession of Lord Amherst of Hackney; and two chalices of rare mediaeval craftsmanship, 'melted down for bullion' after having been removed from the Chapel of St George—the 'Garter Chapel'—at Windsor, are now to be found in the possession of two churches in Milan.

I mention all these things, because the Most Venerable Relic of England—the Palladium of English Chivalry—may yet be found, for all that it was 'destroyed' at the Reformation. This was the jewelled reliquary, brought to England in 1415, by the Emperor Manuel II Paleologus, as a gift to the Most Noble Order of the Garter. The Emperor was met, at Blackheath, by the King, with all his great officers of state, and Emperor and reliquary were conducted solemnly to London.

Well might this gift have been accorded such honour: in the reliquary was nothing less than the Heart of St George. Where is it now? Too many personal experiences of treasure-finding have made me wary of stating too definitely that such-and-such a treasure is gone for ever.

Sometimes the 'losing' is no more than a mislaying or a misplacing as when, following a hunch, I found *A Lytle Booke with a Crucifixe*—the Saxon gospels on which the monarchs of England used to take the Coronation Oath—in the British Museum. Then, though all the MSS left by Camden, which were unaccounted for, were presumed to have been destroyed in the disastrous Temple fire of 1644, I identified Camden's own MS copy of the *Black Book of Arundel*—the copy hastily prepared for the coronation of Edward VI—on the site of the very Inn, in Fleet Street, in which Camden had studied law.

Until the Reformation, not only Westminster Abbey, but almost every other church in London contained some relic of sanctity: in the case of the Abbey, these relics totalled many dozens.

From the time of King Sebert, who founded the Abbey Church of St Peter for Bishop Mellitus, to Henry VIII himself, the kings and queens of England had endowed the Abbey with relics, the most generous donors being King Edward Confessor and King Henry III—the monarch who brought the drinking-water from Tyburn to the City.

The list of relics given by the pious Edward is too long to give here; but among the treasures dispersed at the Reformation were 'many pieces of the vestments of the Virgin Mary; of the linen that she wore; of the window in which the angel stood when he saluted her; of her milk; of her hair; of her shoes and her bed; also the girdle which she worked with her own hands, always wore, and dropped to St Thomas the Apostle at her assumption'. There were relics, too, of the Abbey's patron, in the shape of hairs from St Peter's beard. There were also pieces of the True Cross.

About 1250, Henry II made some splendid presents to the Abbey: these included some drops of the blood which came from Christ's side, some thorns from Christ's crown, and the stone, with the impressions of His feet left upon it, at His Ascension, 'and also great part of the Blood *de Miraculo*'. Close to the tomb of the King is a little niche in the wall. It is the opinion of Mr Lawrence Tanner, Librarian and Keeper of the Muniments at the Abbey, that this niche was intended to hold the phial containing the Blood.

The relics, indeed, were so many, that it is unthinkable that all should have been destroyed. History rejects the supposition that public opinion can be changed overnight, or changed completely; there are 'reactionaries' to every revolution.

There is, in fact, one such relic still to be found in a City church: that of St Magnus Martyr, that strange old church which lies among the business of fishmongers and wine-merchants in Billingsgate, which has been a port for close on two thousand years.

This church, rebuilt by Wren after the earlier church had been destroyed in the Great Fire, is named after Magnus, 'a Christian who suffered in Caesarea in the time of Aurelian the Emperour, Anno Dom. 276, under Alexander the governour'. It is the only London church to have had a public roadway driven through its lower story, just as St Mary Woolnoth is the only London church to have had an underground railway station built in its crypt.

In 1760, a passage was made through the church tower, from north to south, so as to afford a footway to Old London Bridge (which stood about 200 feet to the east of the present Rennie bridge).

'Wren', says Mr A. E. Daniell, 'seems to have foreseen the probability of this communication being required, and had so constructed the arches that no difficulty was experienced in opening them out.

'Since the formation of the present bridge, the footway has, of course, been no longer needed, and a portion of the carriage road to the old bridge has been acquired as a church-yard, and enclosed by a wall.'

As one walks off London Bridge, and on to London Bridge Street, one sees the old church beneath one, though the spire— the loveliest of all Wren's spires—rises even above the modern bulk of Adelaide House.

How many who pass the old, now neglected church daily know that within its soot-stained walls is one of those sacred relics in which once London was the richest of all the cities of Christendom?

Yet here, they say, is preserved a piece of the True Cross.

From the *Pax Romana* to the *Pax Christiana* was no long step; let us take a step backward, and pass from Christ to

Rome, in a short walk down Fish Street Hill, under the shadow of that Monument which, recording one Great Fire of London, defied a later burning.

The Coal Exchange is immediately opposite Billingsgate fish-market, and is an early Victorian building in the classical mode—so classical in a scholarly way that I always think that the classicism is rather that of Berlin than of London. It would be interesting to know whether it was before, or after, the finding of a Roman building on the site, some thirteen feet below street-level, that the architect, J. B. Bunning, designed his carefully classical structure.

The foundations of the Roman structure—it was either a private house, or an office building with private quarters attached—had been laid upon a 'raft' of timber, itself supported by wooden piles driven into the marshy foreshore of the Thames.

When excavations for the Coal Exchange were being made, the level at which the floor of the Roman building was found was held to be as remarkable as the finding of the building itself. For the floor was only one foot above the then High-Water Mark; and, on one morning, the workmen arrived on the site to find that the Thames had overflowed into the excavations.

Much of the Roman building as originally uncovered is now buried once again beneath the more modern premises abutting on the Coal Exchange, but one room—the 'bath room'—has been preserved, and may be visited. This is not the only intact room of a Roman building to be preserved below street-level in London, but it is the only one whose interior walls have not been covered over at a later period. Here you may see the plain Roman plaster, and sit on the seat built into the north wall for the convenience of the bathers as they sweated in the heat rising from the hypocaust or hot-air duct built beneath the floor.

It was as recently as 1951 that the hypocaust was discovered, and then only by accident, for the floor of the 'bath room' was intact when discovered, though it was damaged during the actual construction of the Coal Exchange. Today, through a purposely enlarged gap in the floor, the visitor can see the construction of the hypocaust—short tile pillars supporting the floor, so as to leave a hollow space beneath, through which the hot air (supplied by a furnace situated outside the original building) circulated.

'When this feature was cleaned in 1951', says Mr Ivor Hume [*Treasure in the Thames*], 'it was discovered that the ground was still extremely wet, and that damp was damaging the fabric of the building. As the remains [*i.e.* of the Roman building] had been open to the public for nearly a century, there seemed little likelihood that the cleaning operations would reveal any hitherto unsuspected details.

'The gaps between the pillars had been packed with soil, presumably, it seemed, as a recent measure to give added support to the crumbling floor. At first, this proved to be the case, for all that was found in it were fragments of milk bottles, electric light bulbs and a forged Roman coin. But right at the back, at a point that could only be reached by wriggling face-down between the pillars, was found a deposit of wet, evil-smelling mud in which were discovered a number of late Roman potsherds and one virtually intact pot. These had clearly been undisturbed since the fourth century A.D., but how they came to be there will always remain a mystery.'

Billingsgate Market itself rests on a site which yielded an even older relic: a relic which makes one wonder how much of truth lies in the legends of a Trojan foundation of London—'Troynovant', 'New Troy'. The scientific examination of folklore has proved the existence of so much historical fact in 'wild legend' that there are now people who claim that all legend, no matter how 'wild', is simply truth fancified through its being passed down, by word of mouth, through many generations. Such a theory is to deny the human race of its essential faculty of 'romancing'; but many a legend, now regarded as historically baseless, may well be proved to contain more than a mere substratum of truth.

One asks whether or not Geoffrey of Monmouth was simply romancing when he told of our Trojan ancestors, because of the finding of articles in the London earth—and especially the Thames mud—dating from periods centuries before the Romans had even conquered Italy.

It was while excavating the site of the present Billingsgate Market, hard by the 'Roman bath' under the Coal Exchange, that two such thought-provoking objects were found. These were a beautiful Greek rhyton of the second century B.C., and a miniature hydria (or water pitcher) of the sixth century B.C. The latter matches in antiquity the Trojan or Italic kylix—another beautiful vessel—found at Barn Elms.

This shallow-bowled drinking-cup, which is dated to the fifth century B.C., is decorated, on the side of the bowl, with the figure of a crouching boy, painted by the artist whom we identify as 'the Pythos Painter'. Barn Elms is near Reading, and it was near Reading, on the River Kennet, that another relic from a pre-Roman past was found: a bronze arrow-head, bearing the monogram of Queen Pherenike of Cyrene. This arrow-head is dated to the third century B.C.

Reading is not London, nor is the Kennet the Thames. But a relic of even greater antiquity was found, in London itself, during excavations at London Wall. This is the bronze figure of an Egyptian god.

Of course, all these may have been brought to Britain centuries after they were made—are not antiquities constantly being exported to America? Yet ... there they are: the relics of centuries before Rome was more than a market-village in Latium. One hesitates to read too much into the fact of their being discovered in Britain: but, on the other hand, it would be a pity to read too little.

We have already mentioned the barber's shop—with the waste-water-runnel cut in its floor—which was discovered, after the recent bombing, at the church of All Hallows Barking.

This ancient church, which has now been largely rebuilt, lies only a few hundred yards from Billingsgate. The damage caused by the bombing made an investigation of the building's structure not possible before.

It was found that within the mediaeval walls were concealed an undercroft, built of Roman brick, and a solid wall, on the river side, dating from Roman times. A fragment of a carved and inscribed Saxon cross was also found, buried beneath a Norman pillar to which we can confidently assign the date A.D. 1087.

This district is indeed among the richest in Roman remains: and though the eastern River bastion, which developed into the Tower of London, did not mark the site of the first Roman fortification of London, the proximity of the Tower area to the River would early have given it a position of importance within the City, hardly second even to that of the Basilican area around Gracechurch Street.

Much of what has been found in excavating has either been removed to our museums or covered up again—among them the fragments of a large building at the east end of St Bride's: what Professor W. F. Grimes calls 'the first undoubted Roman building to be recorded between the River Fleet and Westminster'.

One may read about these discoveries, but one may no longer see them, save in pictures. There are, however, two relics of Roman architecture which are not only wonderfully preserved, but may be visited by the curious London perambulator.

The first lies in Newgate Street, under the 'King Edward' Post-office—or, rather, underground, but a little to the back of the building. When, in 1902, the Governors of Christ's Hospital —the public school which numbers both Charles Lamb and William Thackeray among its distinguished scholars—sold the site to the Postmaster-General, the demolition of the old school revealed that generations of Blue Coat boys had been studying and playing above a nearly intact bastion of the Roman wall of London. This bastion—No. 19—and part of the straight wall adjoining are preserved under the yard at the back of the Post Office building. Mail-vans rumble overhead, but within its specially built cellar the bastion, unique in the excellence of its preservation, still keeps watch over memory. There is much of the wall standing above ground; and parts not visible before the last war were uncovered, either by the bombing, or by the demolition of ruined buildings that bombing had made inevitable.

One such building was badly damaged by air-raids—though it is now in course of reconstruction—but the Roman building on which it stands passed unscathed through the Great Fire of 1940 as through the Great Fire of 1666. The building which was nearly destroyed, both in 1666 and in 1940, is the historic church of St Mary-le-Bow, in Cheapside. What lies beneath it is a Roman building—obviously an official building: and possibly a magistrate's court—which stood on the south side of the east-west main road (the *decumanus maximus*) which connected the western entrance of the Basilica of Londinium with the eastern entrance of whatever building it was which occupied the site of St Paul's Cathedral in Roman times.

Just after the last war, an appeal for funds to rebuild St Mary-le-Bow carried a brief history that I had written of this most famous church; and in the pamphlet I put forward the suggestion that we have, in the surviving crypt of St Mary-le-Bow, an intact Roman building—almost certainly a minor basilica, or court-of-justice, lying a few yards to the west of the great palace—on the site of which the Guildhall now stands—housing the Imperial Prefect.

If my view was not universally accepted, it has never been seriously challenged; and so here I shall maintain, what I maintained more than ten years ago, that the crypt of St Mary-le-Bow is a Roman structure, possibly as early as of the first or second century A.D.

The old church of St Mary-le-Bow ('Sancta Maria de Arcubus') was burnt down in 1666, and, in 1671, Wren, who had been commissioned to build a new church on the site, set about clearing the ground, preparatory to rebuilding. Only when the ground had been cleared did Wren discover that, beneath the church, there was a barrel-vaulted crypt. There was no means of access to this crypt and, after having failed to find a hidden entrance, Wren ordered the roof to be broken through, when he descended into the crypt by a ladder.

The memory of the crypt had been lost; though Stow records that the church was called 'de Arcubus', or 'of the Arches', because 'in the reign of William Conqueror', it was 'the first in this city built on arches of stone'.

The assumption generally held is that the builders of the church built the arched underloft, also; but two facts are against this opinion: the first that the arched crypt was not originally a crypt, and stood at street-level; and the second that, though round-headed arches are used, these are not Norman in design, but Roman.

The ecclesiastical Court of Arches—which has been held in St Mary-le-Bow from at least A.D. 1172 onwards, was named, it is said, after the church; but it is possible that the ecclesiastical court was merely successor to a civil court which had held its sittings here since Roman times.

It is certainly not without significance that the pleadings of this court, unlike those of the civil courts, were formerly held in Latin, and not in Norman-French.

There is further evidence that the crypt—for so we now must call it—is Roman. When Wren was digging the foundations for the new St Mary-le-Bow—being extremely careful not to harm the 'crypt' that he had discovered and entered—he found, at a depth of eighteen feet below the existing ground-level, a Roman road, four feet in thickness, which passed the 'front door' of the 'crypt'.

When Mr F. L. Stevens visited the crypt just before the last war, he saw, as he reports in his *Buried London*, 'one or two loose Roman bricks lying on a shelf of the vault, with other displaced stones which carry the story of London building right through the centuries'.

In Norman times, typical capitals had been added to the plain Roman pilasters which carry the springs of the arches;

and Wren, strengthening the walls with a facing of brick, was careful to leave these Norman capitals untouched, so that they can be seen through the strengthening facing that the great architect built around them.

Windows—no longer looking on a busy Cheapside—have been driven through the walls of the crypt in Saxon and mediaeval times; but, as the shape of the room testifies, here is a Roman basilica, in which fines and imprisonments were meted out in a Latin which was probably hardly more classical than that used, a thousand years later, by the judges and lawyers of the Court of Arches.

Not far from Bastion 19, that I mentioned earlier, is another church whose crypt is Roman—that is to say, a Roman building which once stood on ground-level. It was in the year A.D. 1123, that Rahere, jester to King Henry II, founded, in discharge of a vow, the great monastic foundation of St Bartholomew the Great. While on a visit to Rome—so the old story goes—a mosquito from those Campanian marshes which were drained only during Mussolini's rule infected Rahere with malaria. He recovered from the sickness, and in gratitude resolved to build a great priory and hospital (in both the mediaeval and modern meanings of that word).

The foundation was dissolved at the Reformation, in common with all like foundations; but, unlike so many others, the civil part of the hospital was re-founded by Henry VIII, and continues its good work to this day. (It was in 'Barts' that the historic encounter between Sherlock Holmes and Dr Watson took place.)

From Smithfield, famous equally for its cattle-market and its stake-burned martyrs, approach to St Bartholomew's Hospital is made through a mediaeval stone gateway (lovingly, though inaccurately, 'restored').

Little remains now of the vast complex of monastic buildings which sprawled across the lands of John, Duke of Bretagne (commemorated in the name of a nearby street, Little Britain), and what remains has been recovered from sad social decline. Nothing remains now of the great Norman church save the choir, part of the transepts, one bay of the nave, and the aforementioned crypt. Yet what remains is magnificent—so overpoweringly grand, indeed, that the imagination finds it hard to reconstruct, in fact, that superb original of which this great structure is but a small part.

After the Reformation, the Hospital of the foundation continued to discharge its functions, but the purely ecclesiastical part was let out to anyone with a pound or two of rent, and allowed to fall into a seedy decay. From a priory, St Bartholomew's became a stables, a smithy, a tavern, a timber-store, a hop-store and a fringe-factory. During the last century, what remained of the monastic buildings were recovered from base occupancy, restored, and given back to a proper use.

Under the great Norman nave is the Roman crypt—a barrel-vaulted chamber which, like the church above, has seen days of decline; for it was used at one period as a wine-cellar. Today it serves as the local mortuary—a 'bone-yard', to use the blunt but expressive idiom of the district.

Sixty years ago, the parish contained thousands of inhabitants; by the beginning of the last war, the number of actual dwellers in (as distinguished from mere workers in) Smithfield and Little Britain had dropped to under a thousand. Today there is a development of town-planning which has for its aim the re-settlement of the City, and the home-makers may return to this district, which not so much sleeps at sunset as passes into the stillness of catatonia. If the people come back, the district will need cheering up a little. The last time that I passed through it, stopping a moment to read a bronze plate marking the spot near which William Wallace was executed—the notice couched in a prose turgid with a self-conscious Scots nationalism more reminiscent of Drambuie than of Bonnie Prince Charlie—I noticed that two pubs had been turned into banks. It may be more noble to practise usury than to sell intoxicating liquors; but even with the smoke from blazing martyrs, old Smithfield must have been a jollier place than the Smithfield of today.

There is this to be said about the British: when they save, they save, one might say, as lavishly as they waste. During the six years of the last war, Hitler's bombers totally destroyed only three City churches: Austin Friars, St Mildred Bread Street and St Stephen Coleman Street. Many were damaged, of course, and twenty-five were burnt out. All the same, only three were totally destroyed—a small number compared with the deliberate destruction of no fewer than twenty churches (most of them by Wren) which followed the Union of City Benefices Act.

In short, the Church has destroyed eight times the number of City churches that Hitler's men have destroyed. And what Hitler's men merely damaged has, in many cases, been finished off by the type of men who sold the basement of St Mary Wool-noth in 1900, and were restrained with great difficulty, in 1928, from selling the rest of this noble Hawksmoor church.

There are several books which record the lost architectural treasures of London: only those with a thick skin should read them. For every Lord Riddell and Cyril Armitage, there are thousands of tax-subsidized Yahoos or 'developers' who like nothing better than to sever the material links with our past by sweeping away old buildings, especially if they are beautiful as well as historic. Yet, when the Drones decide to spare, with what wasteful and ridiculous excess they set about their exceptional 'saving'.

Beneath a vast white building, whose door bears upon its pediment two obese figures in what passes these days for sculpture, is a room of Tudor brick. The vast white building is part of a block of Government offices which have gone up between Whitehall and the River, their main entrance being in Whitehall Gardens. The Tudor room beneath them is the last surviving part of that splendid palace, White Hall, which was alienated from the See of York by Henry VIII when he deprived Cardinal Wolsey of the Great Seal in 1529.

The room is a large one—62 feet long, by 32 feet in width and 20 feet in height—and, when built, was a wine-cellar, at ground level, though it now lies 19 feet below the level of

Whitehall Gardens. The original brick-stillages on which the wine-casks rested are still in position within the great vaulted chamber.

With the Banqueting Hall, the old Wine Cellar was the only part of the palace of Whitehall to escape the fire of 1698 without damage; and though substantial fragments of Scotland Yard and other mediaeval buildings in Whitehall survived until well into the latter part of the eighteenth century, of the original White Hall, only the Wine Cellar remained—the Banqueting Hall being a later addition, by Inigo Jones.

After 1698, houses were erected on the site of the destroyed palace buildings, and into these the Wine Cellar was incorporated, the room serving, according to an official description sent to me, 'as a luncheon club for the occupying government department', until the demolition of the buildings in which the Wine Cellar was incorporated.

When it was built, though, the Wine Cellar was an intruder among buildings already not-so-new, and the Tudor room itself incorporates work of an earlier date, the east wall of the Wine Cellar being part of a late mediaeval structure against which the Tudor addition was built.

Let me quote the official summarized history.

'Parliament was given an undertaking before the 1939–45 war that in any development of the site the Cellar would be preserved, but on development the Cellar was found to interfere not only with the plan but also with the elevation of the new building.'

In simpler words, the 'developers' found that the Cellar was in their way.

'It was accordingly decided that the Cellar ... weighing approximately 1,000 tons, should be removed to a new position. The whole building was first moved 43 ft. 6 ins. laterally on a staging. It was then lowered by screw-jacks through a distance of 18 ft. 9 ins., and ultimately rolled back 33 ft. 10 ins. to its present position approximately beneath its original site.'

This modestly succinct account does less than justice to the elaborate engineering work involved in moving the Wine Cellar out of the way of 'development', and back to its former site.

'A huge excavation was first made, and here a giant platform of girders was erected, 60 feet long, 50 feet wide and 20 feet high'—thus Mr Harold Clunn. 'Then the cellar was embalmed in steel, brick and concrete to prevent damage. After that it was placed on mahogany cushions, carriage rails and two hundred special steel rollers. It was then shifted a quarter of an inch at a time until it had travelled 43 feet 5¾ inches and rested completely on the platform. Then the original site was excavated to a depth of twenty feet and a concrete floor laid for the cellar to rest again on the ground. By May 1949, nearly two and a half years after the work began, the cellar was rolled back and restored to its original position.'

Mr Clunn adds: 'This gigantic operation cost the Government £100,000.'

It cost the Government, of course, nothing—as the Government has no money with which to buy a tuppenny stamp; but perhaps Mr Clunn means that, in order to effect this laborious and unnecessary undertaking, the Government had to forgo the advantages of sending a troupe of Morris Dancers to perform, under the auspices of the British Council, before selected audiences of Kalmuck Tartars.

Even Mr Clunn does not seem to realize that it would have been cheaper and better merely to have left the cellar as it was.

Not a word is said, in all this description of How the Government Saved the Wine Cellar for the Nation, of the unpardonable destruction of Montagu House, the London palace of the Dukes of Buccleuch, whose demolition was involved in all this 'development'.

When Richmond Terrace is pulled down, as well as the length of houses, some of them of the eighteenth century, which connects Richmond Terrace with Bridge Street, it will be possible to complete the block of which New Scotland Yard forms part.

New Scotland Yard—so called because the first detective-office of the Metropolitan Police was established in Scotland-yard, in 1847—is probably the best-known institution of its kind in the world, not only as an institution, but also as a building. 'Everybody knows' the gloomy yet magnificent brownstone-and-brick edifice which lies between Whitehall and the Embankment, to which the description 'pile' seems so fittingly to apply.

New Scotland Yard is the work of one of the most interesting of our British architects: Norman Shaw, an artist whose taste was so eclectic that he failed to establish himself as a 'style', and so has been largely forgotten by the general public because his work is not easily recognized.

The Gaiety Theatre, which was his brilliant 'sub-editing' of a lesser architect's work, has gone; but the Queen Anne house that Shaw built in 1888 is still to be seen in Queen's Gate, and, of course, New Scotland Yard, though asymmetrical with 'classical' additions uncontemplated by Shaw, remains.

We are concerned with this Scottish baronial structure because of what still lies beneath it: the foundations—including the dressing-rooms—of a great National Theatre, of which the foundation stone was laid by the Duke of Edinburgh, Queen Victoria's sailor-son, on 16th December, 1875. This is the third National Theatre in recent times of which the site has been cleared—the Theatre never materializing. In this case, the site was cleared, and the foundations completed, from designs by Francis H. Fowler.

But work on the National Theatre had to be stopped owing to the fact that funds were not available from a nation of non-national-theatre-lovers; and in 1890 it was decided to erect, on the hardly-begun buildings of the Theatre, the new edifice to house the various departments of the Metropolitan Police.

I am indebted to Chief Superintendent W. C. F. Best, the officer whose unenviable task it is to keep the roads clear for London's traffic, for having pointed out to me that the old dressing-rooms of the National Theatre still lie beneath the grimly castellated battlements of Norman Shaw's Embankment donjon-keep, and that the names of the various dressing-rooms are still to be seen, in faded script, on the doors.

'An obol for Mithras!' said my brother, giving the little girl a sixpence.

It was a sunny day in Dorset, and we had driven along, passing the strip of Roman road that no one has ever dared to plough, past the towering wall of Bulbarrow Beacon, until we came to where the children, a boy and a girl, had set up their shrine by the roadside, under a hedge of flowering quickset. My brother had brought me to see this material evidence of the persistence of a 'dead' religion: a sort of beehive, with the front missing, moulded in fresh mud, and within it, a mud-moulded object which might have been the likeness of a man.

There were flowers placed around the 'beehive', and there were some shells stuck in the mud. As we drew up by the roadside, the little girl, approaching with outstretched hand, said: 'A penny for the Grotto, Mister!'

'An obol for Mithras!' said my brother. 'Dis Manibus!'

Here, where only the track of the Roman road reminds one of the Imperium, the children remember the God of the Roman Soldier. But, indeed, I need not have travelled so far to find the Old Faith still lingering on in the instinctive ritual of children.

In America, on Halloween, the children go from house-to-house, asking for a treat; in London, they do the same thing in connection with an old Fire Feast, 'Guy Fawkes' Day'.

But, though it is rarely heard now, the demand for a penny comes in the summer, too: round about 25th July:

> Please to remember the Grotter;
> It's on'y once a year;
> Father's gone to sea,
> And Mother's gone to fetch him back.
>
> So please remember me!
>
> A penny won't 'urt yer—
> Tuppence won't put yer in the workus!

The 'Grotter' itself—and here let me say that the *correct* pronunciation of 'grotto' is as the Cockney kids say it, and not the 'educated' *grottoh*—is usually a mud-house, decorated with oyster-shells; though sometimes it is a wooden box, shell-covered, not infrequently mounted on the rickety under-carriage of an old perambulator. Until oysters (on which Dr Johnson fed his cat, Hodge) were artificially contrived into a 'luxury', they were a common street-repast of the Cockney; and oyster-shells were common. One doesn't see so many of them now, when even pubs have the impudence to charge a shilling and more apiece for shaggy Portuguese.

Many writers, including the always fascinating Mr H. V. Morton, have been misled by the association of the shell with the Grotto, and have found the origin of the Grotto in the cult of St James of Compostella. The Grotto, not its decoration, is the important aspect of this strange survival. And the Grotto is the 'cave'—the *cella*—in which the God of the Cave, Mithras, was always worshipped.

> Father's gone to sea, and Mother's gone to fetch him back . . .

Better read these words as the rough translation of *'Pater ad cellam it'*; for no women were permitted to attend the Mithraic rites, and Mother could have gone to 'fetch him' only as far as the entrance.

In 1953, archaeological excavation enabled us to state exactly where that entrance was outside of which Mother would have had to wait.

The story of the discovery begins in 1884, when a sewer was laid at the side of the street now called Walbrook; the excavations for the sewer having necessitated the taking up of Bond Court, a small tributary of Walbrook, on the east side of the street. Five years later, a well-known Victorian collector, William Ransom, bought three pieces of Roman work from an East End dealer who specialized in dug-up relics. Ransom's questioning led him to believe (what later discovery has shown to be the fact) that the three pieces came from a site near Walbrook: almost certainly Bond Court.

These three Roman relics were a headless stone statue of the god Bonus Eventus, depicted as standing on the prow of a ship; the marble head and torso of a river god; and a stone slab showing the god Mithras slaying the Bull.

Assuming, as Ransom did, that these pieces had been dug up in London, and assuming further (again as Ransom did) that the three pieces had been dug up in close proximity to each other, the finds seemed to indicate that a temple had stood upon or near a bank of the Walbrook River, and that the temple was almost certain a *Mithraeum*.

It was left to the year 1954 to prove the correctness of Ransom's suppositions, which were by no means accepted, even by experienced archaeologists, since Ransom had never definitely established that the three sculptures had come from the Walbrook area, and a sculpture of Cautopates, one of the two minor divinities always shown as in attendance upon Mithras, was found in Drury Lane. This could have meant that there were—at least—two *Mithraea* in London; or it could have meant that the Cautopates found in Drury Lane and the Mithras bought by Ransom all belonged to one Mithraeum— and one not necessarily originally sited either in Drury Lane or Walbrook.

Post-war conditions, with over fifty acres of London-within-the-Wall flattened by German bombs or burnt out by German incendiary missiles, offered archaeology an opportunity unique in its history. In earlier City devastations, such as that, for instance, which resulted from the Great Fire of 1666, archaeology had not yet developed into a science, and so there was no organized archaeology to take advantage of the opportunity to excavate beneath the waste land. The fission and fusion bombs of future wars will lay much more than a mere fifty acres bare of buildings; but, on the other hand, they will probably exterminate the whole race of archaeologists.

Economic and financial considerations prevented archaeology from taking anything but a small advantage from the presence of so much 'excavable' London land; there was, for a start, no real money to clear the land of its accumulations of rubble, and to clear the basements and foundations of the bombed buildings, but something was done; and that something yielded important results.

On the initiative of the Society of Antiquaries of London, the Roman and Mediaeval London Excavation Council was formed in 1947 and, in the words of Professor Grimes: 'The Excavation Council set itself an all-embracing objective covering the post-Roman as well as Roman archaeology of the City.'

The Excavation Council—its officers all honorary, save for a small paid labour force—has worked in the closest collaboration with the staff of the Guildhall Museum, which has not only provided a worthy and permanent home for most of the finds, but has, through its skilled staff, repaired, evaluated, dated and described the finds, to the furthest extension of our knowledge of Roman and post-Roman London.

Two sites in the City yielded the most dramatic results: the Cripplegate area, where a hitherto unsuspected Roman fort was discovered; and the Walbrook area, where discoveries surpassing even that of the Cripplegate fort in interest were made.

Earlier finds in this area—I have noted one or two—had made it evident that the area around the Walbrook area was one of the most densely settled in Roman times: I have mentioned the finding of the tessellated floor under the predecessor of the National Safe Deposit Company's building in Poultry, which lies on the west bank of the Walbrook.

Archaeological work on the Walbrook area began in 1949, when a 'bombed site' between Walbrook and St Swithin's Lane, behind the Mansion House and St Stephen's Church, came to be cleared so that a large office-building could be erected.

The Excavation Council commenced their excavation of this extensive area the moment after the workmen had cleared away the rubble and the foundations of the bombed buildings, which included Salters' Hall.

This was not the only site in the City to have been excavated, but it is certainly the site which has been most rewarding. In the words of Mr Ivor Noel Hume, who took over the excavation of the Walbrook site after the resignation of Mr Adrian Oswald,

'the building operations have brought to light what is probably the largest quantity of Roman remains to be found in the City since the Bank of England excavations in 1934. The site was ideally placed archaeologically, for it covered part of the area that was probably the most thickly populated in Roman times.'

Domestic and toilet articles, a foot-rule, remains of buildings, vessels of pottery and bronze—all wonderfully preserved in the peat laid down by the flood waters of the Walbrook—were found; but what was most interesting was the great quantity of leather recovered, including an almost perfect Roman sandal. Did this suggest, as Mr Noel Hume thinks, the presence on the west bank of the Walbrook of Roman tanneries?

As I write, news comes from another part of the Walbrook. From the *Sunday Times* of 6th November, 1960, I extract this paragraph:

TUDOR DISCOVERY

Excavations under Finsbury Square, E.C., for the underground car park have unearthed what may be the most comprehensive assortment of Tudor leather work, including parts of shoes, a decorated scabbard, and various straps, yet found in London.

Whether or not the finds of Roman leather in the upper part of the Walbrook indicate the presence of Roman tanneries, that the leather-workers of London liked to set up their places of business beside the Walbrook seems to have been a custom which extended from Roman to Tudor times.

In 1952, it became clear that an opportunity would soon be

afforded to the Excavation Council of work on the site lying to the west of the modern street named Walbrook.

One point which was cleared up in the course of the second stage of the Walbrook area excavations was that the original river had been only some 12–14 feet in width, relatively shallow, being contained, in Roman times, within timber revetments. The bottom of the stream lay 32–35 feet below the modern street level, and some hundred feet to the west of the street now bearing the river's name.

Excavation presented considerable difficulty because of the presence of subterranean water; but here, again, the work was eminently rewarding. After the discovery of a tiny fragment of wall and a scrap of tessellated pavement in the north of the site, towards Bucklersbury, the great archaeological discovery of the post-war period took place.

Let me quote the words of the discoverer, Professor Grimes:

The first indications of this building presented themselves at an early stage in the most easterly cutting. By good fortune they appeared immediately under the cellar floor. As the section was deepened successive floors were uncovered. The latest of these (that is, the first to be encountered), was continuous over the whole surface; at a lower level earlier floors were associated with a sleeper wall aligned with the jamb of the apse, and carrying spaced-out concrete 'pads' or 'settings' for columns. On the limited view given by the cuttings, therefore, it was possible to decide that the building had originally been of basilican type—that is, a columned hall with at least one apsidal end—which in course of time had been remodelled internally by the removal of the columns and by the raising and re-laying of the floor to convert it into a single compartment.

On 14th June, 1954, *The Times* reported Professor Grimes's opinion that the building just uncovered in the excavations alongside of Walbrook had had a religious significance. As the remains were uncovered, this guess became a certainty. What had been discovered was no less than a temple of Mithras, a

Persian god whose cult, having made a great appeal to the Roman soldier, followed the legions to the further limits of the Imperium.

Mithras, the 'Bull-slayer', was the God of Light, and so was related to the Sun and the Moon. Statues of him, used in the Mithraic ritual, invariably show him in the act of killing the primaeval bull, 'representing in the minds of a pastoral community the strongest and most potent source of life and strength that they knew'.

Like the Sacrifice of Christianity, this Mithraic sacrifice was something enacted once and for all; and the worshippers of Mithras, like the worshippers of Christ, commemorated the Sacrifice in ritual symbolism. Mithraism resembled Christianity in its high moral teaching; and for long was a powerful rival to the religion of Christ, failing to conquer, in all probability, because the churches of Christendom threw open their doors to men and women of all ages, professions, classes and races, while Mithraism was even more selective than Judaism.

Mithraea have been found in many places in Britain—notably where the Roman soldier had a permanent encampment. Temples have been found in Housesteads and Carrawburgh, forts on Hadrian's Wall, at Colchester, Silchester and elsewhere; and, as I have noted, there is an indication that a Temple of Mithras may have stood in the neighbourhood of Drury Lane. But there was no doubt that the building uncovered to the west of Walbrook was the first complete and positively identified *Mithraeum* to have been found in London.

What made the identification possible was the finding, on 18th September, 1954, of the head of Mithras in the north-east corner of the nave—a discovery which was destined to make the site famous far beyond the relatively restricted interests of archaeology.

Further finds came quickly. On 26th September, Mrs Audrey Williams found what appeared at first sight to be the head of a youth, which was afterwards identified as that of the Roman goddess, Minerva. On the hyacinthine curls of this head a helmet was once placed. Near by, on October 4th, were found more pieces of statuary: the head of a bearded god, identified as the Egyptian god of the harvest, Serapis, by the modius, or corn-measure, worn as a head-dress; a huge stone hand clutching the pommel of a dagger; a reclining figure of Mercury; and a stone laver—for ritual baptism formed part of the ceremonies of Mithraism.

'The group of marbles as a whole', says Professor Grimes, 'is without parallel in Britain: all are of foreign workmanship. The Serapis particularly is in almost perfect condition; but Mithras, with the upturned eyes which shew that it was derived from a Bull-slaying, stands apart from the others in its sensitive rendering.'

Other finds—all confirming the nature of the building—were a fragmentary Cautopates, the attendant who stands on the left of Mithras, holding his torch downwards, to signify that Cautopates represents night and death; two fragmentary male torsos; part of another Bull-slaying, in limestone; and a small circular plaque 'representing a complex of Oriental deities of a type which occurs in Mithraic contexts on the continent'.

All these sacred objects had been hurriedly buried by the worshippers, as though under the immediate threat of trouble —no doubt from official Christianity. Yet, as the fact that at least two floors were laid after the sculptures had been deposited in their pits shows, the temple survived the trouble; and a stone block, set in position in the centre of the apse from an altar-base, has been dated to about the middle of the reign of Constantine the Great (A.D. 307–337). The temple was then in use at least as late as the first quarter of the fourth century.

Not all was clear when the site had been completely excavated: did the gigantic hand, for example, belong to an equally gigantic statue—one which, in proportion to the hand, must have stood at least eleven feet high?

But soon these academic questions were to pass beyond the limits of purely academic circles, and to become matters of discussion by the Man-in-the-Street. On 20th September, 1954, *The Times* carried a leader, 'A Temple for Destruction', and those who claim that *The Times* is read only by 'the Top People', must have wondered at the number of Top People who flocked to the site of the Temple of Mithras, after 'The Thunderer' had thundered against 'the bulldozing out of existence' of an important antiquity 'almost before it had been seen'.

In their tens and hundreds of thousands, Londoners queued up to see the devoted excavators at work; hoardings had to be erected to restrain the eager crowd from falling into the pit.

The building of the office-block, which was going ahead, was halted, so that people could see the Temple; and, at one time, eighty thousand Londoners stood patiently in a queue (in the rain), to be admitted to the railed-off space from which they could say, *Ave atque vale!* to the God who had once challenged Christ. For this was the Temple of Mithras right enough: Ransom's surmise of seventy years earlier had been vindicated in a manner which would have gladdened that notable amateur antiquary's heart.

But all things, as Pantagruel and his fellows found graven on the Temple of the Holy Bottle, move towards their end; and the end of the Temple of Mithras, though delayed these many centuries, was certain.

The proprietors of the land were willing to sell the site of the Temple to the public, but they wanted half a million pounds for it; and, much as London had come to love Mithras, it did not love Mithras to the extent of forking out £500,000 for him—the equivalent of one pint of mild ale per head of the population of Greater London. The Legenland Property Company Ltd. made the offer: London did not accept it.

The stones of the Temple were carefully uprooted, carted away, and reassembled in the disused churchyard of St John Baptist-upon-Walbrook. And here, in its new home, though the Temple was open to inspection by the public, it was as neglected and forgotten as though, for all the world, it had never been found beneath the rubble of bombed Walbrook. No one came to see it.

The Managing Director of the Legenland Property Company Ltd. was made a Commander of the Most Excellent Order of the British Empire for his generosity in having made the excavations possible, in having handed over to the Guildhall Museum the valuable objects which were found on his Company's land, and for having, at considerable cost to his Company, held up work on Bucklersbury House, so that the public might see the Temple.

Hagiologists may find cause for reflection in the fact that the Temple of Mithras—the God who once rivalled Christ for supremacy throughout the Roman world—has come to rest in the churchyard of the (equally neglected and abandoned) church of St John Baptist-upon-Walbrook.

How much remains to be discovered can be a matter only of conjecture. In this respect, I have been amongst the greatest pessimists; yet, when it seems that there can be nothing more to find and uncover, treasure trove reveals itself to confound the gloomy certainties of such as myself. For instance, workmen, recently clearing the site of what, up to the Reformation, had been the great abbey of St Mary of Graces, east of Tower Hill, found the lead-wrapped corpse of Lady Anne Mowbray, buried in the chapel in the 15th century. There was much outcry because the surgeons, somehow claiming the five-hundred-year-old body of Lady Anne—she was only thirteen when she died—proceeded to 'anatomize' the relic in all the fine old tradition of Barber-Surgeons Hall.

Now that London has been deprived of its position as one of the world's oldest and greatest ports, the demolition of the vast areas of warehouses and other buildings adjoining the doomed docks (themselves to be filled in and overbuilt) may reveal treasures unguessed at when I first began to plan this book, and when the doom of London the Port had not yet been officially pronounced.

12. Each in his Narrow Cell . . .

WHEN, to build his 'window on the West', Peter the Great cleared, on the marshy banks of the Neva, the site of a great city, so many men died in the task of raising Petersburg upon the marsh, that it was said of Petersburg that 'it was a city whose foundations are the bones of the dead'.

In a larger—and even more literal—way, the same remark may be made of London. There are still many of the old burial-grounds to be seen, scattered about London and Westminster: but, until the middle of the last century, almost every London church had its cemetery: quiet places where, for all that Dickens so contemptuously deplored the churches and their churchyards, the City clerk could rest—eat his paper-lunch or read a book—during the mid-day break. For there were trees as well as tombs in these churchyards; and, indeed, the trees are still there, though most of the tombs have gone.

It is interesting to see what has happened to the tombstones: when the tombs have been emptied of their bones—which, after a 'faculty' has been granted by the Bishop of London, are removed for burial in some out-of-London Metropolitan Cemetery—the tombstones are not always destroyed. Some are used to flank walls in orderly ranks, as has happened in the churchyard of Chelsea North Church, in Sydney Street. Some fulfil a purely utilitarian function, as those—dating from the end of the seventeenth century—which paved the garden of a house that I once had in Chelsea.

Others are left *in situ*, as in the little burial ground at the corner of Bream's Buildings and Fetter Lane: on one of these tombstones you may see a child's name, spelt 'Samewell', proof that the pronunciation of his own son's name by Mr Weller was no invention of Dickens, but a survival of a London pronunciation testified, by this Fetter Lane tombstone of 1633, as having been established at least two hundred years.

We saw how, in Fen Court, the family vault of the Westons —a mere cenotaph now—still stands in the paved-space walled in by modern skyscrapers. There are many such empty tombs in London, and there was a time, hardly a century ago, when many people could have wished that there were more.

Burial within the church was a practice prompted by a mixture of superstitious piety, vainglory and a sort of posthumous-practical desire to guard the tomb from rifling by the grave-robbers. It was a practice which went against all the strict Roman urban laws; against, indeed, all the counsels of hygiene and common convenience.

The accounts of the stenches which used to rise from the floors of the City churches—Dickens has much to say on this subject—are too many and too detailed that we should doubt that City congregations must have had to put up with far worse things than a droning sermon, when they went to church.

Few, indeed, of the tombs that one sees on the surface are now harbouring their dead; though the ancient slab-tombs have corpses beneath them. And there are many dead, lying in London's earth, whose place of sepulture is marked by no stone. Some, indeed, have neither earth to cover them or coffin in which to lie: among them, the mummified body of the man known as 'Old Jimmy', who is a sort of perpetual incumbent of the crypt of the still-awaiting-repair church of St James Gar-lickhithe, the church to which the Vintners go in procession each year, their seniors wearing the crowns peculiar to the dignity of this important Mistery.

But where lie the bodies of the three great regicides: Oliver Cromwell, Ireton and Bradshaw?

The history of Cromwell's head has been fairly accurately charted—after having remained for long, mouldering on a spike above Westminster Hall, it was blown down in a high wind, and picked off a street pavement by a doctor.

In the *Morning Chronicle* of 18th March, 1799, the following notice was printed:

THE real embalmed head of the powerful and renowned usurper, OLIVER CROMWELL, with the original dies for the medals struck in honour of his victory at Dunbar, are now exhibited at No. 5, in Mead Court, Old Bond Street (*where the rattlesnake was shewn last year*) [author's italics]; a genuine narrative relating to the acquisition, concealment and preservation of these articles to be had at the place of exhibition.

The 'exhibitor' was a man named Cole, who had purchased the head from a member of the Russell family. When Cole dispersed his collection of 'curiosities', he sold the head three times, the object coming back into Cole's possession each time that the purchaser met a sudden death. The daughters of the last owner, 'being nervous at the idea of keeping in the house a relic so fatal', sold it to 'a medical man named Wilkinson'. It is now supposed to be in a Norfolk vicarage.

But what of the bodies of Cromwell and the others? It is certain that they lie buried—unless they have been moved since 1660—in the little garden of Red Lion Square, through the western edge of which a new road has been driven to connect Theobalds Road with High Holborn.

When Oliver Cromwell died in 1658, he died as a king, and was buried as a king. In his cabinet were found samples of the coins which, had he lived, would have been issued. The legend on these coins talks of him as 'Protector, by the Grace of God', and his head is crowned with the laurel. The reverse of the coin shows the new arms of Great Britain, bearing an escutcheon of pretence quartering Cromwell and Bourchier (his noblewoman wife), crowned with the Imperial Crown.

Louis XIV ordered his court into mourning; and every Prince in Europe sent a special ambassador to represent him at the funeral procession which carried Oliver to his tomb in Westminster Abbey, to be buried among the Kings of England. This funeral was tricked out with all the panoply of a royal burying, the corpse of Oliver being mantled in an imperial robe of ermine-trimmed yellow.

As soon as the Restoration became an accomplished fact, the bodies of Cromwell, Ireton and Bradshaw were dragged from their graves, they were 'tried' at Westminster Hall [There are some curious minor 'repeat patterns' in that master repeat-pattern, History. Oliver's great-uncle tried a man posthumously for High Treason—Thomas à Becket—for 'rebellion against the King'.], condemned to the deaths of regicides, and—save that the condemned men were already dead—the sentences were carried out. They were hanged, drawn, disembowelled and decapitated.

The record states that the bodies, after having been dis-interred at Westminster, were dragged on sledges to Tyburn and, after hanging till sunset, were cut down and beheaded; that their bodies were flung into a hole at the foot of the gallows, and their heads fixed upon poles on the roof of West-minster Hall.

A difficulty in the narrative has been found in the statement that the bodies were dragged to the Red Lion Inn, in Holborn (after which Red Lion Square was named). Why drag them, *east*, to Holborn, when they were due to go, *north-west*, to Tyburn?

The difficulty is resolved if we remember that the word 'Tyburn' applied—as I have already mentioned—to any place of execution; and that there were two such well-used 'Tyburns' near the Red Lion Inn: one at the extremity of St Giles's parish, near the present Tottenham Court Road; the other at the Holborn end of Fetter Lane.

That Cromwell and the others were 'executed' at either of these eastern 'Tyburns' would account for the fact that the bodies of Cromwell, Ireton and Bradshaw were brought in carts, on the night previous to their exposure on the gibbet, to the Red Lion Inn in Holborn, 'where they rested during the night'.

When the bodies were cut down, the Royal prerogative of quartering, and sending the quarters to be exhibited in various places of the kingdom (George IV was the last sovereign to decline this prerogative) was not exercised; and the corpses were buried in what is now Red Lion Square, then a convenient field at the back of the Red Lion Inn.

The odd fact about this burial of the regicides is that they *did* have their tombstone—or, at least, their memorial. A mysterious obelisk used to stand in Red Lion Square, which bore only this baffling legend, cut in the stone:

OBTUSUS OBTUSIORUM INGENII MONUMENTUM
QUID ME RESPICIS, VIATOR?
VADE

If the 'apothecary' to whom local legend credited the erection of this enigmatical obelisk was a man named Ebenezer Heathcote, then the cryptic legend must refer to what—or those who—lie buried beneath. It has been established that this apothecary, who was living at King's Gate, Holborn, soon after the Restoration, had married the daughter of one of Ireton's subcommissaries.

No bodies have been reported as having been found beneath the earth of the garden in Red Lion Square. Perhaps they are there to this day. When—and if—they are found, we shall know whose bodies they are.

That line on Cromwell's monument—*Quid me respicis, Viator?*—recalls another inscription, this time to be found beneath London's surface. On a plain stone-slab, cemented into the wall above a tomb cut in the floor:

SUBTUS CONDITUR
HUJUS ECCLESIAE ET URBIS CONDITOR
CHRISTOPHORUS WREN
QUI VIXIT ANNOS ULTRA NONAGINTA
NON SIBI SED BONO PUBLICO
LECTOR, SI MONUMENTUM REQUIRIS
CIRCUMSPICE!

'... who lived upwards of ninety years, serving not himself, but the Common Good. Reader: do you seek his monument? Then look around you!'

There are nobler tombs in the crypt of St Paul's Cathedral—
though few nobler epitaphs.

And why, as the legend asks so clearly, should Wren have
a more impressive memorial than the plain stone slab on the
wall, and the plain stone slab covering his tomb? His monument, grander than anything any more vainglorious man could
desire, lies all around him: covers him, overshadows, laps him
around.

Both the St Paul's Cathedrals—Old and New—are to be
found in this huge, white-walled crypt, in which so many of
Britain's Great Names are buried. Here, for the curious and
reflective visitor, are the mortuary fashions of five centuries—
from the mid-Elizabethan tomb of

NICOLAVS: BACON: EQ: AUR: OB 1579

—he was father to the great Sir Francis Bacon, Lord Verulam—
to the equally plain (though infinitely more moving) inscription on a small wall-tablet:

PILOT OFFICER
WILLIAM MEADE LINDSLEY
FISKE III
Royal Air Force
An American Citizen
Who Died
That England Might Live
August 18 1940

Above the tablet, in a small glass case, are a pair of faded-
cloth pilot's 'wings'.

But surely it is not by accident that, from the opposite wall,
the face of W. E. Henley looks down on the simple record of
Mr Fiske's short but perfected life. Henley's love of England
was a passion—with him, patriotism was not, in Johnson's
cynical phrase, 'the last refuge of a scoundrel', but rather the
last guerdon of a poet. As with many another passion, this
passion of Henley's led him often into bitterness, not infrequently into narrowness: in loving England too much, he loved

other lands too little. He was no lover of the United States of America.

It is fitting, then, that, in a corner of this crypt which houses so much of England's fame, the great drama of reconciliation is played out, in silence, hour after hour, with two such protagonists: 'England-my-England' Henley and Pilot-officer William Meade Lindsley Fiske III, 'who died that England might live'.

Here they all are: the great captains, the great poets, the great painters, the great architects.

Depending upon the taste of their executors, their tombs are as plain as that of the jaunty Beatty—just a name beneath a naval crown—or as elaborate as that of the austerely-living Wellington: his grand tomb is upstairs, in the nave; but here, in the crypt, is the vast carriage, made from melted-down French guns and weighing eighteen tons, which carried his coffin from Chelsea Hospital to St Paul's.

Jellicoe—the admiral son of a merchant-captain—struck us as no figure to inspire men to enduring sentiment. Yet here, on his plain tomb, are wreaths from men who, the cards say, 'had the honour of serving in his flagship'.

There are the good craftsmen, who achieved only a lifetime recognition, among those whose fame has survived their death: there are Blake, Landseer, Millais, Sargent, but there are also Randolph Caldicott, Wilson Steer, Muirhead Bone, Poynter and the American Royal Academician—one out of many— Edwin Austin Abbey.

For every Arthur Sullivan, there are dozens of now forgotten musicians: all good, and all rightly recognized in their day.

Yet no one here—though he be but a mere lieutenant of infantry—has got in under false pretences. There is the great Horatio, Viscount Nelson, and—great in a different (and some would say a nobler) fashion—Sir Alexander Fleming, F.R.S., the man who gave the world penicillin. Arthur, Duke of Wellington, has his pompous burial carriage here (though the man who slept on a three-foot iron bed would never have countenanced such show), and there is a plaque to Sir George

Williams, the St Paul's Churchyard linen-draper who established an empire of a different kind when, in 1844, he founded the Young Men's Christian Association.

They should all be here: for this, more than any other place, is England's testimony to those who, each in his fashion, have striven to contribute something towards her greatness, whether by war or peace.

A place has been made within this crypt for the new chapel of the Most Excellent Order of the British Empire; and already there is something outdated, and so anomalous, about the Order's title. But whatever that Empire develops into; no matter how it change in pattern and aim; the men who lie here in this crypt, famous and not-so-famous, will all have had some hand in the shaping of that pattern.

It is true that Westminster's 'Honour' is a Dukedom, though few of the hundreds of thousands who live within this most prosperous of Great London's many boroughs think of it as 'the Dukedom of Westminster'.

The reason for Westminster's being called a 'city' is that, in 1541, the abbey-church of St Peter—'Westminster Abbey'—was elevated into a bishop's see; and thereupon Westminster became a city. Ten years later, the new see of Westminster was abolished—but Westminster did not 'revert to its substantive rank'. It had enjoyed the rank of a city for ten years, and it was not going to resign the privilege. A 'city' it has remained ever since—a city without a bishop, just as Horthy's Hungary was a kingdom without a king.

About Westminster there has always been a touch of that not-quite-what-it-seems—and this is true, too, of the famous Abbey itself. It is certainly an old building, even allowing for the fact of several 'restorations' which were practically complete re-buildings.

Of the Saxon church that Edward the Confessor—who still lies in his despoiled shrine within the Abbey—built on the site of Sebert's and Mellitus's early seventh-century chapel, little remains. Some foundation stones, possibly an arch, a few of

the lower courses in the cloisters, and a low, dark passage:
these are all which may be stated, with any certainty, to
remain of the Abbey which was consecrated on 6th January,
the Feast of the Epiphany, 1065.

There is, indeed, little to see of the Abbey, from the outside, which is of any great antiquity: the two great western
towers, which are the most recognizable architectural characteristic of the Abbey are mid-eighteenth-century work, from
designs by Wren; and so much of the outer stonework has had
to be replaced—stone suffering greatly from London's sulphur-
laden air—that very little of the exterior stonework is original.

The rose window above the north door was rebuilt in 1722,
and a great part of the north transept was likewise rebuilt in
1828.

On the other hand, though this great church, like all the
others in England, was deprived of its relics and treasures of
gold and silver at the Reformation, and suffered, like all the
others, at the hands of the iconoclast, not only under Henry
VIII, but under Cromwell, in the next century, the Abbey is
still extremely rich in antiquities: perhaps not precious to the
goldsmith (which is why they were spared) but precious to the
artist and the archaeologist.

The tombs of the kings buried here have been rifled,
'officially' and 'unofficially', but their royal occupants are still
within them.

The only king buried here to suffer the indignity of being
moved from his tomb—because he was a Saint as well as a
King—was Edward the Confessor; but when, in the reign of
Mary Tudor, he was moved back to the shrine from which all
the gold and jewels had been stripped, he was not moved again,
though, on various occasions his coffin was opened.

But it is with the underparts of the Abbey that we are concerned in this book.

Our monarchs are no longer buried in Westminster Abbey,
but after the Restoration, while the custom of burial within the
Abbey was still practised for royal personages, they were buried

within vaults, and no longer in tombs within the body of the church.

In a vault in the south aisle are buried, in this fashion, Charles II, William III, Mary, William's Consort and Co-Sovereign, Queen Anne and her husband, Prince George of Denmark. In the 'new' royal vault, between the knights' stalls in the Henry VII Chapel, are buried George II and Caroline, his Queen, as well as their son and daughter-in-law, the Prince and Princess of Wales, two Dukes of Cumberland, the Duke of York, Prince Frederick William, and the Princesses Amelia, Caroline, Elizabeth, Louisa and Anne.

The crypt beneath the ancient Chapter House—which was once the depository of the regalia of the Scottish kings, and the treasury of England—was, in past times, the chapel of the Chapter House. The underground parts of the Abbey are not only in good condition; generally, they have escaped that mis-guided 'restoration' which has so changed the character of much of the work above.

But, though you may see the Royal Waxworks in Abbot Islip's Chapel, and see the great names on the tombstones which crowd the Abbey itself, there is nothing in the Abbey's crypts but silence and that not-oppressive sense of great age.

When Emma Hamilton was servant to Mr Dane (they say that the film of her romantic life was almost Stalin's favourite), she lived in Littlington Tower, one of the Abbey's older parts. One may imagine that the crypt of the Abbey, as deserted then as now, could have afforded the gallant Emma a handy place of assignation.

There are no legends of treasure buried in the vaults of the Abbey; though, in 1871, a treasure was found in nearby Tothill Street.

The 'Cock and Tabard' had once been a fashionable tavern, much frequented by the gentlemen of the Court; but, in its latter days, like most of the older houses of Westminster, it had suffered a sad decline. In 1871, it was pulled down, and the rest of the thieves' kitchen into which Tothill Street had degenerated was swept away. But, when the workmen were clearing away the rubbish-heap in the tavern's back-yard—an unseemly accumulation little older than the tavern itself—they found a hoard of rich silver plate, which proved to be worth many thousands of pounds. The quality of the silver showed it to have been the property of some great nobleman or churchman; and it is assumed that the thieves had hidden it in the midden, intending to return for it 'when the coast was clear'. Seized while executing some other villainy, they never returned, and the plate lay there, to be found only when the 'Cock and Tabard' was demolished centuries later.

Considering how much treasure was collected by the King's Commissioners at the Reformation, the ecclesiastical wealth of England must have been very great, for there is strong evidence that the Commissioners—who travelled slowly around the country, and thus gave ample warning of their visitations—missed much of treasure that the owners had time to hide.

Traces of the lost treasure of Westminster Abbey were, in fact, found in 1878, at a time when the development of London's sewers, water-supply and Underground railways entailed a lot of digging, and thus an opportunity to turn up the remains of the past.

A valuable discovery of mediaeval church plate, much of it, jewel-encrusted and of the richest kind, was made when some old buildings were being demolished in Long Acre. Now 'Long Acre' was the 'long acre' which bounded Covent (originally 'Convent') Garden, and this property was a possession, up to the Reformation, of the Benedictine monks of Westminster.

When the workmen had cleared the old building away, the foundations of an older were found beneath. No archaeologist was present to record or identify these older buildings; but that they were originally part of an ecclesiastical structure, there can be little doubt. Within a cellar in these older buildings the workmen came across a great wooden chest, banded with iron, which, for all that it had been buried in the clay for three hundred years, was in good condition.

In his book *Buried Treasure*, Charles Quarrell has described how, when the workmen had failed to lift the chest to ground level, they broke it open and discovered a solid, glittering mass of precious metal, stones and coins. The fact that none of the coins was of a later date than Henry VIII supported the theory that the chest may have been the property of the Abbey. Besides some magnificent gold plate, it contained a bishop's or abbot's mitre and crozier, a chain, cross and episcopal ring, and a set of church vessels, including a chalice or ciborium and a jewel-encrusted cross.

It is supposed that this hoard was taken from the Treasury at Westminster, and hidden by the monks, to keep it out of the hands of the Commissioners. (It is an odd freak of circumstance that, three hundred years later, it did get into the hands of the Crown.)

A famous London treasure which, apparently, has no such ecclesiastical connection is the renowned 'Cheapside Treasure', found when some workmen were digging the foundations for new premises at the corner of Wood Street and Cheapside in 1912. Sixteen feet or so beneath the present street-level, the workmen came across the contents of a large wooden box, the wood having perished, leaving only the hinges and handles behind. When the contents were brought to the surface, it was apparent that the finders had here what must have been pretty well the entire stock-in-trade of a jeweller of late Elizabethan or early Jacobean times.

Later digging found other pieces; though there is some mystery in the manner in which the City authorities handled this important find. No Coroner's inquest was ever held, and attempts were made to keep the carefully-recorded details of the treasure from the Press.

The explanation of this decision not to hold a Coroner's inquest came later from Dr Waldo, the City Coroner. He explained that the find did not belong to the Crown, but to the Lord Mayor and Commonalty of the City of London. By the time that Dr Waldo explained all this, the treasure had been moved to the London Museum, and was thus safely out of his power to have it called back. It is now divided among the

London Museum, the Guildhall Museum and the British Museum.

The *Illustrated London News*, in its Ladies' Supplement of July 1914, published a coloured plate, showing fifty-two of the pieces recovered, and specimens from the 'Cheapside Treasure' have also been illustrated, again in colour, in the pages of *The Saturday Book*.

This treasure of a Cheapside jeweller which was found brings up another Cheapside jeweller's treasure, which was never found, despite the efforts both of Samuel Pepys and a party of volunteers from the Speleological Society. Pepys's own practice tells us how such treasure comes to be where we find it: when the Great Fire threatened a break-down of order, Pepys buried his money in the garden of his father-in-law's house in Bethnal Green.

The treasure that Pepys sought was supposed to have been hidden in the Tower of London by Colonel Barkstead, whom Cromwell had made Lieutenant of the Tower. Barkstead, in civil life, was a wealthy Cheapside jeweller; and—so the story goes—he added to his wealth, while Lieutenant of the Tower, by the uncivil practice of extracting money from the state prisoners placed under his care. Barkstead was one of the regicides and, though he prudently made his escape to Holland on the Restoration, he was brought back, tried, sentenced, and hanged, drawn and quartered.

That was the end of Barkstead. It was not, however, the end of all official interest in him. Barkstead was executed in July 1662: in the following October, Pepys was summoned by his cousin and patron, Lord Sandwich, and informed that Barkstead had hidden a treasure worth £7,000 in the Tower. The informant, a Mr Wade, of Axe Yard, was to have £2,000 for having reported the treasure; Lord Sandwich was to have another £2,000 for having listened to Wade and having carried the story to the King; and the King himself was to have the remaining £3,000. Sandwich had obtained the King's warrant for Pepys's searching out the hidden money.

The search was made 'in the cellars' of the Tower, under the

Bell Tower; but the treasure was never found. Three hundred years later, Colonel E. H. Carkeet James, O.B.E., M.C., Tower Major and Resident Governor, gave the Speleological Society permission to search for the Barkstead Treasure; but though they were provided with electrical metal-detectors of which Pepys had never dreamed, the speleologists were as unsuccessful as the Great Diarist had been.

The Crown Jewels of France, too, have never been found; though much rebuilding has taken place in Pall Mall, a house in which Madame du Barry, mistress of Louis XV, took lodgings when she came to England in 1792 may survive.

It is known that she came to this country bringing with her several outstanding pieces of the French royal treasure, to raise money for the counter-revolutionary 'underground'. In the following year, she returned to France; and, as she was carefully—not to say, indelicately—searched on her arrival in France, it is certain that she was carrying no more with her than her travelling expenses and a few private papers. She was guillotined on 7th December, 1793; and the secret of the Crown Jewels' hiding-place died with her.

I open my *Evening Standard*, and read this story:

Man digs up gold coin minted during Roman invasion
BUT HE WON'T SELL TO BRITISH MUSEUM

A dirty, bent disc dug up in an Acton garden has turned out to be a valuable gold coin struck more than 1900 years ago. At first company director Mr Richard T. L. Hands dismissed his find as an emblem of some kind. He put the disc in his trouser pocket and went on digging the garden at his Creswick Road home, preparing the soil for some prize dahlias. But his biggest prize was in his pocket and he did not know it.

The gold coin bears the shortened names of Cunobelinus and of his capital, Camulodunum.

I read of an urn full of rose-nobles, found when workmen

were digging a trench for a water pipe. And there must be many such finds of which neither I nor you will ever read.

Even in places where 'they know every foot', finds of rooms are often made. It was as late as 1894 that the old dungeons of the Collegiate Church in the Tower of London were discovered and opened up. There was no treasure within them; but they were enough of a treasure in themselves.

How many Pepyses were there, who buried their treasure in the face of some disaster? And how many were overtaken by death before they might recover what had been buried?

Common-sense gives the answer to both those questions as thousands. We shall never finish writing the record of treasure lost and treasure found.

13. Miscellanea Subterranea

IF, like the hero of Le Sage's novel, we were given the power to see, not through the roofs of the houses, but through the road and pavement of our great City, what should we see? In one respect, more than the past could ever have shown; in another respect, less. We dig deep, as well as build high; but our basements are being used more and more for commercial, and less for domestic, purposes.

A book much larger than this might be written on what has been done in basements and cellars. It was in a cellar that the vile Mrs Brownrigg whipped her girl-apprentices to death. Authority had more trouble with the crowd than with the sadistical murderess, who would have gone quietly to the scaffold had the mob only let her. It was with great difficulty that Mrs Brownrigg was got safely to her hanging.

Then again, it was in a cellar that mousy little Dr Crippen—for ever famous as the first man to be caught by wireless telegraphy (as Thurtell was the first man to be apprehended by land-line telegraphy)—buried, not so much the remains of his wife, as the unassailable evidence by which he was later to be convicted.

It was under the kitchen floor that the Mannings—also apprehended by the electric telegraph—buried their victim, O'Connor.

When I was younger, all sorts of minor naughtinesses took place—or were reputed to take place—in cellars, fitted out either as 'tea-rooms' or 'clubs', though the greater naughtiness was always attributed to the 'tea-rooms'.

Certainly, a City tea-room was closed down after it had been shown that something more than tea was sold there: and how the discovery came about has its ludicrous side. Into this respectable-looking cellar tea-room went a country housewife, intent upon a refreshing cup of tea. She asked for it and got it. But the foolish waitress could not discriminate between the house-wife and her regular customers, and insisted that the lady pay the usual five shillings which, ordinarily, purchased more than a solitary pot of tea.

Under protest, the lady paid and, full of indignation, com-plained of 'robbery' to the first policeman whom she encoun-tered. The policeman had no interest in profiteering, against which there is no law: but his curiosity was sufficiently aroused for him to wonder why they charged five shillings for tea. The tea-room was closed down.

In Victorian times, an ancient tradition, was still being per-petuated: the tradition of subterranean jollification. That it is ancient is attested by the verb *fornicare*; for just as 'to contem-plate' is to think deeply, as one might in a temple; and 'to consider' is to think deeply, as one might under *sidera*, the stars; 'to fornicate' is to behave as people often do under arches —cellars—vaults—*fornices* in Latin.

The cellar-tavern probably reached its apogee in that Alsatia which developed out of the disestablished monastic founda-tions: all abbeys and, indeed, most mediaeval buildings, had extensive cellarage; and though the crumbling ruins might be patched up above, or even rebuilt, the cellars remained intact—just the thing for intimate conviviality, such as was loved of the Alsatians who set Authority at defiance for close on two centuries.

That the noisome dens of Whitefriars bounded the Temple, the centre of English legality, only made the scandal worse; but it was a scandal that time, and not Authority, had to abolish.

We know the name of one of the most notorious of the riverside 'clubs' of seventeenth-century Alsatia: the 'Bucket of Blood'. It had not one but many openings through its floor on to the River, and robbery of the too intrepid visitor was merely the traditional prelude to his murder.

When Alsatia, at last, was deprived of its legally terminated 'sanctuary', the eighteenth century developed a taste for classical music at concerts given in coal-cellars. (Thomas Britten, the Singing Coal-Man, entertained his guests in a room *above* his coal-yard; but most of the coal-cellars were downstairs.)

The prohibition of cock-fighting opened up the underground cockpit; but the generation which succeeded were more interested in another sort of bird; and the underground Singing Rooms, such as are associated with the names of Evans and 'Chief Baron' Nicholson came into fashion.

Nicholson, who adopted the style of 'Chief Baron' so that he could preside over the mock-trials (almost always for divorce based on the evidence of 'crim. con.', or 'criminal connection') that he staged night after night in his famous dive, 'The Coal-Hole' (observe the name), made a fortune from his Judge-and-Jury entertainments. The Victorians loved them; and though Nicholson was often before the courts—for debt as well as for indecency—it was observed that the bailiff and even the learned magistrate addressed him as 'Baron' or 'My Lord'.

The most famous of the 'respectable' Victorian underground haunts of the *bon vivant* was Romano's, about which Mr Guy Deghy has written a whole book. Romano's was not originally an underground restaurant-and-bar, but a small Italian restaurant in the Strand, of the type from which Gatti's started, and from which Pratti's never strayed. However, success came to Romano, mostly through his having attracted the raffish set of sporting-journalists—some of them connected with the Best Families—who made up the staff of the *Pink 'Un*.

If one may mix one's colours a little, a job on the editorial staff of the *Pink 'Un* was the *cordon bleu* of 'downiness', so far as a journalist was concerned.

I remember the last days of the *Pink 'Un*—I remember what a dog I felt when I bought my first copy, and flicked it negligently open on the counter of Birch's, while I called for an eightpenny dry sherry and a penny spiced bun. Good lord! I couldn't have puzzled more over the *Pink 'Un*'s cryptic contents on that far-off day than I puzzled only last week, when I turned up an old file. I looked in vain for the smut with which each Victorian youth, and many a Victorian woman, were certain the *Pink 'Un* was stuffed.

I realize now what Colonel Newnham-Davis, its staff 'gourmet', and all the other Pink 'Uns realized sixty, seventy years ago: that no one ever found any smut in the *Pink 'Un*, because it wasn't ever there to find.

What a fool-proof racket: to sell a journal as indecent, and because it is held to be indecent, whose contents not even a Chartres Biron could fault!

Romano's is gone: but it took a depressingly long time to die.

A shoe-shop now stands on the site: it is called Romano House.

Romano's was always 'respectable', even when the Pink 'Uns livened up the place with their characteristic horse-play; but there were other underground places which, as frequented by the Idle Rich, were not so well-conducted.

One such was the old Alsatia, popular with young Guards officers of the just-post-Ouida period. A friend of mine who, as a subaltern in the Scots Guards, used to go often to the Alsatia, once told me how, on a particularly boisterous night at the Alsatia, Frank Otter had arrived with an outstandingly beautiful strumpet, more than whose company at the Alsatia he was unable to afford. What was more, he was in debt to the lady.

'So Frank told her to take all her clothes off, and get up on a table. There she was, without a stitch on—and, by Jove!, she was a stunner! "Now, gentlemen," says Frank, "you all observe this delectable filly. I can't afford her—but some of *you* can. I'll start the bidding at five guineas!" And, d'you know, that blessed tart was auctioned there and then. My goodness! how we all laughed.'

I passed up Whitcomb Street the other day, and saw, painted over a pair of tall doors, this legend:

The Rt. Hon. Lord Sandhurst and the Hon. R. Mansfield Licensed to Sell Wines, Spirits and Tobacco for Consumption Off the Premises

Behind those tall doors there is a cobbled yard, and in this cobbled yard there is—or was, some years ago—a trapdoor, leading to an underground room. When I first visited this underground room, it had been fitted up as a bar; and my memory of the 'club' is that it was the most respectable place that I have ever visited. Why on earth one should have had to clamber down a vertical ladder to drink pale ale at a penny over the odds, I did not know then, nor can guess now; but there was no wickedness in this place, for all the exciting promise of its unusual approach.

Then there were the subterranean tea-rooms, fitted up in the coal-cellars of old houses in Jermyn Street and the other parts of St James's. I recall tea in 'The Tea-Rooms of the East', in Jermyn Street, with a lady who is now a famous film actress: here, again, was dreary respectability, for all the Benares brass and the whiff of joss-sticks. Another tea-room of the subterranean kind, in Agar Street, was reputed to be something more than a tea-room, but, if it was, I never found out to what lengths of depravity the management went. It seems to me, looking back, that it was what we *expected*—and never, by any chance, got—which made these places so tempting and frequented.

I mentioned, earlier in the book, Mrs Meyrick, whose daughter married Lord de Clifford; other daughters marrying Lord Craven and Lord Kinnoull—excellent titles, all of them.

Mrs Meyrick was the Night Club Queen of the Twenties; and her most famous 'club' was 'The Forty-three', at 43, Gerrard Street—now the offices of *The Tailor and Cutter*.

Mrs Meyrick has only recently been re-written-up for the hundredth time; with each re-writing, she becomes less and less as I remember her: a plain, plump woman, with knotty bow-legs and untidy hair above a round Irish peasant's face.

One went to 'The Forty-three' to dance with the 'hostesses', and buy drinks at about double the usual price, and cigarettes (always Players, I remember) at half-a-crown for twenty, instead of the statutory eleven-pence-halfpenny.

The only sign of 'wickedness' that I saw were the packets of condoms which were pinned up to the partition of rough-planking which divided the 'Gents'' from the grimy wash-hand basin over which the bored attendant presided.

Sometimes we were raided, and that meant an appearance next morning at Marlborough Street Court, when the Magistrate, 'Freddy' Mead, handed out fines of a pound or two; and we all trooped back to 'The Forty-three' (looking unbelievably dingy in the first light of a London day) to 'celebrate'.

If only our parents had known how innocently we spent our nights! How difficult—almost impossible—it was made for us to fall into serious trouble!

The 'clubs' are still there, of course; but a different class of person now frequents them. I dare say that the present type of club-frequenter is less naïve; he wants (and probably gets) more value for his money.

One memory comes back to me: a night in the Jermyn Street brasserie of the Criterion, an hour or so after the Alhambra had closed down. Now the promenade of the Alhambra was the mincing-place of London's catamites, young and old; and, to take a farewell of the Alhambra, they had turned out in force. Hannen Swaffer was at this famous old music-hall on the closing night and, in the following morning's *Daily Herald*, he protested as vigorously against the nancies as they had protested against the closing-down of their gathering-place.

After the Alhambra—though not without a cheer from the Queers—had closed down for good, this huge hissing of ingles wandered over to the 'Cri.' to hold an overflow meeting in the below-ground brasserie. It was rather alarming: for the uranians took over—as they always do, when in numbers. (It is for that reason, and not for reasons of 'morality', that they are suppressed in Russia.)

Famous old queers of pre-world-war-one vintage had emerged from retirement for this sad occasion; and 'Maud Allan', 'Madge Titheradge', and 'Gladys Cooper' were tottering from table to table greeting painted friends. It was a sad occasion, in more senses than one.

The underground theatre would seem naturally to belong

to an age which liked underground restaurants and bars; but, if contemporary reports are to be believed, the opening of the underground Criterion Theatre in March 1874, aroused considerable interest.

This theatre is all underground, even those holding tickets for the gallery having to descend steps to reach their seats. This, all the same, was no innovation: both the Olympic and the (old) Gaiety Theatres, which were built back-to-back between the Strand and Holywell Street, being underground.

Today, there seems to be a revival of the practice of building places of entertainment beneath the surface: the new Royal Theatre, in Kingsway, built upon the site of that masterpiece of Standard-Oil-classic, Hammerstein's Opera House, lies below street-level. Improvements in ventilation and 'air-conditioning' should take away most of the old objections to the underground place of entertainment.

The Criterion Theatre is still popular. It was an enterprise of Spiers and Pond, two men who went to Australia, during the gold-rush of the 1850s, to make their fortune. Felix Spiers and Christopher Pond did well. Spiers ran the Café de Paris at Melbourne, met Pond, joined up with him, and together the young men secured the contract for supplying the refreshments on the Melbourne and Ballarat Railway.

They came to England, collected a team of cricketers, and shipped them off to Australia—the first English XI to visit the Antipodes.

Then, having made another financial success out of their cricketers, Spiers and Pond returned to England, to branch out as the greatest chain-hoteliers and restaurateurs of their day, and for long afterwards.

They started in England by opening up a buffet at Farringdon Station (Metropolitan)—'a buffet,' said the London *Evening News*, on 28th September, 1896, 'that was gazed at with wonder and admiration by all comers, since it was the first of its kind organized in this country. The Metropolitan, you know, only ran from Farringdon Street to Edgware Road in those days.'

Spiers and Ponds prospered. They built and opened hotels, and some of those hotels have changed their character, and some have gone out of existence, both as hotels and as buildings. But Spiers and Pond have a link with the past—and with this book—in that they still hold the licence to run the cosy little buffets which 'humanize' the District and Metropolitan lines, as distinguished from all other Underground railways. You may still get a drink, 'during licensed hours', in these secret little bars; and only a few years ago, some of the bars seemed to have 'licensed hours' of their own.

I know of only one bar which has a direct connection with the Underground—a bar, that is, which is not licensed by the railway board. That is the 'White Bear' Bar of the Criterion, which has a passage leading into one of the subways of Picca- dilly Circus underground station. This makes up for a pair of swing-doors at the end of a short passage, which used to lead from the central lobby of the underground urinal at Piccadilly Circus.

This was a place in the grand manner—architecturally speak- ing—and must have gladdened the heart of the connoisseurs of such places. One descended to it by a precipitous flight of iron steps and, long before one entered the rotunda, one was aware of it by a curious smell of hot carbolic—or of carbolic- flavoured steam. All the stonework of the stalls was of some pinkish, marblish stone, and the water to flush these unseemly halting places was held in reserve above one's head in vast glass- walled tanks, held together at the edges with brass strips bright, half with Bluebell and half with verdigris. Not infrequently a wag used to introduce a gold-fish into a tank. It's not important, but all the metalwork was vast and complicated, in the most aggressive aspect of Marzipan; and all was painted a shiny aluminium.

Well, a pair of brass-bound swing-doors led from this cloaca to Ward's Irish House: when I was younger, I used to wonder if Wards had built this convenience for their Guinness-drinking customers.

Talking of Guinness reminding me of the Liffey, and

thinking of the Liffey reminding me of the Thames, I am reminded of the last serious time that the Oldbourne burst its underground channel. I heard about it when I was visiting the vaults of the new Chancery Lane Safe Deposit, the oldest business of its kind in London, which now has many such.

In the new building, which was designed by Sir Albert Richardson, PP.R.A., the materials and mechanism are of the latest kind; but the principle of the safe-deposit was established when the original building was opened. The only difference is that the guards are no longer permitted, either by the Law or by Public Opinion, to carry arms.

The Safe Deposit was the invention—or, at any rate, the dear *protégé*—of Alderman Thomas Clarke, afterwards Lord Mayor of London. One cannot accuse the Alderman of using arson in the interests of publicity; so that what happened when a party of the City's most influential business-men sat down to dinner in the Safe Deposit's office must be put down to luck of the most incredible kind. As the company were sitting at dinner, a brass-helmeted fireman rushed in: Stone Buildings, Lincoln's Inn—just across the street—had caught fire, and was blazing fiercely.

'Don't worry, gentlemen,' said Mr Robert Stagg, the secretary, getting to his feet, and waving the startled diners back to their chairs, 'you would be safe at this table, even though the Safe Deposit building itself were on fire!'

He could have added, at the proper time, that they were safe even from Fenians. Each member of the armed patrol, wearing quasi-military uniform, complete with shako, carried a sawn-off shotgun and a revolver.

As a rhyming advertisement issued by the firm in 1893 said:

R stands for Revolver—each watchman has one,
To shoot any housebreaking son of a gun!

But those sentiments belong to the barbarous late Victorian age. We are gentler now. We never look when we drop an atom-bomb on a Hiroshima.

The opening banquet was held on 7th May, 1882; and business boomed from the very beginning. By 1889, there were three thousand 'tenants', paying yearly sums ranging from £3 3s to £13 13s.

What secrets those vaults could tell! is the sort of *cliché* that this place makes tolerable—indeed, inevitable. The private papers of Lloyd George, Asquith and the first Astor to wear a British coronet were all housed here, as were the archives of the Spanish Republican Government.

In 1889, two thousand more safes were added, and prices were 'adjusted', the safes now ranging from One Guinea to Five Guineas a year—cheap enough, in all conscience!—and the strong-rooms from Eight to One Hundred Guineas.

When the last war came, and the building was bombed and shattered, and the River Oldbourne rose and burst through its retaining tunnel, it became necessary to open some of the safes —an action that only unavoidable necessity ever counsels or permits. But the old safes had to be emptied of their contents, and those contents brought over to the new safes in the new building.

Many of the 'tenants' had not communicated with the Secretary for tens of years. Advertisements were inserted in the papers, asking them to communicate with the Safe Deposit— all to no avail.

At last, with Notaries Public as witnesses, the safes whose tenants could not be traced were opened, and what was valuable was put aside to be sold to cover the outstanding rent— often outstanding for fifty years and more.

What was so astonishing was the nature (no less than the variety) of the contents. There were jewels, of course, and private papers. There were gold watches with curious markings (such as would show the High Water Mark at London Bridge), uncut stones, rouble bank-notes in vast quantities. There was one box which contained nothing but a penny and a lock of hair. Another contained only an envelope with six revolver bullets inside: the envelope was marked 'One for each of the Directors'. One box contained only the headlines cut from the newspapers, in reference to the battles of the first world war—the progress of the dates ceasing abruptly at about 1917: was the collector himself a victim of a *putsch*?

But the most curious box of all contained only a pair of frilly woman's drawers, period circa 1908. Their lacy frivolity lent much weight to the words written on the luggage-tag attached to the drawers: 'My life's undoing'.

This was the only time in the Safe Deposit's history that the boxes were opened. In all normal circumstances, the privacy of the safe is inviolate. It is the same with all the other safe-deposits in London—as elsewhere: the National, Pall Mall, Great Winchester House, Hatton Garden, Selfridges, Harrods, the hundreds of banks offering safe-deposit facilities.

The National recalls the story of the triangular plot—by the Mansion House—on which it is built. When this plot was empty, after the opening of Queen Victoria Street in 1867, the Metropolitan Board of Works received, from a deputation of City men, a request to preserve this triangular site as a garden. The Board referred the deputation to the City Corporation, which offered to sell the site—to be used as a garden—for £200,000. No more was heard of the garden idea; but, in November 1871, the Corporation leased the site for the then gigantic sum of £5,500 a year—£1 a square foot.

Apart from the interest that we might properly take in considering the ingenuity which has gone into the designing and maintaining of these underground fortress-treasuries—they have always been a little in advance of the fashion; the Safe Deposit, in 1882, was fully equipped with electric light and telephones—we might consider the opportunity that they give us to see ourselves as others see us: a rare privilege, of which we should take more advantage.

Our weather is frightful, our food worse; our ideas of physical comfort conform more to those of St Simeon Stylites than to the people of Sybaris; we have surrendered our personal liberty to the 'Authorities' so completely that the streets of our capital city are virtually cleared by half-past eleven at night on weekdays, and by half-past ten on Sundays. Without a by-your-leave, our wages and salaries are docked, each week, by a steadily augmenting payment for the poll-tax against which Jack Cade and Wat Tyler fought. Every one of us, above mere subsistence level, who works productively, keeps another man's wife—out of the taxes that the productive worker pays on his productivity.

Yes: but, while the foreigner sees (and shudders at) all these things, he sees, too, that—call it 'innate love-of-order' or 'cringing slavishness' as you will—he, and his money, will be safer here from arbitrary arrest than in any other place that he can imagine.

He may be wrong, of course: but that he thinks so accounts for all the wealth which pours into this country from countries far richer. And much of that wealth is stored away in the vaults of the various safe-deposit companies.

For one thing, the accident of war has established a subterranean shopping-centre in the vaults of the Chancery Lane Safe Deposit. Like so many other developments in Britain, this 'just happened'. Some silversmiths, who used the Safe Deposit to store their stock, were bombed out. They began to take their clients around to the vaults; and later requested permission to receive customers in the vaults. This permission was granted; other silversmiths joined the original cellar-trading silversmiths, and now the London Silver Vault is an established shopping-centre of London, attracting such visitors as Mr Antony Armstrong-Jones, who came here, before his wedding, to buy himself a piece of Georgian silver.

But such newsworthy visitors neither make up the bulk of the London Silver Vault's customers, nor do they provide the solid backing of buying on which the prosperity of this subterranean Aladdin's Cave depends. There are now thirty dealers in antique silver and jewellery; a dealer in modern porcelain has just joined the 'shopkeepers', which fact may presage a coming diversity of trades—and the nationality of their customers affords a sober comment on what the phrase, 'a wealthy country', means.

The principal buyers of costly and fully authenticated silver

come from wealthy Latin American states, from prosperous
Italy, from comfortably progressive Finland. Then come the
Dutch, the Australian and the New Zealand buyers.

'All these countries', it was explained to me, 'have practically
no antique silver of the finest quality, such as you find here in
almost unlimited supply.' And this remark after two wars
which, according to some 'experts', 'have stripped us of all our
wealth'!

'What about the Americans?' I asked.

'*North* Americans? Well, they're not among the big, the
consistent, buyers today. They do come, of course; but privately
—to buy a souvenir to take back with them to the States. And
they're cautious, these days. They want good value. Somewhere around the ten dollars mark. And they want ten dollars'
worth.'

The professional writers on economics should be guided less
by Board of Trade statistics and more by who is buying and
what is being bought, in such places as the London Silver
Vault.

It depends upon how you regard subterranean places. To
some of us, they represent danger; to some of us, safety.

To see subterranean places regarded in their dangerous
aspect, you may go to the Palace of Westminster just before
Parliament opens, and see a squad of Yeomen of the Body-
guard of Our Sovereign Lady the Queen, bravely habited in
scarlet and gold, with starched and pleated ruffs and flat velvet
caps, carry out the search of the cellars under the Houses of
Lords and Commons.

In spite of the fact that the cellars are now lighted with
electricity, the Yeomen take oil-lanterns with them. They have
carried out this search, before each sitting of Parliament, since
1605, when a search really did bring results, in the shape of the
100-lb. barrels of gunpowder that Guy Fawkes had purchased
at ninepence a pound.

That demonstrates the dangerous aspect of hidden places.
They have also their comforting aspect: possibly an older

aspect, since it must have been to caves that primitive man first instinctively fled to escape wild beasts or the bolts of the Sky Beings.

In our times, this aspect of the subterranean has almost forced itself upon our collective notice: long-range guns and bombardment from the air have turned our thoughts instinctively to the Safety That Lies Beneath Us. There is nothing new about seeking safety in a cave or a tunnel—indeed, one of the biggest air-raid shelters constructed just before the last war was made by converting to modern use the extensive system of caves to be found at Chislehurst, a few miles to the south-east of London. Possibly it was for the first time in history that these caves were thoroughly explored and mapped, when the surveyors for the Home Office explored their mysterious and miles-long meanderings.

A book dealing with the London Beneath Us would have been sadly incomplete without some reference to the impressive complex of underground shelters which had been constructed 'between the Wars'. Even during the first world war, art treasures and archives had been stored for safety in disused railway tunnels, some of them 'tubes'. The abandoned under-river 'tube' of the City and South London Railway was so employed, as was the unfinished Post Office 'tube'.

During the air-raids of the first war, when the sky grew menacing with those almost forgotten names, Taube, Gotha and Zeppelin, the population crowded down into the basements of the big stores, into churches, into the Underground railway stations.

After the end of the first war, outside of London, in remote valleys in Wales, great caverns were scooped out of the granite, in readiness for the treasures of food, of art, of record, which would be transferred to these caverns on the imminence of war.

On my way to South Africa, at the very beginning of the last war, I wrote a book which described the social condition of our nation—especially its mental attitude—during the years immediately preceding 3rd September, 1939. The book has been lost: it was commissioned by an American publisher; the top copy, that I posted to New York from Durban, never reached its destination; the carefully-guarded carbon-copy was still in the temporary orderly-room when the Germans arrived. They may have read it—but I doubt it. Paper was scarce, then and there; and a hard-living soldier can find another use for a sheet of paper than to read it.

I recall this book because, in one important particular, it went against the popular opinion: that 'we were totally unprepared' for war. This is nonsense, and I said so.

No nation can be more than prepared for *what it may expect* —and what it may expect can be based only upon the experience of the most recent war. Every war begins where the last war left off; only in the course of the war does the new pattern make itself manifest.

For such a war as we had finished in 1918 (taking into account the new weapons which were ready by 1918, but which had not yet come into use), we were adequately prepared. Especially in the matter of air-raid shelters of the underground type.

While I was gathering material for this book, I wrote to the Ministry of Works for details of the shelter-system devised before and during the last war for the protection of the population. I had asked particularly about the deep shelters.

I received the following letter:

Dear Sir,

I have been a long while following up my letter of 3 May about deep shelters, because we have only recently received a direction from the Cabinet Office. Even now I am not able to give you much satisfactory information. In underground accommodation for the use of the Government, much of the information available is classified as 'security'.

Yet we should be prepared to arrange for you to visit the 1939–45 Cabinet War Room in Great George Street, which is open to the public and does afford a good example of the type of accommodation. Because of the considerations of security mentioned, we should have to ask you to let us see before publication anything you proposed to write on the subject of underground accommodation under Government control.

In other words, in return for permission to visit a hidey-hole 'which is open to the public', I should be required to submit 'anything I proposed to write on the subject of accommodation under Government control'. The bargain seemed to me to be an unreasonable one; though I understand that my American colleagues, wishing to write on the subject of the American Civil War, encounter the same jealous guarding of 'secrets' which are secrets no more.

However, since by visiting the Great George Street cellar I may seem to acquiesce in this impudent proposal, I shall leave it to my non-writing readers to visit the place; and quote information which has already been published.

As regards the Cabinet War Room, there is what appears to be an excellent description in *The Finest Hours of Winston Churchill*, by Reginald Pound, serialized in the London *Daily Mail*; the Cabinet War Room being described in the instalment titled, *This Fantastic Hole in the Ground*, published in the issue dated Friday, 16th September, 1960.

The sub-title of the article pretty well sums up the description:

SIX ACRES OF BOMBPROOF
ROOMS . . . FORTY FEET DOWN UNDER

With regard to the deep shelters, about which the Ministry of Works is so reticent, fifteen years after the end of the war, a full description of their construction was published in *The Engineer*, over four issues of that respected journal: in the issues of 18th September, 27th November, 4th December and 11th December, 1942.

It is true that *The Engineer* does not give the siting of the shelters that it describes in such technical detail: but anyone who would like to supplement *The Engineer*'s information

with a list of the places in which the deep shelters were constructed has only to wander in and about London to see the
great protective shields of the main entrances towering above
the street or common.

For a start, one may go up the Tottenham Court Road, as far
as Store Street (in which Dickens's father died), and see the
entrance to the deep shelter blocking up the narrow street.

Again, many foreign visitors have since been accommodated
in the deep shelter at Clapham; were they conducted to their
simple beds blindfold?

Anyway, according to *The Engineer*, the deep shelters were
mostly constructed to link up with existing Underground lines
when the war should have finished.

'It was in December 1940, that the Ministry of Home
Security decided that it was advisable that a certain amount
of accommodation should be provided in London by means
of such shelters to meet the needs of the large number of
people who too shelter nightly in the tube railway stations.'

The description of how the Ministry's decision was realized
reflects nothing but credit on all concerned, even on—I should
say, particularly—the Government departments concerned.
What was notably impressive was the harmony in which
private enterprise worked with state-controlled organizations.

The (private) consulting engineers for the huge undertaking
were Messrs Mott, Hay and Anderson and Messrs W. T. Halcrow and Partners; it was to Mr Halcrow's credit that a mixed
concrete-and-cast-iron construction was proved practicable.

The London Passenger Transport Board's engineer-in-charge
was Mr V. A. M. Robertson; and Mr J. C. Martin was specially
appointed by the Board to act as liaison-officer between the
Board and the private firms involved.

The Board itself employed its para-governmental authority
to make necessary labour, materials, and transport available to
the task. It not only found the men, but supplied 24,000 tons of
cast-iron lining, as well as one hundred and twenty lorries,
procured from the Board's own Coach and Bus Section. A

pleasing note is introduced into this solemn business by the (apparently quite serious) remark that the Board's Legal Department had 'done its bit' by the acquisition of land.

The length of the tunnels is given differently in two parts of the series: at one time they are stated to have been 1,200 ft. in length, at another, 1,400 ft. There is nothing much in the difference.

To quote *The Engineer* of 18th September, 1942:

Eight new tube shelters in the London area, it was announced last week, are now so nearly completed that in an emergency they could be brought into use without delay...

The article mentions that the tunnels will use concrete in part, instead of the completely cast-iron structure formerly used.

...it is interesting to note that the place of the more usual cast-iron lining has been taken to a considerable extent by pre-cast cement blocks. The use of this alternative material was referred to by Mr Halcrow, in his Thomas Hawkley Lecture before the Institute of Mechanical Engineers last week...

After all this time, there cannot, therefore, be much of a 'state secret' about the substitution of cement for iron in deep tunnelling.

...for their special use as shelters, the tunnels are divided by a concrete slab forming upper and lower 'floors'. Each shelter is about 1,200 ft. long, and capable of holding 2,000 people. Cross-passages provide space for medical aid posts, control rooms and the like. The tunnels lie at levels between 75 ft. and 110 ft. below ground level, and to each there are several alternative entrances. Four of the shelters are north and four south of the Thames.

The three other articles on the same subject deal in detail with construction, design, lay-out, sleeping accommodation, ventilation, sanitation, telephone communication, and so on.

To accelerate the pace—eminently suitable to a Civil Servant, but not to a Civil Servant in need of shelter from a bomb—Kinnear, Moodie & Co. rigged up a rudimentary shield, built, on the site, from material available. With this shield, and working three shifts, the progress leaped from two rings a day to over twelve.

Precautions against flooding were taken, of course; but most attention had necessarily to be paid to the ventilation of the tunnels, for, in the event of a gas-attack, the entrances would have to be sealed. The condition of the tunnels in hot weather, and with the doors sealed, would, in the opinion of the writer of the articles, be 'intolerable'.

During a gas-attack, when the entrances to the pill-boxes [at ground level] would have to be closed by gas-doors, fresh air is introduced by means of sheet metal ducting above the pill-box, filter chambers being provided in the more heavily built-up areas to keep back dust from bombed buildings.

What a way to run a world!

But I'd better stick to quotations from already published works.

Said Mr F. L. Stevens, in his *Under London* (1939), to which the Right Honourable Herbert Morrison, P.C., M.P., gave his blessing—his *imprimatur*—in a foreword:

Westminster is not alone in the thoroughness of its preparations.... A model system of trenches has been built in Lincoln's Inn Fields, under the seven acres of which is an underground network, one thousand four hundred and twenty-nine feet long, seven feet deep and covered with concrete and two feet of earth. Seating accommodation is provided for one thousand three hundred people.... Finsbury is to dig deeper. The Borough Council have a plan for a combined car park and air-raid shelter thirty-four feet below ground-level, to cost £263,000 and to hold twelve thousand people.

From the same authority I learn that the City of Westminster were building eight systems of underground shelters to accommodate upwards of fourteen thousand people, and 'built at a cost of about £5 or £6 a head'.

As I said before, what a way to run a world!

In a topsy-turvy world, dealing with a topsy-turvy subject, I feel that I can reverse the common procedure, and end this book with a dedication.

Gods are created—or resurrected—by pressing human need.

I shall, then, dedicate this book with an old dedication, which has been given a new significance:

DIS MANIBUS
To the Gods of the Underworld

London: by the banks of King's Scholars' Pond
October 1960

Bibliography

In acknowledging the principal sources of my information, I have endeavoured, as far as possible, to cite the authority, either in the body of the text or in footnotes.

I have not thought it necessary to mention, in the Bibliography, such standard works of reference as are now household names: Caesar, Stow, Strype, Besant and the rest; but, in listing the references, I have omitted, so as to avoid over-loading the Bibliography, such works as have contributed, at most, a stray mention or passing thought.

I have thought it more convenient to the reader who wishes to pursue the subjects of which this book is no more than a synoptic epitome to group the references under the main subject-heads.

It should be emphasized that the works listed below are merely the *principal* among those which have been consulted.

PALAEONTOLOGY

BUCKNILL, J. A. and MURRAY, H. W.: *Mammalia,* in *Victoria County History of Surrey,* Vol. I

COLLENETTE, C. L.: *The Invertebrate Fauna of Hyde Park and Kensington Gardens: Insects. London Naturalist,* 1938, 48–49

DARBY, H. C., *ed.*: *An Historical Geography of England before* A.D. *1800*

FITTER, R. S. R.: *London's Natural History*

GOMME, Sir L.: *London*

GRINLING, C. H., INGRAM, T. A. and POLKINGHORNE, B. C.: *A Survey and Record of Woolwich and West Kent*

HALL, H. R.: *Unwritten History*

HARTING, J. E.: *The Birds of Hampstead* (in *Lobley*)

HICKS, H.: *On the Discovery of Mammoths and Other Remains in Endsleigh Street, etc.* Quart. J. Geol. Soc., *48,* 453–468

JOHNSON, W.: *Animal Life in London*

LONDON NATURAL HISTORY SOCIETY: *Unpublished Records of Mammals, Birds, Reptiles and Amphibia in the London Area* (1900–1944)

OWEN, D. J.: *The Port of London Yesterday and Today*

PAGE, W.: *London, its Origin and Early Development*

REID, C.: *The Plants of the Late Glacial Deposits of the Lea Valley.* Quart. J. Geol. Soc., *71,* 155–163

Sᴵɴᴄʟᴀɪʀ, R.: *Metropolitan Man*

Sᴘᴜʀʀᴇʟʟ, F. J. C.: *Early Sites and Embankments on the Margins of the Thames Estuary.* Jour. Roy. Arch. Inst., 42, 269–302

Vᴜʟʟɪᴀᴍʏ, C. E.: *The Archaeology of Middlesex and London*

Wᴀʀʀᴇɴ, S. H.: *Further Observations on a Late Glacial or Ponders End Stage of the Lea Valley.* Quart. J. Geol. Soc., 71, 164–182

Wɪʟʟᴀᴛᴛs, E. C.: *The Land of Britain: part 79—Middlesex and the London Region*

Wɪɴʙᴏʟᴛ, S. E.: *Britain B.C.*

Wʀɪɢʜᴛ, W. B.: *The Quaternary Ice Age*

HISTORY

Bᴇʟʟ, W. G.: *Unknown London*

Bʀᴜᴄᴇ-Mɪᴛғᴏʀᴅ, R. L. S. (*ed.*): *Recent Archaeological Excavations in Britain*

Cᴀʀʏ, M.: *The Geographic Background of Greek and Roman History*

Cʟᴜɴɴ, H. P.: *The Face of London*

Dᴀɴɪᴇʟʟ, A. E.: *London City Churches*

Gᴏᴍᴍᴇ, Sir L.: *London*

Gᴜɪʟᴅʜᴀʟʟ Mᴜsᴇᴜᴍ (London)—Publications:
Finds in Roman London, 1949–52
Discoveries on Walbrook, 1949–50
Small Finds from Walbrook, 1954–55
Sculptures from the Temple of Mithras, Walbrook

Hɪʟʟ, W. B.: *Buried London; Mithras to the Middle Ages*

Hᴏᴍᴇ, G.: *Roman London*

Hᴏᴍᴇ, G.: *Mediaeval London*

Hᴏᴍᴇ, G.: *London Bridge*

Hᴜᴍᴇ, I. N.: *Treasure in the Thames*

Hᴜᴛᴛᴏɴ, A. W.: *A Short History and Description of Bow Church, Cheapside*

Qᴜᴀʀʀᴇʟʟ, C.: *Buried Treasure*

Tʀᴇᴠᴇʟʏᴀɴ, G. M.: *English Social History*

Wᴀʟғᴏʀᴅ, E. (Tʜᴏʀɴʙᴜʀʏ, G. W.): *Old and New London*

Wᴀʀᴅ, J.: *Romano-British Buildings and Earthworks*

Wɪʟʟɪᴀᴍs, E.: *Early Holborn and the Legal Quarter of London*

Wʀɪɢʜᴛ, T.: *A History of Domestic Manners and Sentiments in England During the Middle Ages*

WATER-SUPPLY AND SANITATION

Hᴏʟʟɪɴɢsʜᴇᴀᴅ, J.: *Underground London*

Jᴇᴘʜsᴏɴ, H.: *The Sanitary Evolution of London*

Mᴇᴛʀᴏᴘᴏʟɪᴛᴀɴ Wᴀᴛᴇʀ Bᴏᴀʀᴅ: *The Water Supply of London*

REYNOLDS, R.: *Cleanliness and Godliness*
STEVENS, F. L.: *Under London*
WRIGHT, L.: *Clean and Decent*
WYLIE, J. C.: *The Wastes of Civilisation*

GAS

CHANDLER, D. and LACEY, A. DOUGLAS: *The Rise of the Gas Industry in Britain*
MACKENZIE, Sir C.: *The Vital Flame*
STEWART, E. G.: *Town Gas: Its Manufacture and Distribution*

ELECTRICITY

THE ELECTRICIAN: *Forty Years of Electrical Progress* (A Reprint of articles which appeared in the 2,000th number of 'The Electrician', September 15th, 1916)

UNDERGROUND TRANSPORT

BAKER, B.: *The Metropolitan and Metropolitan District Railways* (in Minutes of Proceedings of the Institute of Civil Engineers, session 1884-5)
BAKER, C.: *The Metropolitan Railway*
BENNETT, A. R.: *London and Londoners in the Eighteen-Fifties and Sixties*
HOWSON, H. F.: *London's Underground*
LASCELLES, T. S.: *The City & South London Railway*
LEE, C. E.: *The Metropolitan District Railway*
NEURATH, M.: *Railways Under London*
PASSINGHAM, W. J.: *The Romance of London's Underground*
SOMMERFIELD, V.: *Underground Railways—their Construction and Working*
STEVENS, F. L.: *Under London*
WILSON, B. G. and HARAM, V. S.: *The Central London Railway*
WROTTESLEY, A. J. F.: *Famous Underground Railways of the World*

GENERAL

ANON: *London As It Is Today* (Pubd. H. G. Clarke & Co.: 1851)
HARBEN, H. A.: *A Dictionary of London*
HARPER, C. G.: *A Londoner's Own London—1870-1920*
HOLDEN, W. H.: *They Startled Grandfather—Gay Ladies and Merry Mashers of Victorian Times*
LAVER, J.: *Victorian Panorama*
WHEATLEY, H. B.: *London, Past and Present—Its History, Associations and Traditions*
WRIGHT, J. D.: *London's Old Buildings*

INDEX

Acheulean Man, 6, 13–14, 121
Adams Hydraulics Ltd, 269
Air-raid shelters, 265–70
Albert, Prince Consort, 88
Allhallows Barking Church, 135, 216–17
Allhallows Staining Church, 202
Amherst of Hackney, Lord, 211
Anderida, 18
Anglo-Saxon Chronicle, The, 33 ff.
Archaeological research and discoveries, 42 ff., 52 ff., 194 ff.
Armitage, Rev. C., 198, 222
Asbestos, 185
Ashfield, Lord, 164–5
Asia, 14
Augustine, 33
Austin, H., 81
Austin, W., 68, 92, 191
Australia, 14–15

Baker, Sir H., 204
Baker Street and Waterloo Railway ('Bakerloo'), 163–4
'Balass Ruby, The', 211
Bank of England, 34–5, 204 ff.
——Museum, 205–6
Barlow, P. W., 133
Battersea Power Station, 71
Bazalgette, J., 2, 11, 85, 101, 102, 104
'Beaker Folk, The', 6–7, 15–16
Beckton outfall, 84
Bell, Graham, 156
Benedictines, 41
Benest, K., 142
Bennett, A. R., 153–4
Besant, Sir W., 10
Best, Chief Supt W. C. F., 225–6
Bidder, 11, 102
Billingsgate Market relics, 215–16
Billingsgate as port, 24–5
Blackstone, 52
Blackwall Tunnel, 136
Blackwell, 102
Blurton, J. R., 25, 200

Boadicea, 23–4, 49–50
Boulton and Watt, 173–4
Bracton, 51
Brindley, 61
British Archaeological Association 196–7
British Museum, 28, 205, 248
Britton, 51
Brompton and Piccadilly Railway, 163
Brougham, Lord, 176
Browne, Sir J., 46, 53
Brunel, M. I., 131–3
Buffon, 53
Bulmer, B., 57

Caesar, 9, 11, 18–19, 21–2
Camden, 43, 211–12
Carmelite monastery remains, 194–7
Caroline, Queen, 112, 145
Carr, Sir E., 193
Cassius Dio, 10–11
Cassivelaunus, 22
Celts, 6–8, 16–18, 29
Central London Railway, 160–1, 167
Chadwick, E., 72, 74–5, 86, 93
Chalmers, Dr J., 175, 176
Chancery Lane Safe Deposit, 259–62
Charing Cross, Euston and Hampstead Railway, 163
Charles I, 60, 128, 210
Charles II, 37, 47–8, 87, 245
Cheapside Conduit, 105
'Cheapside Hoard, The', 53, 247–8
Chellean Man, 13
'Cheshire Cheese, Ye Olde', 41, 197
Cholera, 74 ff., 82
Christianity in Britain (Roman), 26, 32
City and South London Railway, 158–9
City Corporation, 137
Clapham A. W., F.S.A., 195
Claudius, 18, 31
Clayton, Rev. J., 172